A New Railway to Scotland

A New Railway to Scotland

Building the Settle to Carlisle Railway
from newspapers of the time

DAVID OCCOMORE

HAYLOFT PUBLISHING LTD

First published by Hayloft Publishing Ltd., 2020

A CIP catalogue record for this book is available from the British Library

ISBN 978-1-910237-43-4

Designed, printed and bound in the EU

Hayloft policy is to use papers that are natural, renewable and recyclable products and made from wood grown in sustainable forests. The logging and manufacturing processes are expected to conform to the environmental regulations of the country of origin.

Climate neutral
Print product
ClimatePartner.com/12667-1910-1001

This book was printed with the offset of carbon emissions and support for Forest Protection in Pará, Brazil.

Hayloft Publishing Ltd,
a company registered in England number 4802586
2 Staveley Mill Yard, Staveley, Kendal, LA8 9LR (registered office)
L'Ancien Presbytère, 21460 Corsaint, France (editorial office)

Email: books@hayloft.eu
Tel: 07971 352473 or +33 (0) 380 896760
www.hayloft.eu

Frontispiece: Cowburn Tunnel on the Hope Valley Line, Derbyshire, built in 1891. Miners being lowered down a shaft to the tunnel headings. The reporter for the *Penrith Herald* in August 1873 was lowered in the same way to view the headings on the Black Moss tunnel on the Settle and Carlisle (photograph courtesy of *Picture the Past*).

*To all those unknown navvies and boys who toiled
in the mud and dark to build a railway*

Acknowledgements

Writing this book has taken some six years of research, during this time I am indebted to many newspaper sources for material and these are acknowledged in the text. I would also like to thank the Cumbria Libraries for their on line access to the national newspaper archive, also to the staff at Penrith Library for their help in using the micro film viewer and access to the local newspaper files. I would like to thank Lazonby Local History Society who have given me access to their files on the Settle and Carlisle Railway and the Friends of the Settle and Carlisle Railway for the use of the photograph of Lazonby railway staff. I would also like to thank the Cumbrian Railway Association for the use of photographs from their extensive archive.

Notes on illustrations

Fredrick Williams's book contains a number of reasonably accurate line drawing of viaducts and bridges, although his landscapes were drawn rather fancifully. On the other hand it is with regret that there were no photographs taken of the building of the railway, except for some of the viaducts. With this in mind I have drawn on railway construction photographs taken of other lines around the country to help illustrate my text. Although these photographs were taken much later in the century, over the intervening years many of the methods of railway building had not changed, the pick and shovel, along with horse power, still very much in evidence.

Contents

We're the blokes that have to go rough that others may go smooth.
We walk in the mud that others may ride in a train.

Navvy sayings gathered by Missioner Mr Gisson

Introduction

Building the Settle and Carlisle Railway was without doubt an enormous civil engineering project for late Victorian engineers. Even today with all our advanced techniques and equipment it would still be a major undertaking. The very terrain that this railway crossed insured that there would be bridges, tunnels, and viaducts every few miles.

Written accounts of the Settle and Carlisle Railway started almost as soon as the line opened with Frederick Smeeton Williams (1829-86), a pioneer railway author, writing his book *The Midland Railway: Its rise and progress*, as the Settle to Carlisle was being built and included significant information about the line, his account was finally published in 1876 (republished David & Charles 1968). Williams of course, reflects the best of the Midland Railway Company, and leaves out all the events that the company would find embarrassing.

Over the years the line has gained an iconic image, that has spawned a not inconsiderable, number of further books. A good number of these have been photographic albums, with views depicting steam and diesel trains traversing the wilder reaches of the line in all the panoramic beauty of the different seasons.

In more recent times W. R. Mitchell, whose books are highly recommended reading, has researched and written extensively about the Settle and Carlisle Railway in the vicinity of Ribble Head viaduct and the associated navvy hut encampments of that area. However my book, through no deliberate intention of mine, contains more accounts about the line as it passes through the northern Eden Valley from Kirkby Stephen to Carlisle.

Many column inches, in the newspapers of the day, were devoted to describing the 72 miles of the Midland Railway's new line during its construction, and the early years of its operation. *A New Railway to Scotland* is, as far as I am aware, the first major collection that has been put together, of these contemporary accounts. Altogether these news reports form an almost monthly diary of events taking place at the various construction sites.

Because of the magnitude of the new line, construction reports of the Settle to Carlisle line found their way, not only into the local papers, but also the national newspapers. I have transcribed most of the text verbatim, with some editing where it was thought necessary. This is so that we can savour a sample of the lost language of our ancestors as they portrayed those times, in the vivid and colourful sentences that the reporters used. The newspaper reporters provide us today with the closest description of Victorian railway construction that we have available. I cannot claim this book is a definitive collection of these newspaper reports, as I am sure that further stories will surface as more research is undertaken.

We must also remind ourselves that before the advent of radio and television, people relied on the word pictures in the newspapers to provide them with detailed accounts of events taking place up and down the country. Victorian journalistic reporting, was by modern standards, sometimes graphic. We have often heard our television news presenters say 'some of the images you are about to see you may find distressing, and so it was with nineteenth century newspaper accounts of accidents, only they gave no prior warning about content in the descriptions the reader would meet.

My intention is to allow the newspaper reports with as little alteration as possible, to be the focus of the book although I have made an exception by adding sub-titles to excessively long accounts for the 29 October 1872, 2 August 1873, 2 June 1875, and 5 October 1877. My time span has been set from 1865 to 1908 when the Midland Railway staff were with drawn from Carlisle at the time when the Citadel Station passed into the hands of a station committee.

I have also added footnotes where I think they may be of some assistance. I have not just written the book for railway historians, but for those interested in local history and likewise family historians whose ancestors had connections with the building of Victorian railways. But above all I am writing for anyone, who like me, find reading old newspaper accounts addictive.

Dent Dale viaduct on the Settle and Carlisle Railway with timber scaffolding around the rising piers. Once the piers are at the correct height, the arches can then be turned. Photograph courtesy of Cumbria Railway Association.

Chapter One
1865-1869

The Midland Railway in 1859 were working trains to Ingleton, with an agreement with the London North Western Railway (LNWR) to forward their carriages on through Kirkby Lonsdale and Sedburgh, to Tebay and then on to Carlisle.

Much to the Midland Railway's annoyance and the inconvenience of their passengers the London North Western Railway were attaching the coaches to the rear of slow goods trains. The Middland Railway solution was to build its own line from Settle to Carlisle, with this in view an Act was passed in 1866. By 1868 the relationship between the London North Western Railway and the Midland Railway had thawed, so the Midland Railway, who were financially heavily committed to extending into London St Pancras, asked parliament for an abandonment bill. This was refused, so the Midland Railway had no choice but to go ahead and build their own railway between Settle and Carlisle.

Constructing the line took some 6,000 men with a range of skills and trades including: labourers, navvies, bricklayers, masons, carpenters, smiths, strikers and miners, platelayers, boys, one horse carts and drivers and two horse carts and drivers. The impact of all these extra men with their families living in huts erected all along the route would have almost doubled the population of the villages they were close to. Alongside these men came the engineers and contractors men who would need rented houses or hired rooms near their work sites. This need for accommodation and provisions, would have had a positive effect on the local economy

Blackburn Standard, 11 October 1865

NEW RAILWAY ROUTE TO THE NORTH

The Midland Railway Company are at present surveying the country between Settle and Carlisle, with a view to promoting in the ensuing session of Parliament a bill empowering them to make an independent line to the border city. When, on a former occasion, the Midland Company adopted measures to secure to themselves an independent route to the north they were induced to abandon their intention, and enter into arrangements with the London and North Western Company. Those arrangements have not, it appears proved satisfactory, and the Midland Company have determined to possess, if possible, a line of their own.

Starting at Settle, the line, as at present projected, will pass along the valley of the Ribble, and thence along the vale of the Eden to Kirkby Stephen, in Westmorland, where communication may be made with the Stockton and Darlington by the Eden Valley line. Pursuing the vale of the Eden the line will enter Cumberland at Culgaith, and having crossed the Eden will follow closely the course of the river to the village of Armathwaite, passing through some of the most picturesque woodland and river scenery in Cumberland, which has hitherto been a *terra incognita* to the generality of tourists. From Armathwaite the line will pass on to Scotby, on the Newcastle and Carlisle section of the North Eastern Railway, and thence running parallel with that line for a couple of miles, enter the Citadel Station at Carlisle, where it will join the North British line, and with the 'Waverley route' form a new route from the south of England to Scotland.

Derby Mercury, 21 February 1866

MIDLAND RAILWAY COMPANY

The Half Yearly Meeting… The Chairman at considerable length supported the proposed line from Settle to Carlisle, which would give the Midland access to Scotland. Having explained at some length the reasons which had induced the directors to propose the Settle to Carlisle line at an estimated cost of £1,638,043, the Chairman said there were many reasons why the project should not be delayed. They believed it would be remunerative; that it would fortify their position and make the Midland system one of the great arteries commencing at London and terminating at Carlisle.

Derby Mercury, 23 May 1866

…The Chairman – The next bill is number one on the list. A bill for the enabling of the Midland Railway Company to construct railways from Settle to Hawes, Appleby, and Carlisle, and for other purposes. This bill is one which will enable us to extend the Midland system from Settle to Carlisle. It will intersect the North Eastern system of railways and proceed on to Carlisle, where it will effect a junction with the lines of six companies who have their termini there. It will be about 80 miles in length and the estimated capital required is £1,650,000, with the usual borrowing powers. Some parts of the gradients are rather difficult, and will be expensive, but the great bulk of the route is comparatively easy and inexpensive, so that we calculate the average cost per mile to be £20,000.

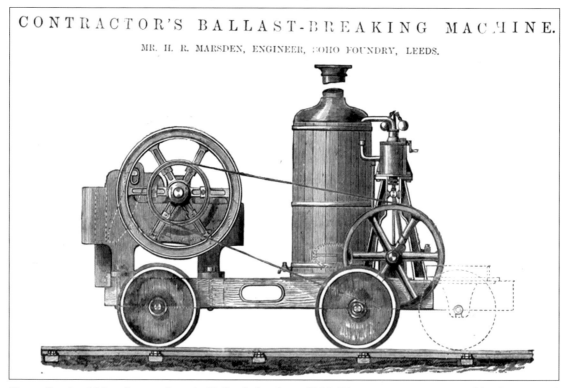

CONTRACTOR'S BALLAST-BREAKING MACHINE.

MR. H. R. MARSDEN, ENGINEER, SOHO FOUNDRY, LEEDS.

Henry Rowland Marsden was born in Holbeck, Leeds, in 1823. His parents were poor and he began work in a local mill at the age of ten, becoming an engineering apprentice at fifteen. In 1848 he emigrated to the United States where he made a successful career in mechanical engineering, and returned a wealthy man to Leeds in 1862, setting up a factory for patent stone-crushing machinery to take advantage of the demand of the time for road building stone. He became mayor of Leeds in 1873 and died suddenly on 19 January 1876.

There will be considerable local traffic, but that alone would not have induced the directors to propose to you so large an amount of capital to be expended; the main object we have in view is to secure for you a fair share of the traffic between England and Scotland. That traffic amounts to more than £1,000,000 a year and we are told that our proportion would be £300,000, as awarded to us under the English and Scots agreements. We have tried by protracted negotiations with the other companies to obtain redress, but hitherto we have failed and we have not been able to obtain that fair division of traffic which we would justify us in withholding from making an independent line of our own. The worst gradient is 1 in 100, whilst the Lancashire and Carlisle have 1 in 70 for a considerable distance In the interest of all parties we have looked at the matter again and again but we cannot see any other way of protecting and developing the traffic of the Midland Company, but by prosecuting the bill now under your consideration. I will not detain you further; the bill has passed the House of Commons.

Leeds Mercury, 11 February 1867

...The preliminary surveys are also in progress upon the Settle and Carlisle Railway, so that the tunnels and some of the other works which will require a considerable length of time to complete, may be commenced at an early period.

Leeds Mercury, 14 August 1867

The Berleigh Rock Drill was invented in America in 1866. It was a pneumatic drill using compressed air. This tool was capable of drilling holes up to five inches in diameter, to a depth of thirty feet, at two to ten inches per minute. At the same time the air also helped to ventilate the tunnel.

That considerable progress has been made in staking out the line of the Settle and Carlisle Railway, the time for the completion of which will be governed by the tunnel through Blea Moor, and the viaducts and cuttings adjacent thereto. The necessary preparations have therefore been made for proceeding at once with these portions of the work.

The Lancaster Gazette, 15 May 1869

THE NEW RAILWAY LINE TO SCOTLAND

The Midland Railway (Settle and Carlisle) Bill, to which royal consent has recently been given has for its object the construction of a line between Settle and Carlisle, to give an independent route to the Midland Company. With respect both to goods and passenger traffic, from the south of England to Carlisle and places north, and visa versa, together with powers to use the Citadel Station at Carlisle for the accommodation of such traffic. The new route in addition to offering such facilities for traffic and passenger communications between Scotland and the Midland counties, will open for tourists some of the most picturesque scenery in Cumberland.

Leaving the Midland line at Settle, the new railway will take the course of the Ribble and thence passing into the vale of Eden, will reach Hawes, and then go to Kirkby Stephen, where connection will be made with the newly constructed Eden Valley line. Thence passing Brough, where large annual fairs are held, the line will run almost parallel with the Eden Valley Railway for some distance, and cross over the border of Westmorland into Cumberland to Culgaith. Through Skirsgill Wood the line will pass on to the village of Langwathby; thence along the east side of Little Salkeld to Mill Pool, where it will cross the River Eden, and then make straight for the village of Lazonby, which lies within a few miles of the town of Penrith.

From Low Wood, which is the next place put down, the route will be by the riverside, close past Sampson's Chamber, and then through the middle of Barron Wood, still following the course of the Eden, to Armathwaite, passing through High Wood, and on the west side of the village. Thus some of the most secluded woodland retreats of Cumberland, which at present are visited only by the solitary angler, or occasionally by a select picnic party, will be rendered easily accessible to all. The district around Armathwaite is perhaps one of the finest in the county for pleasant scenery. From Armathwaite the line leads on past Eden Brow to Dancowfield, and thence stretches on to Cumwhitton, a village of considerable size, which is provided with railway accommodation.

The run is next to Scotby, a village distant about two miles from Carlisle at which the trains over the Newcastle and Carlisle line call. Passing within a short distance of the south end of this village the new line will effect a junction with the Newcastle and Carlisle line at Durran Hill Crossing, which is equidistant from Carlisle and Scotby, and by this means will get into Citadel Station at Carlisle, and communicate with the Waverley Route.

In November 1869 John Ashwell (1822-1911) signed the contract No1 from Settle to the Marble Works, Dent. He expected to complete it in 1873. William Henry Ashwell (1844-1913), his agent, laid the first stone of the Ribblehead Viaduct in October 1870. In 1871 John Ashwell got into financial difficulties, and the Midland Railway took over the contract with direct labour, a total work force of 8,200 men, on a semi-contractual basis with William Ashwell. The resident engineers were R. E. Wilson and Edgar O'Ferguson and the agents were James Hope and W. H. Ashwell with Midland agent A. Terry.)

Chapter Two
1870

Penrith Observer, 1 February 1870

MALLERSTANG: SETTLE AND CARLISLE RAILWAY

In a few months the contractors for the construction of this railway will probably have disturbed the quietude of most on the picturesque villages in Westmorland. The interesting ceremony of cutting the first sod in Mallerstang was performed by Mr Parkin Blades (Sir Richard Tufton's agent for the township) on Monday week, and the event was fraught with much interest. It is the first step towards opening out a wide tract of land, the inhabitants of which have hitherto been debarred from ready access to the busy centres of industry.

(Sir Richard Tufton, Appleby Castle, Director of the Eden Valley Railway.)

The Lancaster Gazette, 19 March 1870

THE SETTLE AND CARLISLE RAILWAY

The contracts for the Appleby section of the Settle and Carlisle branch of the Midland Railway Company have recently been entered into. The distance taken is fourteen miles, and the amount of the contract is said to be about £300,000. Mr J. Firbank, of Newport, is the successful competitor for the work.

Contract No 3 of 15¾ miles from the northern end of Smardale Viaduct to Crowdundle Viaduct near Newbiggin. The resident engineer was Jesse Drage. The contractor was Joseph Firbank and the contractors agent was J. Throstle.

Cumberland and Westmorland Advertiser, 12 April 1870

SETTLE AND CARLISLE RAILWAY

On Tuesday the last contracts for the formation of this line was accepted by Messrs Eckersley and Baylis for the sum of £330,000. The portion of the line extends from Carlisle to Newbiggin, is 25 miles in length, and will contain some heavy work. There were five estimates put in, the highest of which was £450,000.

Contract No 4 of 23½ miles, between Crowdundle Viaduct and Petteril Bridge, Carlisle, was given to Eckersley and Bayliss. The resident engineers were John Allen and Samuel Paine and the contractors agents were J. Lambert and E. Williams. The rails were to be delivered to Appleby on the Eden Valley line and Scotby on the Newcastle to Carlisle Railway.

The Leeds Mercury, 19 May 1870

ACCIDENT AT SETTLE

An accident, which had well nigh terminated fatally, happen on Tuesday last to a man in the employ of Mr Ashwell, the contractor for that portion of the new line of railway (Settle and Carlisle) now in the course of construction, commencing at Settle. The man was engaged with others, on the works near Settle winding up a huge stone with the help of a moveable crane, when suddenly it upset, and before he could get out of the way of the falling crane he was knocked down. His fellow workmen fortunately escaped unhurt. He was speedily removed to his lodgings in Giggleswick, and on Dr Green being called in it was discovered the poor fellow had sustained severe bruises about the head and face, and one of his legs, from the foot to the knee, was found to be badly crushed.

The Carlisle Journal, 20 May 1870

SETTLE AND CARLISLE RAILWAY: to Engineers, Contractors and Others

To be Let, at LAZONBY, TWO Good FURNISHED ROOMS (Sitting and Bedroom) in a private house. Apply at the Office of this Paper.

The Carlisle Journal, 24 May 1870

FIRE AT COOMB WOOD, ARMATHWAITE

On Thursday shortly after mid-day, a fire broke out in Coombs Wood, near Armathwaite, the property of the Earl of Carlisle, and, before the devouring element could be subdued, it spread over an extent of 50 acres doing much damage to the trees, and completely destroying the brush wood. Consequently the picturesque scenery above the rocks, for which Armathwaite is famous, has been robbed of much of its natural beauty. Lately some men have been employed in the wood, peeling bark. It was at the place where this operation was being carried on, just above the rocks, that the fire occurred, and it is conjectured, though there is no direct evidence of the fact, that the brushwood was ignited by fire which fell from the tobacco pipe of one of the workmen.

The fire, it seems, was first observed by Mrs Harrison, wife of the wood-keeper, who gave an alarm. This was while the workmen in the wood were absent at dinner; but with the greatest promptitude Mr Hope, of the Dukes Head Inn, hastened to the Midland Railway works for aid, and Mr Bell the engineer, very willingly allowed the whole of his men, 50 in number, to proceed at once to the wood to render assistance. Every one worked with the greatest energy. The railway workmen, under Messrs Wilson, Fleming, Dudley, and John Robson, who superintended the whole affair, deserve much praise for the manner in which they strove to prevent the fire spreading… Of course Mr Harrison is much concerned about the fire, he having had charge of the wood for several years.

Lancaster Gazette, 4 June 1870

LARGE ENGINE

On Monday evening last, the streets at Ingleton was all in commotion in consequence of Mr Ashwell, railway contractor, having an engine conveyed to Batty Wife Hole, in Ingleton Fells. They had seventeen horses to it and thirty men, and when they got further up the dale they were obliged to add another eight horses. They arrived safe at their destination.

The Lancaster Gazette, 16 July 1870

MIDLAND RAILWAY EXTENTION

The progress of railway works and bustle and activity are inescapable, and in no case is this more apparent when quiet country neighbourhoods are invaded by gangs of labourers, teams of wagons, and their attendant wagoners, joiners, masons, smiths. We are experiencing this change in our district at the present time for the works required to extend the Midland System are now in full progress, particularly at Newbiggin, in Westmorland, Culgaith, Barron Wood and Armathwaite. The appearance of these usually quiet places have with the last few weeks been totally changed. Wooden huts and stabling have been erected, tommy shops are opening, wagons laden with material are constantly passing to and fro, and the shouts of the teamsters and the stroke of the pick are becoming familiar to the ear. Near Newbiggin the railway will cross, by means of a many arched viaduct, the small stream which divides the two counties. The work here is extremely heavy, but even now a considerable length is ballasted and laid. Approaching Culgaith another length is in progress and immediately under the village, brick making machinery is at work, and, as good material is at hand, a considerable number of the bricks required will be manufactured on the spot.

At Culgaith, which, as is well known, stands on an eminence, to which the road is both steep and difficult, the work is excessively heavy. As the line approaches the village its course is along a raised embankment till it strikes the side of the hill on which the village stands. A deep cutting here leads to the entrance of a tunnel six hundred yards long, which passes underneath the road at a depth of about 50 feet, but which further on is considerably above 100 feet below the level. About the centre of this a shaft 100 feet in depth has been sunk, and in this gangs of men work day and night by alternate shifts, and the tunnel has already been extended many yards in both directions. The hill is composed as far as they have yet penetrated, of hard marly substance, which rings like metal when struck by the pick, consequently the progress is slow and tedious. At present the men are engaged only in driving what is termed a head or channel, so as to allow the employment of a larger number of hands at a later period. Blasting becomes necessary every few hours, and so far as we can judge, the tunnel will be a labour of years. Leaving Culgaith the line runs through a fine country to the village of Langwathby, passing it on the high side, and gradually approaching the Eden till it crosses the river between Great and Little Salkeld. The next village Lazonby, and passing on it traverses Barron Wood, where the work is of a very heavy character, tunnelling and deep cuttings being very frequent. The line then runs in a north-easterly direction to Armathwaite, where considerable progress is now being made:- Carlisle paper.

Penrith Observer, 19 July 1870.

RAILWAY EMPLOYEES' SUPPER AT LANGWATHBY.

In honour of the important event of cutting the first sod of the Settle and Carlisle Railway in the neighbourhood of Langwathby, Messrs. Eckersley, Bayliss, and Co., contractors, on Thursday last entertained the workmen in their employ, to the number of upwards of 40, to an excellent and substantial supper at the house of Mr Oldcorn, the Shepherds Inn, at Langwathby. The spread was replete in all its appointments, and did the utmost credit to the worthy host and hostess, whose hospitality, have won for them general esteem. Messrs. Eckersley and Bayliss were present during the evening. The after proceedings, which were pleasant and orderly through out, were kept up until a late hour.

Cumberland and Westmorland Advertiser, 19 July 1870.

SETTLE AND CARLISLE RAILWAY: Public Tea Meeting and Musical Entertainment

With the exception of a demonstration to Admiral Elliott and Wm Hopes, Esq., on the passing of the bill for the extension of the Midland Railway, no festive display has taken place on its account till Wednesday last. Messers. Firbank and Throstle, the contractors for the third or Appleby section, extending from Smardale Gill, near Kirkby Stephen to Newbiggin, a distance of eighteen miles, in order to provide their work people with easy access to the extensive works now in course of construction at a place called Helm, about two miles from Ormside and four from Appleby, have just completed the erection of between 30 and 40 huts, with suitable convenience, capable of accommodating upwards of 200 persons, together with a large building to hold a similar number, to be used on Sundays as a chapel for religious services and for a school and reading room during the week.

The building is upwards of 40 feet in length, and the interior is divided by a folding partition, one portion of which is used during the week as a coffee room, where the workmen can be accommodated with tea and coffee at any time for a small charge. Evening classes are to be formed under the gratuitous superintendence of the Rev. Mr Clark, rector of Ormside who has also further arranged to give two services each Sunday. Mr Thorpe, late of Preston, has been appointed scripture reader, his duties extending from Ormside to Newbiggin, who will occasionally take part in the services. An harmonium is to be bought being raised by voluntary subscription, and Admiral Elliott, and Miss Hill have presented prayer books and hymn books, together with a handsome subscription towards the working expenses of the navvies who will be located on a bleak common, exposed to the violence of a fierce helm wind during the winter will be as well provided for as circumstances will allow.

The opening of the building was inaugurated on Wednesday afternoon last, by a tea drinking and musical entertainment, a large number of people from Appleby and the neighbourhood taking advantage of the fine weather and the festivities to witness the operatives of the excavations and sinking of two shafts in the tunnel, the works of which will extend half a mile underground. The huts, the brick-making machine, the engines, stables, and works at large were all subjects of much interest and curiosity. Tea was provided punctually at five o'clock in excellent style under the management of Mr and Mrs Kirby, a large number of navvies and their wives were present. After the room had been arranged, a public entertainment, hurriedly got up, was given. John Portees, Esq., of Appleby, was called to the chair, and was supported by the Rev. Mr Clark, C Firbank, Esq., Mr James Dickson and the Rev. Mr Lewis. After an introductory speech from the chairman, several songs and duets were given in a highly creatable manner, Mrs Clark alternatively presiding at the piano and harmonium. Several popular songs were given by Mr Throstle, Mr Kirby, and the others, which were vociferously applauded; and Mr C Firbank made an amusing speech in behalf of the ladies. Other songs and speeches followed, and after address from the Rev. Mr Clark and the Rev. Mr Lewis, the meeting was brought to a close by singing the National Anthem, and the company dispersed a little before nine o'clock, all well pleased with their entertainment at the new town of workman's huts called the 'Helm'.

The Lancaster Gazette, 30 July 1870

INGLETON

LARCENY – Henry Perry, a navvy, working on the Settle and Carlisle Railway, was apprehended on the 21st instant, by PC Goodison, and brought the following day before C. Ingleby, Esq. and the Rev Rd Denny, at the Court House, Ingleton, charged with stealing a silver watch, the property of William Hughes at Batty Wife Hole, in Ingleton Fells. The defendant was committed for trial at the next Quarter Sessions.

The Carlisle Patriot, 5 August 1870

MEDICAL APPOINTMENTS FOR THE SETTLE AND CARLISLE RAILWAY

During the construction of the railway from Newbiggin in Westmorland, to Carlisle, the surgical staff will consist of the following gentlemen:- The headquarters will be at Scotby, where a surgery has been constructed. Dr Head has been appointed to the section between Carlisle and Eden Brow, Dr Mitchell, from Eden Brow to Kirkoswald, Dr Williamson, from Little Salkeld to Newbiggin and Dr Dudley, from Little Salkeld to Armathwaite.

The Lancaster Gazette, 6 August 1870

FATAL ACCIDENT – On Tuesday last, about noon, as Mrs. Powell and her sister, Ann Wall, observed a little girl about six years of age, was riding on an engine at the Underhill cutting, on the Settle and Carlisle Railway, in the neighbourhood of Batty Wife Hole, Ingleton Fell, the engine ran off the line at a curve on the tramway, and pitched on one end. The wagons that were attached to the engine came rushing on and threw their load of dirt over the engine and buried the child. When the debris had been removed the child was found dead, being very much scalded and its body having been broken. The stoker jumped off the engine and escaped unhurt, but the driver and Mrs Powell were much scalded. An inquest was held before T. P. Brown Esq., deputy coroner, at the house of Mr John Garlisk, Batty Wife Hole, when a verdict of Accidentally killed was returned.

(Possession of the land being legally secured, the work of construction commenced by the formation of the tramway across the moor, from the road to the foot of the hill. This was a distance of two miles and a half. Mr Ashwell remarked to us, 'we worked like Yankees, and laid nearly a mile a week. A month after we began, we had a locomotive running over it. We used it until within a month of the opening of the line, and some of it was there the other day. It would scarcely, however, done for a main thoroughfare, for there were gradients of 1 in 25, and 1 in 16; and there were curves of two and a half chains radius but up and down and in and out we went till we reached our destination… Williams)

Penrith Observer, 6 September 1870

THE CULGAITH RAILWAY CUTTING

Judging from the rapid manner in which the contract of Messers. Eckersley and Bayliss is being carried out, we may expect that in a short time the Settle and Carlisle extension of the Midland railway will be opened for traffic. Though the cuttings in many places are immensely heavy, the number of hands employed, the systematic method of working, and the modern appliances that have been brought to bear upon the excavations, have in a marvellous degree facilitated the rapid completion of the contract. At Culgaith hundreds of 'line men' or navvies are engaged in forming the monster gullet running through the summit of Pea Hill, which leads to the village. The length of the cutting will be about a quarter of a mile, and its depth from the centre of the hill, at which there is a shaft already at work, is about 104 feet. From this shaft there is, night and day, a continuous raising of earth in formation of the tunnel already opened south wards.

To clear the tunnel an ingenious contrivance has been resorted to. As the tunnel is formed lines of

Navvies building a cutting by moving excavated material down a vertical shaft into the wagons below as they did at Culgaith described in the Penrith Observer September 1870. Here they are shown at East Leake Tunnel on the Great Central in 1897 these navvies are working for Henry Lovatt & Co., (Leicestershire Archives).

rails are laid, and at intervals apertures are bored upwards, terminating at the surface. Bellow each of these holes a wagon is placed, and the work men from the top, numbering about a dozen at each opening, are regularly employed in 'picking' away the soil, which runs down the opening and is taken away by the wagon and 'tipped' at an adjoining 'break'. This process is continued until the line is quite open, and the sides of the gullet sufficiently sloped. A considerable distance has already been opened out, under the direction of Mr Coomb. A brick kiln, a blacksmiths shop, and joiners shop are attached to the works, as well as labourers cottages, stores etc. The place is well worth a visit every facility being afforded of obtaining information.

The Hull and Barnsley Railway was built in the early 1880s, some five or six years after the Settle and Carlisle was finished. This railway required the construction of an 83 foot deep cutting immediately next to Riplingham tunnel. The January 1884 issue of the *Engineer* describes the method used at Riplingham and makes it clear how the cutting was made at Culgaith: 'A number of shafts were sunk to formation level from the surface and a heading was made throughout its length to connect the shafts at the bottom. After working out the shafts and getting the heading laid with rails, the trucks were run under the shafts, and the material from all round the shaft was simply dropped into the trucks, trains of which were loaded as fast as could be wished, and hauled at once off to the tips for the large bank.'

Penrith Observer, 13 September 1870

SETTLE AND CARLISLE RAILWAY

Workmen are employed day and night at Smardale viaduct, near Kirkby Stephen, in preparing for the foundations of two of the largest pillars, which are to rise above one hundred and fifty feet in height. Owing to the late rains it is necessary to have an engine pumping the water out. THE WEATHER Boisterous winds and drenching showers have characterised the weather during the past week. During the whole of Friday night a storm raged with great fury, and did some slight damage to the dwellings exposed to its full force. Sunday was comparatively fine; but yesterday the rain again fell heavily.

The Lancaster Gazette, 17 September 1870

FATAL ACCIDENT – On the 9th inst, John Lee, aged 46 years, a workman on the Settle and Carlisle Railway, now in course of construction, at Batty Wife Hole, in Ingleton Fells, when riding in a wagon on the temporary line, was thrown out of it and severely bruised on his body, legs and arms. He only survived two hours. An inquest was held on the 12th instant, at the house of John Garlick, Viaduct Inn, Batty Wife's Hole before Thomas Brown, Esq., coroner for the district. Verdict Accidental death.

Cumberland and Westmorland Advertiser, 27 September 1870

FATAL ACCIDENT IN WESTMORLAND

The New Settle and Carlisle line of railway has been rather prolific in accidents since its commencement, and we have to record another. On Monday, while a man named John Tramp, 45 years old, was working at the No2 shaft of a tunnel in course of construction at The Helm, in Westmorland, he was killed. He was engaged, along with a boy, in empting skips near the mouth of the shaft, and was seen by a man named John Thompson running towards the shaft. He was not again seen alive, his dead body being found at the bottom of the shaft. An inquest, held in the Chapel at Ormside, the jury returned a verdict of 'Accidental killing'.

Blea moor tunnel

The first work at the tunnel itself was the sinking of the shafts. This was done with the aid of a 'jack roll', which is like a windlass over a common well, until horse gins could be got into position, and these in their turn were superseded by four winding engines, placed at the four principal shafts, with which the work involved in making the shaft and lifting out the debris was accomplished. 'But how in the world did you ever manage to get that lumbering, ponderous engine up here?' we enquired of our friend Mr Ashwell. 'Pulled it up with a crab,' he replied. 'A crab!' we asked, 'what's that?' 'Well a windlass perhaps you call it. We fixed the windlass in its place; laid a two foot gauge road up the hillside in places sometimes as steep as one foot perpendicular rise in two and a half feet length, and then dragged it up… By having crabs placed one above another, we pulled up the boiler, which weighed two tons and a half, and then the engine, the lot weighing very likely six tons. The riveters put it together… When one engine was set to work, we used it for drawing up some of the others… And there for four years and more those engines did their almost ceaseless work, the two at either end winding materials or men up the incline planes from near the tunnel mouths, while the others were lowing bricks and mortar, in skeps down the shafts, or raising the excavated rock or water that found its way into the workings, and threatened, to drown them out… Williams.

The Carlisle Patriot, 14 October 1870

FATAL ACCIDENT NEAR SCOTBY

An inquest was held at the house of Mrs Graham, Scotby, on the 6th inst., upon the body of a man named Luke Fitzgerald, a native of Carlisle, who met his death upon the previous day near Durran Hill by a quantity of earth falling upon him. Deceased, who was 45 years of age, was employed as a labourer on the line of railway now in formation between Settle and Carlisle, and it appears that whilst working in a cutting near Scotby, the embankment rushed in, burying the deceased and instantly killing him. His body was immediately got out, but life was quite extinct. A verdict of 'accidentally killed' was returned.

The Sheffield and Rotherham Independent, 19 October 1870

FIGHT BETWEEN NAVVIES

Scenes of violence and bloodshed were enacted on Saturday night and Sunday morning at the village of Armathwaite, about twelve miles south of Carlisle, where a large number of navvies are employed upon the contract of Messrs. Baylis and Eckersley, in the construction of the Settle and Carlisle extension of the Midland Railway. Saturday was 'big pay' and the navvies, after receiving their wages, repaired in gangs to their respective quarters. The men consisted of Englishmen, Irishmen, and Scotsmen, divided into distinct gangs who work together, drink together, and fight together, too. The English appear to have fancied that the Irishmen were working for less money than themselves, and this suspicion engendered much ill feeling, which vented itself in a very forcible manner when men had drunk deep.

A company of navvies were on Saturday night drinking in the New Inn, about a mile from the village, and tossing for a gallon of ale, when another gang came up and demanded admittance. The inn being already full, they could not obtain admission but by way of effecting a forcible entrance, they stormed the house smashing the windows with stones and making a complete wreck of the place. A general fight ensued, in which many heads were broken and one man fatally injured; this was a navvy, named Cornelius Cox, an Irishman, who, it is stated, had been held up and kicked in a very savage manner by two navvies, while a third battered his head with a spade. After being thus abused he was thrown over a wall, where he was discovered two or three hours afterwards so much injured that his case was at once seen to be hopeless. He died on Monday afternoon.

A Scotsman named Campbell was pursued by a dozen navvies to a store belonging to the contractors, and there brutally kicked and mutilated. Another navvy was left on the road with his ribs broken, while broken heads and bruised faces were very numerous. Sunday was spent in drinking and disorder, but as the New Inn had been wrecked, and the principle public house of the village drunk dry, the violence somewhat abated, and the arrival of a body of police to reinforce the local constabulary tended to preserve order.

On Sunday, however, a combined plan of action had been arranged. The Irishmen all working in a cutting known as Dickenson's cutting, and two strong gangs of Englishmen, much more numerous than the Irish, are employed in Low Wood cutting and Barron Wood cutting. On Monday morning, a gang from each of these places began simultaneously to march upon Dickenson's cutting, with the avowed intention of driving the Irish from the works. The Lowwood division was found in the village four deep, armed with bludgeons. But the timely appearance of a body of the county police across the road with cutlasses had the effect of checking the march.

The other gang from Barronwood, however, did succeed in making its way to Dickenson's cutting, and driving the Irishmen from the works. This done, they broke up into groups and spent the day in loitering about the roads, and there were frequent fights, all work suspended. Three men have been apprehended on the charge of being concerned in the murder of Cox, and three others as ringleaders in the riotous affray. On Tuesday, the English and Scots resumed work, the Irish having left the neighbourhood.

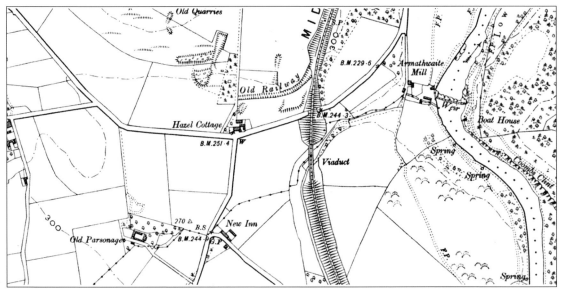

Map of 1896 showing the New Inn at Armathwaite and its proximity to the railway viaduct. It was at the New Inn that the Armathwaite navvy riot took place in October 1870. The inn was in existence before the railway construction started. Note the disused railway that the contractors used to extract stone from the quarries for the railway works.

The Aberdeen Journal, 19 October 1870

Yesterday, while two navvies employed on the Settle and Carlisle Railway were drinking together in a public house, near Appleby, one of them accidently shot the other dead, with a loaded gun, which he took down from the ceiling to examine. The two men were on friendly terms, and lived together.

The Lancaster Gazette, 29 October 1870

At the Penrith petty sessions, on Tuesday, Charles Parker, alias 'Punch', John White, and William Kaisley, three English navvies, were charged with wilful murder of Cornelius Cox, at Armathwaite. The three prisoners were committed to Carlisle assizes on a charge of wilful murder.

The Evening Gazette, 2 November 1870.

THE POACHING AFFRAY IN CUMBERLAND

Armathwaite, the scene of the recent murderous riots among the navvies engaged in the construction of the Settle and Carlisle Railway is becoming notorious for violence and bloodshed. Another affray, which very nearly resulted in another murder has occurred there. In this instance, a gamekeeper in the employment of Sir George Musgrave, Bart., of Edenhall, was the victim. It appears that on Saturday the gamekeepers of Sir George Musgrave found some snares in Barron Wood set for the capture of hares. Knowing that the owners would in due time return to take the game out of the snares, they arranged to meet at a certain hour on Sunday morning and watch.

At the appointed time, only one of the keepers, a man named Harrison, appeared at the rendezvous. After he had watched for some time, he saw two men approach, whom he recognised as navvies upon the railway works; and having seen enough to identify them with the ownership of the snares, he emerged from his hiding place, and attempted, single handed through he was, to seize the two poachers. One of them, however, took to his heels. The other, who was made of sterner stuff, remained behind and made a desperate attack upon the watcher.

A fierce encounter ensued, in which the poacher ultimately had the best of it, for he left the watcher lying insensible upon the ground, with one leg broken and with many severe wounds upon his head and face. On Monday, Superintendent Parker, of Appleby, Westmorland, apprehended two men at Kirkby Stephen, and removed them to Penrith for identification, where they were identified. The game keeper is more seriously injured than was at first thought of, and the police believe that both poachers must have engaged in the attack upon him.

The New Inn, Armathwaite, where the navvy riots took place in October 1870. The building on the right, now a private house, was the original inn and was later extended to the left (author's collection).

Cumberland and Westmorland Advertiser, 22 November 1870.

BOY KILLED ON THE SETTLE AND CARLISLE EXTENSION LINE

On Monday week, at Barron Wood, near Armathwaite, an accident, which terminated fatally, occurred to a boy of the name of Hughes, ten years of age, whose father is the owner of two wagons on the line now in course of construction. It appears that the foxhounds were hunting in the neighbourhood, and in order to obtain a better view of them the little fellow climbed on to one of the wagons. Whilst in this position another wagon came up the line, striking the one he was standing upon with such force as to cause the lad to lose his balance and fall upon the line, one of the wheels instantly passing over his head injuring him to such an extent that he died within a quarter of an hour.

Cumberland and Westmorland Advertiser, 6 December 1870.

ROBBERY AT LITTLE SALKELD

The construction of the Settle and Carlisle extension having brought together great numbers of navvies and other workmen, in various places along the route provision stores have been opened in obedience to the inevitable law of 'supply and demand', by the tradesmen living in the adjacent towns. On Friday morning the 24th ult., one of these stores opened at Little Salkeld by Mr H. G. Pattinson, grocer, Penrith, was discovered to have been forcibly entered, and a quantity of goods together with a sum of money, stolen from therein.

The extemporised store had previously formed a portion of a dwelling house, which it now adjoins, and the business is conducted by Mr Joseph Pattinson, a brother of the proprietor, who left it as usual on the previous evening, and proceeded to his lodgings at a little distance, having first double locked the door with both an ordinary and a hang lock. Next morning, it was found that the staple holding the hang lock had first been forcibly wrenched from its place, and, as was proved by the state of the other lock, the door had been burst in. Having obtained admission, the thief or thieves had ransacked the place, and taken all the money which had been left, consisting of some two and sixpence in copper.

They had also evidently had a penchant for tobacco, as two rolls containing together about 16lbs. had been removed, but in addition to these, the only other articles missing were a loaf of bread and some butter, which had probably been used for present necessity. The drawer in which the tobacco was kept was found lying on the road near the store. Particulars were at once communicated to the police, but as yet no trace of the depredators has been discovered.

Hugh George Pattinson, Greenfield House, Brunswick Road, Penrith was a grocer at 47 King Street, *Post Office Directory,* 1873.

Penrith Observer, 13 December 1870.

THE NAVVIES AT LAZONBY

Mary Ann Dixon, landlady of the Joiners Arms Inn at Lazonby, was charged with knowingly permitting drunkenness, tippling, and other disorderly conduct in her house, against the tenor of her licence, on Saturday, the 6th ult. Police constables Taggart and Musgrave, who proved the offence, stated that the house was tenanted by two navvies, who were drunk and creating a great noise, which was continued after they had been turned out of the house at the request of the defendant. P.C. Robinson stated that when Mrs Dixon refused to supply drink the men insisted upon helping themselves. In reply to Mr Cant, witness admitted that when the police arrived Mrs Dixon said to the navvies, 'Out you go'. Mr Dowson:- The disturbance was the result of the defendant supplying drink to those men. She ought to have stopped the tap before they were drunk. Mr Cant contended that defendant had followed the instructions of Supt. Fowler as far as possible. Defendant and her mother had occupied this house for forty years, and there had been no previous complaint. Case dismissed on defendant paying the costs of five shillings.

Chapter Three
1871

Cumberland and Westmorland Advertiser, 3 January 1871

APPLEBY CHRISTMAS CHEER

The mechanics, along with several of the officials connected with the construction of the Appleby section of the Settle and Carlisle Railway extension, celebrated their annual festival at the house of Mr Joseph Longrigg, the Crown and Cushion, on Monday afternoon. For years past it has been the custom of the mechanics under Mr Joseph Firbank, in whatever part of the globe they were located, to meet in interchange of those civilities which at this festive season are universally recognised. A substantial repast was prepared by the hostess, which included not only the substantials, and the most delicacies common at this festive season, and the highest eulogiums were passed by the company, which numbered between 30 and 40, on the handsome manner in which Mrs Longrigg had catered for her guests. After the removal of the cloth Mr Johnson was called to the chair, and Mr James Jenkins occupied the vice chair. The health of the contractor, Mr Joseph Firbank, was enthusiastically received. Mr Throstle, the engineer, and the general staff were in turn duly honoured, as well as the chairman and vice-chairman, and a very pleasant and agreeable evening was spent with toasts, songs, and recitations.

The Sheffield and Rotherham Independent, 6 January 1871

THE LATE COLLISION BETWEEN IRISH AND ENGLISH NAVVIES IN CUMBERLAND

At the Cumberland Quarter Sessions, on Wednesday, three navvies named Jos French, Joseph Draper, and Thomas Jones, were each sentenced to twelve months imprisonment, for rioting at Armathwaite on the 17th October last. It will be remembered that the riot occurred between Irish and English navvies on the Settle and Carlisle Railway, and that a man was killed in the affray. The prisoners took an active part afterwards in exciting the others to riot in driving the Irish off the line.

Cumberland and Westmorland Advertiser, 10 January 1871

ACCIDENT ON THE SETTLE AND CARLISLE RAILWAY

In works of such magnitude as the formation of a long line of railway, and the great danger to which the men engaged upon them are exposed, it is wonderful that accidents are not more frequent occurrence than they are. On Friday last a catastrophe occurred on the Settle and Carlisle extension near the village of Culgaith. While engaged in a cutting, a rush of earth took place, and one of the men was buried beneath a covering six or seven feet in depth. At the time the 'slip' occurred he was standing upon a plank, which was tilted into an upright position and formed an aperture through which the poor fellow was enabled to breathe. A strong body of men were soon upon the spot, and energetic measures adopted to rescue him from his perilous position. This, however, was a work of some time, and when at length the debris was removed it was found the unfortunate man had sustained injuries of a most severe character.

Penrith Observer, 10 January 1871

LOCK-UP AT LAZONBY OR KIRKOSWALD

The Rev. J. Heysham drew attention to the want of a lock-up at Lazonby, or Kirkoswald especially during the progress of the works on the Settle and Carlisle Railway. The Chief Constable stated that he had in accordance with the request of the Penrith Petty Sessions made inquiries as to whether he could obtain a house or a room in a house to be fitted up as a strong room, but such a place could not be found in either of the villages. After some discussion it was left to the Penrith Magistrates to take the matter into consideration and see what temporary arrangements could be made to meet the requirements of the case, and report to next Sessions.

The Reverend John Heysham, MA., was the vicar at Lazonby from 1846-77. He was also Justice of the Peace. He was 78 years old at the time of the census in 1871 and unmarried. He lived at the Rectory with a housekeeper, gardener, coachman, two male servants and a female domestic servant.

Penrith Observer, 31 January 1871

FATAL ACCIDENT IN BARRON WOOD

Last Monday, a man, 31 years of age, a labourer, named Barney Clarke, was killed in Barron Wood. Deceased was at work, along with several others, on the new Settle and Carlisle line, and a large piece of rock fell from the roof of the tunnel, struck him, and killed him on the spot. The roof was considered quite safe, having been finished as progress was made. The dead body of Clarke was removed to the New Inn, where on Tuesday an inquest was held and the jury returned a verdict of 'Accidental killed'.

Cumberland and Westmorland Advertiser, 31 January 1871

FATAL ACCIDENT AT NEWBIGGIN

Another of those accidents, now so frequent, occurred on Tuesday last, and was unfortunately fatal in its character. The deceased (whose name was Joseph Jackson, from Beverley, in Yorkshire) was in the employ of Mr Coombes, contractor, and was engaged in 'trimming' a wagon at Haggs Wood, near Newbiggin, Temple Sowerby, on the above day, and the wagon being accidentally upset by a root, deceased was killed on the spot. His body was conveyed to the Black Swan Inn, Culgaith. No inquest was held.

Manchester Times, 4 February 1871

FIRE AT THE WORKS OF THE SETTLE AND CARLISLE RAILWAY

A fire broke out on Saturday morning at the tunnel mouth on Section 2 of Messrs Benton and Woodiwiss's contract, and destroyed the store shed containing material used in the prosecution of the work. The damage to property is great, and the excavation will be delayed for a short time.

Contract No 2 was from Dent Head to Smardale Viaduct near Kirkby Stephen, a distance of about seventeen miles. It was let in November 1869 to Benton Woodiwiss. John Story was the resident engineer. Assistant engineer Frank de Lynn. James Hay was the contractors agent.

Abraham W. Woodiwiss was born in 1828 in Belper Derby the fourth son of Duffield stone merchant George and his wife Dorothy. In 1841 he was living at Hopping Hill, working as a labourer. He married Emma in 1848, and moved to Derby Dale. The 1871 census finds him at 41 Osmaston Road, Derby, now a contractor with six children. By 1881 he had moved to 117 Osmaston Road, and was employing three servants. He became mayor of Derby from 1880-82 and was knighted in 1883 by Queen Victoria at Osborne House. He died in 1884 at Menton in France, where he went on doctor's advice. By all accounts he was a generous, kindly and fair minded man. After the Settle and Carlisle line contract was completed Benton and Woodiwiss went on to build the Great Northern line from Keighley to Bradford and Halifax.

Penrith Observer, 7 February 1871

CULGAITH: THE RAILWAY TUNNEL

Last week, from some cause at present unexplained, a portion of this immense tunnel fell in. The roof was considered perfectly safe, and the workmen were passing regularly. We are glad to learn, however, that none of them were injured by the accident.

Penrith Observer, 14 February 1871

ACCIDENTS ON THE SETTLE AND CARLISLE RAILWAY

On Thursday a 'tipper', between seventeen and eighteen years of age, fell whilst driving his horse. The wheel of the wagon passed over his leg, which was nearly cut off. The mutilated limb has since been amputated and dressed at the Carlisle Infirmary. On the same day a labourer was seriously crushed by a fall of earth, in the cutting near Appleby.

The Carlisle Patriot, 10 March 1871

WALKING OFF WITH A NAVVY'S KIT

On Tuesday, a navvy named Thomas Atkinson called at the lodgings of a navvy named John Long, in Appleby, and represented himself to be Long's brother and asked for his bundle which contained three shirts, value 8s; a pair of moleskin trousers, value 8s; a woollen cord waistcoat 9s; a new hat, 2s-6d; two navvy's slops, 5s; two pairs of stockings, 1s-6d; and a scarf, 6d. After giving the bundle to Atkinson, the woman thought all was not right and immediately informed Long of what had taken place. Information was given to the police, and pursuit made, when he was apprehended with part of the cloths upon him, and in his hurry to get into the stolen goods the shirt had been put on with its back to the front.

The Lancaster Gazette, 11 March 1871

Inquest: An inquest was held at the Craven Inn, Giggleswick, on Saturday last, before Mr J. P. Brown, deputy coroner, on the body of George Dripple, a single man, aged 36 years, who was accidentally killed on Friday last near Helwith Bridge, Settle, on the Settle and Carlisle Railway now in the course of construction. The deceased was employed as a 'tipper' and whilst thus engaged he stumbled and fell across the rails, the wheels of the laden wagon passing over his body, and crushing him badly; he died whilst being conveyed to the hospital. No blame was attached to anyone, and the jury returned a verdict that the deceased was accidentally killed by a railway wagon running over him.

The process of 'tipping' was used to make embankments. A tramway was made from the cutting to the embankment and at the extreme end, a stout baulk of timber was fastened to prevent wagons going over the edge. The truck of spoil had a horse fastened to it, walking by the side of the line it began to trot and then gallop. The man running along side then detached the halter and both stepped to one side as the truck hit the baulk of wood allowing the contents to tip down the face of the embankment. The empty truck was then taken back by the horse and man to be refilled.

Lancaster Gazette, 18 March 1871

USING THREATENING LANGUAGE

Edward Burgoyne, of Batty Wife Hole, bookkeeper, who had been apprehended under a warrant the previous day, and was remanded on bail from the 9th to the 10th inst., was brought before the Rev. B Richard Denny, charged with threatening the life of Frederick Taylor, of Hewitt Bridge, Horton Parish, provision dealer, in the words or to the effect following: 'If you do not deliver up those papers I will fire at you.' Several witnesses were called on each side, when it was proved that the complaint had threatened to strike defendant with a hammer, whereupon Burgoyne said, 'If you strike I will fire.' After evidence of Mr Cox, who stated that complainant was under his employ, and that the day previous to the alleged threat he examined Taylor's books and invoices and had found he was deficient in his accounts to the amount of £34 and, also, that he Cox sent Burgoyne to Helwith Bridge to take charge of the shop. The defendant was then discharged, complainant having to pay costs.

Mitchell provides us with some background information:– Messers Burgoyne and Cocks, a name that varied in its spelling, had premises in Settle and Batty Green. From here they supplied smaller shops at Stainforth, Helwith Bridge, Horton, Selside, Ashes, Sebastopol, Jericho, Tunnel Huts and Dent Head. So successful were the two businessmen that in 1871, within a year of commencing to supply the railway families with provisions, the partners moved to new premises in Duke Street, Settle. 'This establishment is a great improvement to the street, on this account the firm last week gave their customers 500 glass jugs and sugar basins.' At Settle, using two large ovens, Messers Burgoyne and Cocks produced 4,000 loaves of bread daily and nearby was a large butchering shop where four fat cows and from ten to fifteen sheep, besides porklings and fat pigs were slaughtered weekly. The partners also supplied from the Batty Green premises newspapers and periodicals. Mr Cocks appears to have been the financial wizard. He pored over the books, and was quick to detect discrepancies, such as those occurring in the ledgers being kept by the manager at Helwith Bridge. Mr Cocks immediately instructed his partner to investigate, and to ensure that no further goods were taken until legal proceedings began from, *Shanty Life on the Settle and Carlisle Railway*).

Lancaster Gazette, 18 March 1871

Assault: On the 15th inst., at the Court House, before C. Ingleby, Esq. and the Rev Richard Denny, James Rixon, of Sebastopol, Batty Wife Hole, brick maker, who had been in custody since the 13th inst. was charged, on the information of Emma Shackleton, of the same place, married women, with assaulting her in an aggravated manner, on the 11th inst. at Sebastopol. The defendant, it would appear, has lately had his troubles, having twice lost his better half with in about a fortnight, from the effects of which and 'John Barleycorn' he has approached somewhat to the position of a mad man. After hearing the witnesses on both sides the defendant was fined 1s and 14s-4d costs.

Mitchell quotes from the *Lancaster Guardian* 1871:

The brick making establishment (at Batty Green) is under the management of Mr Rixon. The brickworks cover a large space of moorland and consist of extensive drying sheds, ovens, a large patent brick-making machine by Porter and Co., of Carlisle, a crushing machine, and a traveller seventy yards long to deliver the bricks in the shed above the ovens where they are dried by the waste heat. Porter's machine when in full work will make about 20,000 bricks a day. At present, as only half of it is at work, it makes from 11,000 to 12,000 a day. There are ten ovens with two fire holes to each oven. An oven holds from fourteen to fifteen thousand bricks, and it takes about a week to burn them. The quantity of fuel con-

Earth wagons tipping to form an embankment pictured here on the Hull and Barnsley Railway built between 1880-85. Photograph courtesy of Hull Museum.

sumed at these works is only half the quantity at an ordinary brick kiln. The bed of clay which lies under a thin strata of peat is a mud deposit and much of it on account of its nature is thrown aside. A crushing machine is employed to grind shale which, being intermixed with the clay used at the works, yields bricks of such a superior quality that when thrown out of the ovens they ring like pots. From 26 to 28 persons are employed at the works. Two girls were busy carrying bricks from the never-ceasing traveller. The large quantities of bricks made at these works are used for lining and arching the tunnel, from *How they Built the Settle and Carlisle Railway.*

Lancaster Gazette, 25 March 1871

STEALING TOOLS

John Lamb, alias 'Little Jack' was brought up on remand before J. Birbeck Esq., and the Rev. H. Swale on the 16th inst., charged with having on the 25th ult., stole a quantity of masons tools from the blacksmith's shop in No 1 cutting on the new Settle and Carlisle railway the property of James Thistlewaite. The prisoner was traced by P.C. Taylor from Settle to Batty Wife Hole and Dentdale; from the direction of Kirkby Stephen. Information was furnished to the police authorities in Cumberland, by whom he was subsequently apprehended, and handed over to the Settle police. The charge was fully proved to which the prisoner made no defence. Inspector Ireland, who had charge of the case, said he thought it was his duty to state to the Bench that whilst the prisoner had been in Cumberland he had been of great service to the police there, having run down and secured a man who had stolen some blankets. The

Bench remarked that they were glad that the above circumstances had been mentioned, and in consequences thereof would pass a more lenient sentence than they otherwise would have done. The prisoner was then sentenced to two months imprisonment with hard labour.

Cumberland and Westmorland Advertiser, 28 March 1871

THE NAVVIES AND THE ROYAL MARRIAGE

With the foresight and liberality which ever characterise the acts of the worthy baronet, the owner of the broad and fruitful domain of Edenhall, the robust and hardy sons of toil upon the Longwathby section of the Settle and Carlisle Railway were, on Tuesday last, the nuptial day of Princess Louise and the Marquis of Lorne, enabled to enjoy an unexpected treat in honour of an event which has been hailed with satisfaction among all ranks and classes of the realm. Two casks, containing seventy two gallons of sterling home-brewed, were through Sir George Musgrave's orders conveyed from his own cellars and placed at the disposal of Mr Jones, the travelling ganger, to distribute amongst the navvies. This he did to the satisfaction of every one. Of course the health of the newly-married pair was drunk with ringing cheers; and loud hurrahs which arose when the health of Sir George, his good lady, and respected family was given, might have been heard at the mansion of the worthy baronet. Timely acts of thoughtful kindness like this, and emanating from so high a quarter, cannot be too highly commended, and must tend to create a better feeling amongst a class of men who often look upon the wealthy as enemies of the poor.

Princess Louise 1848-1939 was the sixth child to Queen Victoria; she married John Marquis of Lorne the heir to the Duke of Argyll on 21st March 1871.

Penrith Observer, 28 March 1871

SETTLE AND CARLISLE RAILWAY

The ceremony of laying the first stone of the Helm Tunnel, in the parish of Ormside, near Appleby, on the contract No 3 of the Settle and Carlisle Railway extension, took place on Saturday last. The stone was laid by the resident engineer, Mr Drage, in the presence of Mr Throstle, Mr Christopher Firbank, and a number of workmen, who afterwards united in a toast, wishing prosperity to the undertaking. The tunnel, the only one on contract No 3, is situate about four miles from Appleby, near a farmhouse known as The Helm, where the contractor, Mr Joseph Firbank, has erected a large number of temporary cottages, occupied by some five or six hundred navvies engaged on the work in the district. The tunnel through which a heading or drift way has already been driven, will be 528 yards in length. The ground throughout is of boulder clay and the shale, with a band of limestone rock; and will consequently require a lining of brick and stonework for its entire length. Most of the stone used will be in the tunnel itself, and the bricks are made on the ground by machinery erected for that purpose. It is expected the tunnel will be completed in about nine months.

The resident engineer was Jesse Drage. The contractor was Joseph Firbank and the contractors agent was J. Throstle.

Cumberland and Westmorland Advertiser, 28 March 1871

LARCENY BY A RAILWAY LABOURER

On Tuesday last, the police apprehended, at Crosby Garrett a man named John Banks, railway labourer, 31 years of age and a native of Essex, charged with having stolen from a hut at Crosby Garrett, on the 18th inst., a small wooden box containing eight half-sovereigns, seven shillings in silver, and three pence in copper, a silver watch guard, two jet broaches, a pair of jet earrings, a pair of gloves, and three

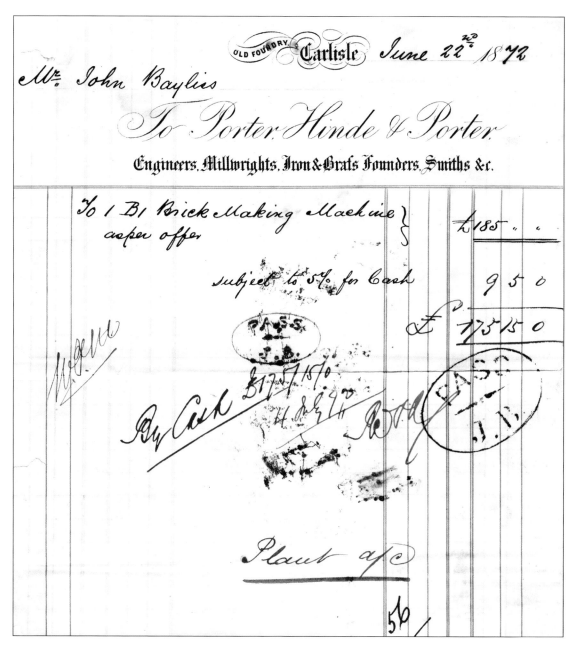

Brick making machines were in use on the Settle and Carlisle Railway. Mr Mitchell in his book 'Ribble Head the Viaduct', mentions machines made by Porter & Co., Carlisle, and notes that 1.5 million bricks were made for Ribblehead Viaduct at the Batty Green brickworks that were run by Robert and John Nixon, two brothers from Northamptonshire.

John Francis Porter was born in Carlisle in 1810 and worked for his father, an iron master. He had no formal engineering training but learne much from his father's works. In 1857 he began, with his brother George Porter, at the Old Foundry in Carlisle, constructing brick making machines for the East India Railway. This bill from an archive fromally belonging to the solicitors Wright Brown and Strong of Carlisle, confirms that Mr Bayliss the contractor, bought a machine from Porter and the date of 1872 coincides with his work on the Settle and Carlisle Railway. (Photograph author's collection).

dog licences, the property of John Stacey, labourer, Crosby Garrett. Prisoner had lodged in the same hut, and when apprehended denied having any money upon him. On searching him the police found something hard inside his jacket lining, and the prisoner said it was a piece of tobacco, but on pulling it out, it was an old necktie with the end cut off and containing six half-sovereigns and 9s 6d in silver. He was taken before the magistrates and remanded.

The Bradford Observer, 1 April 1871

Ellis Parker alias Nelson (25) labourer, was charged with the manslaughter of Christopher Wright at Langcliffe on the 9th January last... It appears from the evidence that the deceased had kept a beer house called the Bay Horse at Langcliffe, a place about a mile from Settle and near where the Settle and Carlisle railway has been constructed. The prisoner is a navvy and was employed on the railway. On Sunday night, the 9th of January, the prisoner with one of his mates went into the beer house. He was under the influence of liquor, and observing this the landlady refused to sell him any drink. There were many other labourers in the house, and the prisoner managed to get more drink among them. At eleven o clock all the company went out except the prisoner and his companion, but they refused to go. Mrs Wright then asked the prisoner if he would go if she gave him sixpence. He said he would, and she accordingly gave him sixpence. He then, however, refused to go, demanded a gallon of ale, and said he would see who was master of the house. He also said that that he was 'the champion' from London. Mr Wright the deceased, who was about 75 years of age, sent his granddaughter out for the parish constable, and as he did not come a messenger was sent to fetch a police officer. There was not one to be found. In the meantime the prisoner commenced to abuse the deceased. He threw him down on the floor and in falling his head came in contact with the long settle. In consequence of the blow Mr Wright died a few days later. The judge said from the evidence he should think it was an aggravated case of manslaughter and would pass sentence in the morning.

Penrith Observer, 11 April 1871

ELOPEMENT AND ALLEGED ROBBERY AT LAZONBY

At the Penrith Police Court, on Saturday, two navvies named John Thompson and Simon Spencer, alias James Mace, were brought up on remand, charged with stealing two shirts, a few knives and forks, two sheets, and a towel, the property of Thomas Fitzpatrick, a railway labourer, residing at Lazonby. It appeared from the evidence of the prosecutor that on Wednesday last, whilst working upon the new line at Lazonby, he was informed by a brother workman that his wife had left the neighbourhood, and had taken with her, besides the principal portion of her own apparel, the articles mentioned above. He arrived at Lazonby in the month of August last, and his wife, who was living in Glasgow, followed him about three weeks afterwards. The hut in which they resided consisted of a kitchen and two sleeping apartments, in one of which there were six beds, capable of accommodating twelve lodgers. Sometimes they had nine men in the house, and at other times the full number. He and his wife slept in a separate apartment. On the afternoon of Wednesday last he found that his wife had left the hut shortly after dinner, and on looking over the premises, found that the property had been taken away. He at once informed the police... I found my wife had gone to Plumpton, and that the two prisoners had gone with her to Penrith... Thompson stated that he had run off with the prosciutto's wife, and thought he had done her a good turn by so doing, as he would make her a better husband than the man she had been living with...

Mr Jameson said the only ground on which they could convict Thompson was that he was aware that the articles had been taken from the husband by the wife. There was however, a possibility he might not know, and though the circumstances were somewhat suspicious, the Bench had decided to dismiss both cases.

Lancaster Gazette, 6 May 1871

ALLEGED THEFT

Amelia Newman, a married woman, residing at Settle, whose husband is employed on the Settle and Carlisle Railway, was charged with having stolen a woollen shawl, the property of Sarah Barton, servant at the Hart's Head Inn, Giggleswick. The prosecutor said the prisoner, along with others, was in the parlour of the Hart's Head Inn, on the 27th December last, and immediately they were gone she missed the shawl. On the 25th ult., she again saw the prisoner, when she had the shawl in her possession. There appeared to be some doubt as to the identity of the shawl, and the Bench accordingly discharged the prisoner.

Lancaster Gazette, 6 May 1871

Two navvies, named respectively George Thompson and James Booth, employed on the Settle and Carlisle railway, were brought up in custody, charged with having committed a violent assault upon P.C. Taylor, on Thursday, the 27th ult. From the evidence it appeared that the prisoner had savagely attacked the police constable on the turnpike road near to Ingfield, Settle, and had thrown stones at him, one of which hit the police constable on the head, and for a time rendered him insensible. Several of the stones were produced in court and were of formidable dimensions. The cries of Taylor for help were heard by two men, who were working in the neighbourhood, and with their assistance both prisoners, who were drunk, were after some difficulty, safely locked up. Both prisoners pleaded guilty, and Thompson was committed to prison for three months, and Booth, who it appeared had been most violent in his conduct, was sent for six months.

Brick making machine made by Henry Clayton, Atlas Works, London. A similar machine was used on the Midland Railway St. Pancras extension in 1865.

Penrith Observer, 16 May 1871

THE NAVVIES AT LANGWATHBY

Last week, on the arrival of about a hundred Irish navvies at the new railway works at Langwathby, the contractors for the line and the villagers, apprehending a collision between the sons of Erin and the English, a body of special constables was taken from Penrith to the neighbourhood of the huts in the above vicinity, with a view to awe the aggressors into submission. On the arrival of the constables there were indications of dissatisfaction; but the night passed over without any serious outbreak. On Sunday one of the new arrivals was severely beaten about the head, etc., and his wounds are said to be almost as serious as those inflicted upon his countryman, Murphy, at Whitehaven, a few days ago. Fears are still entertained of an outbreak of hostilities; but to what extent the dissatisfaction prevails we are unable precisely to state. We are informed that the other special constables will be called later for today.

Carlisle Journal, 30 May 1871

ANOTHER ENGINE IN TROUBLE

Yesterday the agents of Messrs Eckersley and Bayliss, the contractors of the Carlisle section of the Carlisle and Settle Railway, were busily engaged in removing an engine (Scotby) of upwards of twenty tons in weight, to a certain portion of the line now in construction. For this purpose they had a wagon drawn by 22 of the most powerful horses employed on the railway. All went on very smoothly until the bottom of Mirebank Hill, Weatheral, was gained, when the wheels sank in the ground, so much that a screw-jack had to be used in order to facilitate the removal of the ponderous load. However, in spite of the exertions of the men, and the splendid drawing of the team of 22 horses (hich, by the way is worthy of remark as it was all done voluntarily without the aid of 'whip or wattle'), the wagon remains at the bottom of Mirebank Hill, and it is a matter of doubt whether it will be possible to ascend the steep gradient with out putting down a road of stout planks.

Further details of the incident at Mirehouse are revealed in the *Westmorland and Kendal Advertiser,* 10 June 1871.

Lancaster Gazette, 4 June 1871

LARGE ENGINE

On Monday evening last, the streets at Ingleton was all in commotion in consequence of Mr Ashwell, railway contractor, having an engine conveyed to Batty Wife Hole, in Ingleton Fells. They had seventeen horses to it and thirty men, and when they got further up the dale they were obliged to add another eight horses. They arrived safe at their destination.

Cumberland and Westmorland Advertiser, 6 June 1871

FATAL ACCIDENT ON THE SETTLE AND CARLISLE RAILWAY

On Thursday, the 1st inst., a man whose name we have been unable to ascertain, but who we understand belongs to the neighbourhood of Gargrave, near Skipton, was killed by falling off a crane used for the purpose of hoisting stone out of what is called the 'deep cutting', on the new line of railway now in course of construction between Settle and Carlisle. The place where the accident happened is near Settle.

Cumberland and Westmorland Advertiser, 6 June 1871

RIOT EXPECTED AT ARMATHWAITE

Late on Saturday night, a report was brought to Mr Mousley, the manager of the Settle and Carlisle Railway, that the English navvies had arranged to again attack the Irish navvies, and drive them off the

Manning Wardle 341 'Newcastle' sister engine to 'Scotby' used by contractors Eckersley and Bayliss on the Settle and Carlisle Railway. Photograph courtesy of G. Wells.

works. Mr Mousley put himself in communication with the police. The chief constable of the county had a large force of police collected during the night and dispatched to Armathwaite early on Monday morning, under the command of Superintendents Fowler, Taylor, and Bertram. The police were armed, and fully prepared for any emergency. During the day great numbers of navvies were hanging about in groups, but no disturbances whatever occurred. There was to have been also a prize fight on that day. This timely presence of the police also prevented. There was a report in circulation that a collision did take place between the two parties of navvies, and that six men were killed. There is no truth whatever in that statement. The manager of the railway has since issued a notice, which it is to be hoped will have the effect of preventing any repetition of the disgraceful conduct that occurred at Armathwaite last winter. In this notice Messers Eckersley and Bayliss say that having reason to believe that a few evil disposed workmen engaged on the railway are endeavouring to incite some of their fellow workmen to engage in riot and other unlawful proceedings, they 'hereby caution and warn all peaceably disposed men against yielding to such bad counsels, as the utmost rigour of the law will be put in force against all offenders.' The contractors offer a reward of £50 to any of the workmen who will give such information as will lead to the apprehension and conviction of any person or persons who attempt to persuade others to join in disturbing the public peace by forcible interference with other workmen engaged on these works.

Westmorland and Kendal Advertiser, 10 June 1871

REMOVAL OF A RAILWAY ENGINE FROM CARLISLE TO DUNCOW FOLD

On Monday last several of the agents of Messrs Eckersley and Bayliss, the contractors of the Settle and Carlisle Railway, were engaged in the removal of an engine, weighing 25 tons, from Carlisle to Duncow Fold, a distance of about nine miles. The engine was conveyed by means of a strong four-wheeled wagon, the tyres of the wheels being about nine inches in breadth. No mishap occurred until the foot of

Mirebank Hill, Wetheral, was gained, when the metal on the road proved to be too thin for the ponderous load, and the consequence was that the wheels sank into the road to the depth of the nave. They were, however, raised by means of the screw jack on Tuesday, and stout planks placed under them. Early on Wednesday morning the men and horses appeared in full force, and by means of planks cut into short lengths and placed crosswise the top of Mirebank Hill was gained in about 60 lengths, which of course meant so many trials for the horses. The ascent of the hill, which by the way, is very narrow and steep, was considered by the numerous onlookers as a wonderful achievement and great credit is due to Mr G. William for the skill which he displayed in making the temporary 'way'. Such a team of horses has seldom, if ever, been witnessed in the north of England; at times 22 in double yoke, at others sixteen or eighteen in single file, according to the nature of the ground, with a reserve of five or six horses in case of need. Their admirable drawing under the able management of Messrs A. Lanning and J. Simns, the contractor's horse keepers, was the theme of much comment, the only wonder being how horses can be so well trained in such a short time as many of the animals have been in the contractor's possession. At Mr Lanning's word of command they pulled simultaneously, and at his 'wo' they ceased drawing at once. In fact, there was ocular demonstration that perfect horse discipline can be established almost with out the aid of a whip. On Thursday the engine arrived safely at Duncow Fold, amid the almost deafening cheers of the spectators

Lancaster Gazette, 10 June 1871

PETTY SESSIONS

At the Court House, Ingleton, on Friday, June 2nd, James Fassam, a labourer on the Settle and Carlisle railway at Batty Wife Hole, Ingleton Fell, was charged by Henry Heighton, medical attendant at the railway works, with unlawfully aiding and abetting one Fredrick Hoare, to assault and beat the said Henry Heighton. The defendant was fined £1-10s and costs, 13s, in default, two months imprisonment in the House of Correction at Wakefield with hard labour. The fine and costs were paid. The Chairman commented strongly on the case, and wished it to be clearly understood by the workmen and others on the new line, if a similar case was brought before them they should feel disposed to send the offender to gaol without the option of a fine.

Penrith Observer, 13 June 1871

FATAL ACCIDENT IN MALLERSTANG

On Monday week, the 5th inst., a man named John Whitell met with his death on the Settle and Carlisle Railway, at Aisgill Moor, in Mallerstang, deceased was engaged in uncoupling the horse from a team of wagons, which were moving down an incline, when he slipped and fell in front of the wagons, two of which passed over the lower part of his body. When picked up he was quite dead. We understand deceased and others, when engaged in this work were obliged to cross the rails in front of the moving wagons (a practice which cannot be too strongly deprecated), and, in addition , the unfortunate man wore a pair of clogs at the time of the accident, which, it is suggested, caused him to stumble over the rails. An inquest was held on the body by G. R. Thompson, Esq., and a common jury. A lad, who worked with deceased, deposed to seeing him fall, and heard him cry out 'Oh!' two or three times. A verdict of 'accidental death' was returned. Deceased was about 43 years of age, a single man, and a native of Preston.

Penrith Observer, 22 June 1871

SEIZURE OF BEER AT ARMATHWAITE

Last week Superintendent Fowler, of Penrith, seized a quantity of beer in a navvy's hut at Low Houses, near Armathwaite. Sergeant Roche having given the information, the Superintendent procured the search warrant and seized ten or twelve gallons of beer in a half-barrel. Part of this is stated to have been sold without licence in the hut, and the occupier will be summoned before the magistrates.

Carlisle Journal, 18 July 1871

REMOVAL OF A RAILWAY ENGINE TO LAZONBY

Last Wednesday Mr Adolphus Lanning, head horse keeper to the contractors of the Settle and Carlisle Railway, selected twenty of the best horses under his care for the purpose of removing an engine of 20 tons weight from Penrith to Lazonby. Ten splendid animals were yoked two a breast to convey the engine through Penrith, but when at the top of Castlegate, unfortunately the brake gave way owing to the great stress upon it, and the consequence was that the heavy load rushed off down the incline at a frightful speed. With great presence of mind Mr Lanning put the horses into full gallop, and happily the foot of the steep hill was reached in safety. The rest of the journey was got over without a single mishap.

Westmorland and Kendal Advertiser, 22 July 1871 (provides a second description of the above event).

REMOVAL OF A LOCOMOTIVE FROM PENRITH STATION

The interesting ceremony of 'hoisting' the first locomotive for the Eckersley and Bayliss section of the Settle and Carlisle Branch took place at Penrith Station, on Wednesday week, and was witnessed by many spectators. The engine weighs nearly 15 tons, and is neatly constructed. After being fixed upon the wagon, a performance which occupied several hours, ten splendid horses were harnessed, the whole of which were decorated with rosettes and ribbons. When about the centre of the hill in Castlegate, one of the brakes became powerless, and the horses, unable to hold back the ponderous machine, were lashed into a gallop. A scene of the wildest confusion ensued. Scores of spectators lined the footpath at each side along the route of the cavalcade, and as the engine, which was being dragged along at a furious pace, passed within a few inches of the Fish Inn, it was a miracle that either the building was not seriously damaged, or the wagon upset, Fortunately the horses and wagon moved uninjured into the open square, and proceeded at once to Lazonby in safety.

The open square referred to was the Corn Market and the Fish Inn stood facing the market at the bottom of Castlegate, a steep curved hill leading to Penrith Station. What the engine failed to do in 1871 was finally carried out in 1972 when the Fish Inn was demolished to make way for a pedestrian precinct called Poets Walk.

Penrith Observer, 25 July 1871

FATAL ACCIDENT TO A NAVVY

On Thursday week an inquest was held at Culgaith, upon a navvy named George Taylor, who met with his death on the Tuesday previous. Taylor was 30 years of age, and was employed as a driver in the construction of the new line of railway at Culgaith; and at the time of the accident he was on the night shift. He was in charge of a horse, and engaged in removing wagons from the tunnel to the bank. About two o'clock in the morning he was seen by a 'ganger' named Lawrence, to leave the tunnel, with his horse and a couple of wagons, and about half an hour afterwards the same man found him lying between the rails with his head fearfully smashed. The supposition is the deceased was caught with his head between the buffers of the two wagons whilst in the act of uncoupling them. The jury's verdict was accidental death.

Cumberland and Westmorland Advertiser, 8 August 1871

THE MIDLAND RAILWAY AND LANGWATHBY HILL

The Rev C. H. V. Pixell, of Skirwith Vicarage, writes to the newspapers as follows:- Many are the complaints that are raised by the country people living on this side of Penrith against the greater difficulty they find in getting their carts up this hill, in consequence of the alteration made in its gradient by the Midland Railway. On behalf of these people I write to ask you to give us your powerful advocacy, that the trustees of the road may be enabled to induce the Midland authorities to lower the crown of the hill.

Cumberland and Westmorland Advertiser, 15 August 1871

THE SETTLE AND CARLISLE RAILWAY

In their report for the half year, the Midland directors say, Mr Crossley reports that the works on the Settle and Carlisle Railway are proceeding as rapidly as the wet season and the available work force will admit. All the tunnels, except a short one at Birkes, are commenced, and in active progress. The large viaducts at Battywife Moss, Dent, Long Marton, Langwathby, Great Salkeld, Armathwaite, and Drybeck, are all in progress. The under bridges are in a forward state; the earth works are carried on at all the available points; there is abundant plant on all the contracts, the limit to progress being the number of men procurable. The contract for the portion of railway No1, extending to Hawes, has been let.

Penrith Observer, 22 August 1871

FATAL ACCIDENT AT ARMATHWAITE

On Wednesday last another melancholy railway accident occurred at the new works near Armathwaite, by which a young man named William Stewart, 24 years of age, lost his life. The deceased who was a 'driver' went to work about six o'clock in the morning; and in the course of the forenoon, while attempting to unfasten a chain attached to one of the horses, his foot slipped, and falling upon the line of rails, the wagons, which then in motion, passed over his body, inflicting upon him such injuries that he died within half an hour afterwards. Deceased, we believe, belonged to Penrith.

Lancaster Gazette, 26 August 1871

INGLETON THUNDERSTORM

On Friday afternoon, the 18th last, about three o'clock, a thunderstorm commenced in Ingleton and the neighbourhood, and although it lasted for two hours with out much rain, the peals of thunder were not very loud nor the flashes of lighting very vivid. On Ingleton Fell the storm was much more severe. Ten sheep were killed by lighting, and six stone masons, working at the viaduct, who had repaired to a shed for shelter from the rain, were struck by the lighting on the legs, but received no injury save a severe shock.

Cumberland and Westmorland Advertiser, 29 August 1871

FATAL ACCIDENT AT ARMATHWAITE

Another fatal accident occurred on Monday at the Settle and Carlisle Railway works at Armathwaite. One of the workmen, a man named James Laidlaw, was wheeling a barrow along Kirby's cutting, at Barron Wood, about 400 feet above the line of rails. When near the edge the unfortunate man was tripped up, and falling upon his head on to the line was instantly killed.

A boy, sometimes called a 'nipper', like David Payne (September 1871) leading the horse pullling an earth wagon during the building of the Great Central Railway. It can be seen from the photograph how such muddy conditions would lead to boys and men easily falling under the wheels of a wagon. Photograph courtesy of Leicestershire Archives.

Penrith Observer, 5 September 1871

ACCIDENTS ON THE SETTLE AND CARLISLE EXTENSION WORKS AT APPLEBY

A boy of the name of David Payne, fourteen years of age, acting as 'nipper' on the embankment at Battlebarrow, met with a serious accident on Tuesday last. He was returning with some empty wagons, riding, as is usual, on the wagon, when the horse took fright in passing over a wooden bridge, and he was thrown under the wheels by the sudden jerk, two of which passed over his thighs. One leg was fractured frightfully. He was conveyed on a stretcher, and attended by Dr. Dinwoodie, under whose care he is doing as well as can be expected, considering the serious nature of his injuries. Another accident happened the same evening to a navvy of the name of Tommy Todger, resulting in a broken leg. He had been imbibing freely amongst others of his companions, at the Kings Arms, Battlebarrow, and whilst performing some wrestling feat or other with one of his mates, fell on the kitchen floor and broke his leg. He was removed to the works known as New Belgravia, and attended by Dr. Armstrong, who reduced the fracture. This is we are informed, the third broken leg the poor fellow has had; and what still makes the misfortune worse, he had in navvies phrase 'jerked up' with his employers on Saturday night, and consequently will not be entitled to the benefit of the club.

'Jerked up' means left the job.

Carlisle Patriot, 9 September 1871

FATAL ACCIDENT ON THE SETTLE AND CARLISLE RAILWAY

Yesterday week, a man, 50 years of age, named Patrick Murphy, was killed near Armathwaite while at work on the new Settle and Carlisle line of railway in course of construction at that place. He was engaged filling a wagon in a cutting in Barron Wood, in the parish of Lazonby, when a large quantity of earth fell on him and crushed him to death. He had been warned of this danger previously, but had taken no notice. At an inquest last Saturday at Lazonby the jury returned a verdict of 'accidental death'.

Cumberland and Westmorland Advertiser, 26 September 1871

REMOVAL OF A LOCOMOTIVE ENGINE

A correspondent writes as follows:- Of far more interest to the inhabitants of Crosby Garrett than the autumn manoeuvres of the army, or the opening of the Mount Cenis Tunnel, during the past few days, has been the removal of a locomotive engine from the station at Smardale to the works on the Settle and Carlisle line at this village. The engine 'Hunslet' by name was started from the station on Tuesday morning under the superintendence of Messrs Firbank, Jun, and F. West, assisted by a large number of horses and men. It was conveyed across the river and remained all that night near the 'chapel well'. At this point the road is steep and narrow, and turns at almost a right angle. The horses being unable to draw in a straight line, the monster was towed along by ropes and pulleys, attached to the trees along by the road side. After being engaged all day on Wednesday, the men were obliged by darkness to leave it at a short distance from the village. Early on Thursday morning it was brought into the village, but did not reach its destination till dusk on Thursday evening; the last hundred yards being very steep, a line of rails was extemporised to facilitate its journey. The road was of course completely blocked during two days. One person from a distance, who met the procession with a horse and cart, had his vehicle taken to pieces and borne past the obstruction.

Smardale Station is on the Stainmore line just east of the Settle and Carlisle railways Smardale viaduct. The name 'Hunslet' could refer to the engine's builder, it is possable that this was the 0-6-0 saddle tank called Henry Appleby built in 1870 (see appendix A). The engine's name may have come from the birth of Henry James Tufton in 1871 son of Sir Richard Tufton 1st baronet whose seat was Appleby castle. Another candidate for this engine has been put forward by Mr Russell Wear in the *Cumbrian Railways Journal* October 2017: Hunslet works No 7, called 'Hunslet' an 0-6-0 ST, see appendix A.)

Cumberland and Westmorland Advertiser, 3 October 1871

SERIOUS ACCIDENT AT LANGWATHBY

On Friday last a serious accident happened to a man named Anthony Howe, a native of Langwathby, and in the employment of Mr Bayliss, contractor for the section of the Settle and Carlisle Railway extension which runs past the village. He was, we understand, employed in cutting hay and straw, to be used as provender for the horses, with a one-horse machine, when his trousers became entangled in a revolving shaft, and he was thrown to the ground. In falling he instinctively threw out his arms, which with his hand were caught amongst the cog-wheels, and cut and bruised in a frightful manner. The little finger was completely severed, and the limb nearly up to the elbow presented a shocking spectacle. The accident was witnessed by some of his fellow workmen, who stopped the machinery and released the unfortunate man from his painful position. Dr Williamson was almost immediately in attendance and after dressing the wounds he deemed it prudent to remove the poor fellow to Carlisle Infirmary, where he would receive proper and constant attention. He accordingly proceed to Carlisle the same afternoon the doctor kindly volunteering to accompany him on the journey. According to the latest accounts that have reached us he is going on favourably.

Penrith Observer, 17 October 1871

HIGHWAY ROBBERY NEAR LANGWATHBY

On Saturday last, three strangers, in the garb of navvies, made their appearance in the village of Langwathby, and at a public house there, entered into conversation with a ganger named Mr Murras. After a brief conversation, the latter consented to engage the men, and set them to work on the railway on Monday morning. With this object, and after handsomely entertaining the men, he undertook to find them lodgings, and for that purpose accompanied them along the highway. Mr Murras was accompanied by another gentleman, who, after proceeding some distance suggested that, as the night was dark, he should hand his watch over to him, which he accordingly did, and the gentleman returned to the village. Shortly afterwards, Mr Murras was set upon by the three navvies, who abused him unmercifully, felling him to the ground, and taking from him all his money and the remainder of his valuables. The men absconded. It is hoped the scoundrels will be suitably punished.

Newcastle Courant, 20 October 1871

SERIOUS ENCOUNTER BETWEEN ENGLISH AND IRISH NAVVIES

On Saturday night a serious affray took place between English and Irish navvies at Little Salkeld, Cumberland. The disturbance took place in the Druids Head public house, and in the course of which an English navvy, named Thomas Little, was stabbed by three Irish navvies John Whelan, Thomas Daley, and Charles Daley. The three men who attacked Little were apprehended and conveyed to Penrith lock up. Little was in such a dangerous state that his deposition was taken on Sunday before two magistrates, and in the presence of the prisoners.

0-6-OST, 'Henry Appleby' on the Basingstoke and Alton Light Railway. Joseph T. Firbank, son of Joseph Firbank contractor on the Settle and Carlisle Railway, is most probably one of the gentlemen in the open truck. Photographer unknown.

Post Office Directory 1858: Mrs Kidd, Druids Head, Little Salkeld, Kelly's Directory, 1906: Mrs. Jane Banks. Little may have been a local man. Several families of that surname lived in the area.

Cumberland and Westmorland Advertiser, 14 November 1871

Letter to the Midland Railway Company, Penrith, 19 October 1871

Sir, I am instructed by the Leath Ward Highway Board to inform you that Mr Bayliss, one of the contractors for the Settle and Carlisle railway, has opened out and commenced working a freestone quarry in the Township of Armathwaite, which was set out by the Inglewood Forest Inclosure Award to the Surveyor of Highways for the use of the owners and occupiers of land in the township. This quarry is situate a considerable distance beyond the limits of deviation of the railway, and no notice has been given of intention to take it, yet Mr Bayliss sets up a claim under the authority of the Railway Company to work the quarry. I am instructed by the Leath Ward Highways Board, who are surveyors of highways, to enquire whether Mr Bayliss has the authority of the company to enter this quarry, and whether the company claim to work the quarry as a matter of right. I may state that the land owners have been advised and are prepared to contend that the company have no such right.

I am, sir, your obdt servant, Jas Hudson.

Cumberland and Westmorland Advertiser, 21 November 1871

MAN DROWNED AT LANGWATHBY

A most melancholy occurrence took place at Langwathby, on Sunday last, or early yesterday morning. As some navvies were proceeding to their work upon the Settle and Carlisle extension railway, they discovered the dead body of Mr Isaac Dodd, miller, in the mill race, a short distance from his own residence. How the deceased, who was 36 years of age, got into the water we have been unable to learn, but it is supposed that he missed his footing in the darkness when passing along the temporary bridge which spans the river, near the place where the unfortunate man was found.

Langwathby Mill is on the Briggle Beck not far from Little Salkeld Station. The mill building lies at the foot of a viaduct known as Dodds Mill Viaduct.

Cumberland and Westmorland Advertiser, 21 November 1871

FATAL ACCIDENT ON THE SETTLE AND CARLISLE RAILWAY

On Tuesday last a fatal accident occurred on the railway now being made from Settle to Carlisle, at Batty Green, near Kirkby Lonsdale, to a man named John Ashton, who is supposed to be a native of New Mills, Derbyshire. It appears that the deceased tried to get on to an engine whilst in motion, but he missed his hold, and fell between the engine and a loaded wagon. The wagon ran over him and killed him instantly. The body was carried to the Welcome Home Inn, Batty Green, where an inquest was held. The verdict was 'accidently killed'.

Cumberland and Westmorland Advertiser, 28 November 1871

ACCIDENT AT LONG MARTON

On Monday afternoon week a serious accident befell Mr Lewis, foreman at the railway viaduct, at Long Marton. He was standing on the centre of the bridge, when a heavy stone, swung on cranes, struck him on the head and precipitated him to the ground, a distance of twelve feet. His head and shoulder were much hurt, and he was taken to Carlisle for surgical advice. We are glad to hear that notwithstanding his serious injuries, he has returned to Appleby, and from present appearances is likely to recover. Mr Lewis is highly respected amongst his workmen under him.

Chapter Four
1872

Penrith Observer, 16 January 1872

ACCIDENT AT LANGWATHBY

Last week an accident which might have been attended with serious consequences occurred during the process of erecting the new railway bridge at Langwathby. Just as the men were about to place a ten ton girder, at a considerable height, the guy rope snapped asunder, and the immense mass fell upon the road. Providentially all the assistants escaped from being crushed; but the work was considerably delayed.

Penrith Observer, 23 January 1872

NARROW ESCAPE AT BARRON WOOD

On Saturday last a somewhat serious accident occurred to a railway labourer, named William Douglas employed in Barron Wood cutting, near Armathwaite. The unfortunate man was mounting a wagon into which a large stone was being lowered, when one of the 'clasps' snapped, and the stone fell upon his hand, crushing it so severely that it is feared at least one of his fingers will have to be taken off. The stone weighed about two hundredweight. Had the man been a few inches nearer the wagon in all probability he would have been killed on the spot.

A contractor's locomotive taking full earth wagons to the tip at the head of an embankment during the construction of the Hull and Barnsley Railway, photograph courtesy of Hull Museum.

Penrith Observer, 13 February 1872

RAILWAY BRIDGE AT LITTLE SALKELD

The surveyor (Mr James Hudson) intimated that since the last meeting he had communicated with Mr Allan, the contractor under the Midland Railway Company. With reference to the complaint that the arch at Little Salkeld bridge was too narrow, Mr Allan replied that the company's engineer was under the impression that this was an occupation road, in which case they were not bound to extend the arch more than twelve feet. However, as it was a public highway the Board had power to compel the railway company to form an arch 25 feet in width. He (the surveyor) thought it would be sufficient if the bridge were made the same width as the road. Mr Spencer (Murrah Hall) was of the opinion the bridge should be extended to the utmost limit, because it was possible, if the traffic increased upon the road, that it might be widened. After some further discussion the matter was left in the hands of the surveyor to deal with as he thought best.

Penrith Observer, 13 February 1872

ARMATHWAITE QUARRY

The surveyor explained that some time ago complaint was made to him by the Armathwaite way warden of the way in which a township quarry, there situate, was being worked by Mr Bayliss, the contractor for the Settle and Carlisle Railway. Mr Bayliss was accordingly communicated with, and he agreed to pay for the stone used at a certain sum per cubic foot. Mr Bayliss had now prepared an account as between himself and the township, and was prepared to hand over £392-8s, for the stone used up to 31 December.

Mr Lazonby: That is a pretty large sum. They will not know what to do with it.

The Surveyor: That will be the difficulty.

Mr Lazonby: We can keep it until they do.

The Clerk: (Mr S. K. James): the total amount will be about £800.

The Surveyor: Hardly as much as that.

Cumberland and Westmorland Advertiser, 13 February 1872

ACCIDENT ON THE SETTLE AND CARLISLE RAILWAY

A young man of the name of John Carleton, living with his mother, a widow, in Colby Lane, Appleby, met with a serious accident on Tuesday last. He was engaged backing a muck wagon at the end of a cutting which crosses the Roman Road when an empty wagon came up, struck the other with great force and he was knocked down. He was found to have sustained severe injuries on his breast, and his jaw was broken. He now lies in a very dangerous state.

Penrith Observer, 20 February 1872

ORIGINAL CORRESPONDENCE: THE ALLEGED STRIKE AT APPLEBY

To the editor of the Penrith Observer.

Sir, The following paragraph appears in your issue of the 13th inst, "The blacksmiths employed on the Appleby Section of the Settle and Carlisle Railway, under Mr Joseph Firbank, the contractor, struck for an advance of 4d. per day along with the nine hours' movement on Tuesday last. The contractor acceded to their terms on the following day." Will you kindly give me space in your columns to state that the incident upon which the above is based was the demand made by four of the men for an increase of pay, to three of whom a slight advance was conceded, the other was discharged, the nine hours' movement was not mentioned.

I am, sir, yours truly, John Throssel, Manager.

Lancaster Gazette, 2 March 1872
ATTEMPTED ROBBERY OF A RURAL LETTER CARRIER
On Saturday last, as Richard Foster, letter carrier between Ingleton and Batty Wife Hole had proceeded on his journey about two miles, he met a navvy who seized him and threatened to kill him if he did not give up his money. After a severe struggle in which both fell to the ground, Foster at last managed to get away, and went as fast as he could to Batty Wife Hole, the navvy pursuing him for above a mile. When he got to Batty Wife Hole, he gave information to the policeman and they both returned and apprehended the man. They took him to the Ingleton Police Station, and he was brought before Messrs Denny and J. T. Rice, who sentenced him to two months imprisonment; and at expiration of that time to pay 28s cost, or in default to be imprisoned one month.

Lancaster Gazette, 30 March 1872

INGLETON ROBBERY
On Saturday, the 23rd inst., PC Goodison apprehended John Smith, a navvy working on the Settle and Carlisle Railway, in Ingleton Fells, charged with stealing from the person of Joseph Smith £15. Prisoner was taken to the lock up at Ingleton and remanded to the 28th inst.

Lancaster Gazette, 27 April 1872

FATAL ACCIDENT
An accident which terminated fatally happened on Tuesday last to a man named William Peacock, who was employed on the works of the new Settle and Carlisle railway, and was along with others, assisting

Sheriff Brow Viaduct with a contractor's engine on the left and a train of wagons with men working on them crossing the viaduct. The contractor's engine could be a Manning Wardle 0-6-0ST. Photograph courtesy of J. Shevelan.

to lower some timber from a bridge in course of construction across the River Ribble, at Sherwood Brow, near Stainforth, when, as the chain was being unfastened, the crane overturned and fell into the river, the deceased and another man going over with it. Peacock was found to be severely crushed and otherwise injured, the other man also sustained injuries of a serious character. Both men were conveyed to the hospital at Settle, but Peacock died the same evening. The other man, we understand, is progressing favourably. Deceased was 25 years of age and a native of St. Albans. An inquest was held on Thursday last at the Naked Man Inn, before Mr Brown, deputy coroner, when after hearing a statement of the particulars of the accident, the jury returned a verdict to the effect that Peacock was accidentally killed by a crane falling and knocking him off a bridge into the River Ribble.

Sherwood is the local name for Sherif Brow viaduct officially the Ribble Bridge. Built in 1872 with three 30 foot spans, with an arch height of 55 feet.

Lancaster Gazette, 27 April 1872

On Wednesday morning, about 6 o'clock, a man named Thomas Burrow, employed in a cutting near to Stainforth, on the Settle and Carlisle Railway was found dead in a field close by. The deceased, who was only 21 years of age, has only been in the neighbourhood for a few days, and is said to have come from Horton-in-Cartmel. An inquest was held on Thursday last, before Mr J. P. Brown, deputy coroner, at the house of Mr Thomas Greene, innkeeper at Stainforth, when a verdict in accordance with the above facts was returned.

Penrith Observer, 30 April 1872

SHOCKING FATAL ACCIDENT AT BARRON WOOD CUTTING

Another distressing accident occurred on the Settle and Carlisle Extension Railway, near Armathwaite on Friday last, by which a youth, aged fifteen years, lost his life. Whilst unloosing a horse attached to one of the wagons, near the tunnel mouth, in Barron Wood, two other wagons were driven up. By these the youth was knocked down. One of the wagons passed over his arm, whilst the other so dreadfully mutilated his body that he died almost instantly. As no blame was attached to anyone, the coroner did not deem it necessary to hold an inquest.

Lancaster Gazette, 3 August 1872

FATAL ACCIDENT AT THE RAILWAY WORKS

On Saturday morning last, as one of the engines was going towards the tunnel from Batty Green and when near to Jericho, John Jones, the fireman, was in the act of turning one of the taps connected with the engine when his foot slipped and he fell from the engine, two wagons passing over his legs and part of his body. He was at once removed to the hospital, at Settle, where he died in a few hours. An inquest was held at the Joiners' Arms, before J. P. Brown, Esq., deputy coroner, when a verdict of 'accidental death' was returned. The deceased, who was in his seventeenth year, was highly respected by all who knew him.

The York Herald, 19 August 1872

On Tuesday, a navvy employed on the Settle and Carlisle Railway near Sedburgh, named William Taylor, was found guilty of the abduction of Elizabeth Wardle, under fourteen years of age. The prisoner had enticed the girl away from the house of her father, where he had been lodging, and had taken her with him to Kendal and Lancaster, sleeping with her in the first town as his daughter. The judge sentenced the prisoner to nine months imprisonment.

Penrith Observer, 3 September 1872

SERIOUS ACCIDENT AT SMARDALE

On Friday morning last a serious accident befell a lad named Allison, employed in working the crane at the Midland Co's new viaduct, at Smardale. The unfortunate youth was just getting on to the gantry for a days work, when his foot slipped, and he was precipitated a distance of 20 feet, his head striking some timbers in the decent, and fracturing his skull. He was removed to his lodgings close by, and medical attendance procured at once... last night he was living, and even somewhat improving, considering the frightful injuries received, this seems almost miraculous. On the 8th October Allison succumbed to his injuries.

The method by which the erection of such works is carried on in the case of these high viaducts, is indicated by our engraving. A light timber stage, called a 'gantry', is constructed on each side of the work, sufficiently wide to allow of the piers and abutments being built between. A jenny, or crane, is then placed on a movable platform extending from one stage to the other. The materials are wound up either by hand or steam power, and are then moved slowly along till they can be lowered to the exact position they are to occupy. As soon as the masonry is built up to the height of the gantry, a fresh lift of timber is put on, the crane raised to the new height, and so the work continues to another stage. By these means stones of great size can be used. One in this viaduct (Arten Gill) measures fourteen feet by six feet, is a foot thick, and weighs more than eight tons... Williams.

Penrith Observer, 24 September 1872

SETTLE AND CARLISLE RAILWAY – TWO WOODEN SHOPS FOR SALE

Erected where there are a number of workmen employed on the line. Apply, by letter, to Joseph James, Post Office, Carlisle.

Penrith Observer, 8 October 1872

FATAL ACCIDENT ON THE ARMATHWAITE SECTION OF RAILWAY

On the morning of the 2nd inst., while a driver, named John Smith, aged 52 years, was unhooking his horse from a loaded wagon, at the time in motion, he, by some means or other, missed his footing, and was caught by the wagon, the wheels passing over and nearly severing both legs from his body. Dr Allen, of Armathwaite, (surgeon to this line of railway), was promptly in attendance, and rendered him all the assistance that medical skill could suggest, but in spite of all his endeavours, the poor fellow succumbed in about two hours after the occurrence.

Daily News, 29 October 1872

AMONG THE NAVVIES: FROM OUR SPECIAL CORRESPONDENT, GEARSTONES INN, WEST RIDING OF YORKSHIRE

RIBBLE HEAD VIADUCT

I am just in time to miss Mr Ashwell, the contractor, who, I am told, has gone 'up the line', and I set out to follow him. 'The line' is a temporary way which winds deviously across the hollow, already partly spanned by the huge skeleton viaduct. I scramble along some how, through knee deep bogs, on to piers whose foundations are just level with the surface, past batches of stone hewers hammering away industriously at great blocks of blue stone for the piers of the viaduct; then I find myself among these, and in labyrinthine scaffolding that encircles them, looking up at trucks and engines traversing tram roads at a dizzy height, at derricks, and blocks, pulleys, at noisy little fixed engines, and at silent busy masons. From the hollow below the viaduct I make my way somehow on to the embankment leading to it, and pick my road through the deep mire on its surface, now balancing myself on the rails that run along it, now making a stepping stone of a sleeper, now plunging mid leg into liquid mud. I find that the great tunnel is a mile and more from the end of the viaduct, and that the interval is composed partly of cutting through the wild lying moorland morass, with the deep gully of a stream on the left. I step aside to let engines pass with trains of trucks attached, full of earth or stones, the latter going on towards the viaduct, the former, waste as it is, being shot away down into the gully.

The Parson and the School

As I arrive at the beginning of a deep cutting, and pause in hesitation whether to go on or turn back, there overtakes me the clergyman of the navvies, a wiry elderly gentleman with a long white beard. It would do a fashionable curate a world of good to undertake this worthy man's work for a few months in the winter season, traversing these miry cuttings, and plunging through the bogs and the marshes on visitation duties to the outlying navvy settlements. His head quarters are in Batty Wife Hole, his church being the school room, and last Sunday evening, as he tells with something like pride, he had a congregation of ninety. He is one of the missionaries of the Manchester City Mission, and was detailed to this work on the application of the Midland Railway Company. Rough as the place is now, it must have been much rougher when he first came, some fifteen months ago. Drinking and fighting were all but universal; now they are of considerably less common occurrence. Still in such work there is little encouragement to a clergyman, and his influence must be of a passive rather than of an active kind. Every one we passed greeted him civilly, some of the lads even with affectionate respect, and the old gentleman's face glowed again with pleasure when a gigantic navvy, whom he did not know, having sheepishly saluted him said, in answer to a question, that he remembered him some years ago on some works in another part of the country. The 'parson', as most called him, was plodding his muddy way up through Jericho, past the barracks 'up tunnel', and so to Denthead at the opening into the further valley, to uplift the 'school money', and bring it back to the treasury. Mr Ashwell has organized a school system along his contract. At Batty Wife Hole there is a school master, and at Jericho and Sebastopol school mistresses. A nominal school fee is charged, and he sustains the rest of the expense.

The Contractor's Ganger

We again miss Mr Ashwell by a hair's breadth, but meet Frank Moodie,* his henchman, a stalwart Northumbrian, with a fine homely breath of north country accent, a profound pride in his navvies. Frank has the portion of line between Sabastopol and Denthead, the heaviest work in the whole section. Hither come all the best men, where the work is all piece work, and best paid because it is most severe. There had been a slip in a cutting, and 25 men are clearing out the slipped ground, working by the yard. As they toil they are the embodiment of physical force in its fullest development of concentrated energy. No man stops to lean for breath on the head of that pickaxe he wields so strenuously; the heave of the shovels is like clock work. The navvies, bare throated, their mas-

---

*1871 census: Frank Moodie born 1825 Northumberland, onlooker on railway/workshop master, aged 46 living at Ingleton Fell with wife Phyllis 40, John 14, born Northumberland, Francis 11, born Guernsey.

Turning arches on the new piers at Ribble Head Viaduct. The wooden formers were held in position by using putlocks in the pier's stone work. Steam cranes were used to haul up the building materials, photograph courtesy of the Cumbria Railway Association.

sive torsos covered but by a shirt, their strong lissom loins lightly girt, and the muscles showing out on their shapely legs through the tight, short breeches, and the ribbed stockings that surmount the ankle jacks, are the perfection of animal vigour… there is no heaviness in the muscular strength of these navvies; they sway to their work with as much suppleness as a coal porter sways under his load in unison with the vibration of the plank…

THE CUTTING

The stiff greasy blue black melts away bit by bit from before their indomitable, energetic, on-slaught, each man working as if he wrought for his life. A 'waster' among such men would stand ignominiously confessed before the morning's work were half done. Five and twenty more equally fine men are labouring of the face of a harder and deeper cutting a little further on. Seven of them abreast are plying their picks with a persistent zeal that speaks of piece work in every stroke, others are wheeling mighty barrow loads over a narrow bridge, and tipping them down a hollow. Moodie explains with pride that these two gangs are composed of the best men on the working. No ganger is needed over them; indeed, they would not brook supervision. 'The way the country has come to think now,' explains Moodie, 'good men wonna stand to be ordered about.' Only he uses a stronger expression. 'They wonna have a foreman d… their eyes and bulling about among them.' And piece work saves the contractor the expense of supervision. All that is needed is to see that the levels are right, and to have an engineer to measure work done every fortnight, against the pay day settlement. They allot their duties among themselves and 'the best man' among them is the man who can do most work, and a sulker could not live among them for an hour. They are all Englishmen I ask whether there are no Irish among them? 'Irish,' is the reply, 'they'd take up an Irishman by the back of the neck and throw him over the bank into the river.'

THE 'TOMMY' SHOP

These men heap fuel lustily into the furnace of their vital energy. Many of them eat eighteen pounds of beef in the week. Beef is their fare. Mutton they reckon of little account, and bacon as only used to fill up the interstices. As we look at them the 'tommy truck' makes its appearance behind an engine. It is a peaked roofed structure, like the cabins shepherds sleep in on the Downs, and it is full to the eaves of great sides of beef that have been sent up from Settle. A firm in Batty Wife Hole supply nearly the whole of the edibles to the navvy communities along this section, sending carts daily or bi-weekly across the moors to the different villages. There is no truck direct and hardly any inferential truck. I make no doubt any other tradesman, if found it worth his while, might oppose the Batty Wife Hole 'tommy shop'.

JERICHO

We clamber out of the cutting and go to Jericho, Jericho consists of two rows of huts standing forlornly on the shoulder of perhaps the bleakest moor in England. Every thing is sluggish and nasty outside them; but the sweeping breezes that rakes the hill side keeps the place fairly sweet scented, notwithstanding the stationary dirt and the erratic pigs. Every hut in Jericho is as full of lodgings as it can hold, and if he had twenty more, Moodie says he could fill them, owing to the keenness

The piers of Ribble Head Viaduct rising out of the moorland, showing the navvy huts dotted around the site. Those clustered in the distance were called Belgravia and the settlements near the viaduct were Inkerman and Sebastopol. The Batty Green encampment of huts were to the right next to the road, , photograph courtesy of the Cumbria Railway Association.

of the men for the high wages on the neighbouring heavy work, and the propensity to crowd into the tunnel working in the wet and cold weather. The parson, Moodie, and myself are invited into one of the huts, and sit down before a blazing fire in the society of three buxom navvy ladies, one of whom has a pretty child in her arms. A big piece of beef is cooking in the oven, and a pot full of potatoes is simmering over the fire. Everywhere are present the signs of sluttish, wasteful plenty; fragments go for nought when people eat a pound and a half at a meal.

A navvy is sitting by the fire nursing a bruised foot; such accidents are necessarily not uncommon. The mistress draws us a glass of excellent beer, and indeed proffers whisky. Then we hear of the reformation of Jericho. Moodie has passed along the hill side on a Sunday morning, and seen seven fights simultaneously progressing on the strip of level moor in front of the huts. There has not been a fight in Jericho for the last fortnight. True, suggests the impartial quarry man by the fire side, that may in part be owing to the cold weather, since, as it seems, it is in summer that the men drink hardest and fight most; but both the parson and Moodie are impressed with the belief that it is indicative of a real and substantial improvement. Quarrelsome men get their dismissal from Jericho as soon as they expose their foible, and it seems rapidly becoming a happy family of exceptionally stalwart men.

Before we leave, I am shown over the hut which (paper apart) is both warm and watertight. The living room is in the centre, entered through a porch. At either end is a sleeping room, one being for the family the other for lodgers. The room allotted to the latter contains three good sized and fairly clean truckle beds. As I learn that there are six lodgers, I gather that each bed is occupied by a couple. On one of the beds lies a copy of the *Graphic*. The navvy thirst for literature and art is not, however, so strong as to stimulate him to an investment in the *Graphic*. It appears that several copies of that paper, as also of the *Illustrated London News*, many weekly papers, and a large number of *British Workmen*, are every week gratuitously distributed by Mr Ashwell, the contractor for this section, who I am bound to say, appears to make every effort to promote the health and comfort of the thousand men to whom he gives employment.

THE TUNNEL

Bidding adieu to Jericho, after an outside inspection of a chaotic heap of stones, which I am profoundly surprised to find is hollow, and contains what, for want of a better name, must be called a public house, we return to the cutting, which is now nearing the mouth of the tunnel, and which as yet has not been excavated at this point within some thirty or forty feet of the intended level. Within a couple of chains of the mouth of the tunnel we come upon a shaft, down in the depths of which 25 Cornish and Devonshire miners are excavating to right and to left of them along the level intended for the permanent way. They are working in blue stone rock, as hard as the nether millstone, not a spoonful, to use the phrase of my companion, comes out with out powder. We hear the clink of their drills, and every now and then the dulled report of a blast. Tub after tub comes to the surface laden with jagged fragments of the stone. There is still the tunnel to be visited, where some 500 men are steadily burrowing through the heart of the rocky Blea Moor, and where alone Irishmen labour alongside Englishmen. But time does not serve for the present, and I should prefer to be accompanied by Mr Ashwell himself.

THE CONTRACTORS RAILWAY

I came up on foot, but Moodie undertakes that I shall be sent back on wheels. When a man in authority here desires to ride, he calls, not for his carriage , but for his engine. If he had guests, and chose, in imitation of the lavish gentlemen with curricles, to order more engines, I have no doubt that his behests would be fulfilled. 'Your engine waits,' says Moodie, and we ascend. We stand with our feet on a narrow ledge, and clutching with our hands a bar either side of the boiler of the puffing, screeching, impetuous and yet docile little *Curlew*, and having had fastened on behind a few trucks containing stones, we move on. I need not say that the temporary rails laid down for service during the construction of a railroad, differ totally from an orthodox permanent way. You must lay your account with bumps, jerks, miscellaneous and incomprehensible wobbling, and a seemingly tipsified character of things in general. You go, as a matter of course, down declines that would make the hair on the head of a Government Inspector stand on end, and labour up inclines that would wind a foot passenger, Presently there is a shout and the engine halts, the last truck has lumbered off the rails. There is a rush of all surrounding hands, and it is prised and purchased back in an incredibly short time. We make progress, but at the top of an incline over against Sebastopol the engine itself quits the rails, and I quit it preferring to perform the rest of my journey on foot.

BACK TO THE HUTS AND THE NAVVY

Returning to Batty Wife Hole, I explored with some deliberation that interesting collection of habitations, and found it in several respects to improve on closer acquaintanceship. There is a little sequestered colony of employees here; the surveyor and engineer of the company, the staff of the contractor, the doctor, and the clergyman, and very dull times of it I imagine they must have. There is a post office, savings bank, and money order office, very little resorted to by the navvy population, who are given neither to save nor to remit. There is a reading room, or rather the same room serves for chapel, school, and reading room. There is a fever and small pox hospital, happily unattended now for some months, and an accident hospital is being erected. Each workman contributes 1½d per week for the doctor and ½d for the hospital, admissions to which he is entitled to in case of accident. I found out that Batty Wife Hole had tolerable sewerage, then I paid a visit to 'Salt Lake' where there are eight very good detached huts. Returning through Batty Wife Hole, I encounter a gigantic navvy in a huge moleskin monkey jacket with a round bundle on his back… a Whitney pea green jacket with mother of pearl buttons, six flannel shirts, two white linen ditto, sundry pairs of stockings, a pair of boots, and a silver watch, with a gilt chain. Now he was going to try his luck elsewhere, with the meagre remnant of his kit contained in the little bundle on his shoulder.

Cumberland and Westmorland Advertiser, 5 November 1872

SETTLE AND CARLISLE RAILWAY

This line makes very slow progress, the fact being that navvies cannot be got to work more than a week or two in the secluded country places through which the railway runs. They must have the dissipations of town life. At the meeting of the Girvan and Portpatrick Railway, the chairman mentioned as a fact that the contractor had more men on the first eight miles out of Girvan than the contractors of the Carlisle and Settle line, extending to 24 miles.

The Girvan & Portpatrick Railway on the west coast of Scotland was authorised by parliament in 1865. It formed a 31 mile line from Girvan the terminus of the Maypole & Girvan Railway to Challoch Junction eight miles from Portpatrick on the Portpatrick Junction Railway. The construction was carried out under Alexander Galloway an engineer from Glasgow. Work started in 1871 and the line was opened in 1877.

Blake's stone crusher, another invention from the USA. Because of a shortage of labour in the nineteenth century America, something that was not a problem in Great Britain, US engineers turned to mechanisation at an earlier stage than in Britain. British engineers and contractors, in the 1870s, were just beginning to realise the benefits of these machines.

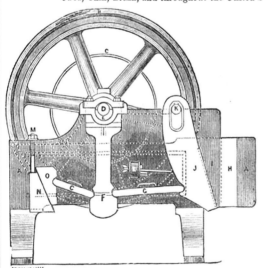

Penrith Observer, 3 Decemer 1872

APPLEBY: SETTLE AND CARLISLE RAILWAY

The chairman (Mr Price), Mr Ellis, and other directors of the Midland Railway Company, accompanied by Mr Crossley, the chief engineer, Mr Drage, resident engineer, Mr Joseph Firbank, the contractor, and Mr Throssel, his manager, inspected the Appleby section (No 3) of the Settle and Carlisle Railway extension on Tuesday and Wednesday last. Notwithstanding the unfortunate weather which has prevailed during the past summer, and the difficulty of obtaining labour, we are given to understand that this part of the line will compare very favourably in forwardness with any of the other sections. All the works have been most substantially executed. The large tunnel at the Helm is expected to be nearly completed by the beginning of the year, and the viaduct over the River Eden, at Ormside, is also in a forward state. These two may be called the heaviest undertakings in the neighbourhood. The works, generally, reflect the greatest credit on the eminent contractor, Mr Firbank, and his able and courteous staff of officials, Mr Throssle, the manager, Mr Crawys, Mr Phillips and others, who are so deservedly held in high esteem in the district.

John Sidney Crossley was born in Loughborough on 25 December 1812, orphaned at the age of two, he was articled by his guardian Mr Stavely, a Leicester architect, to his son Edward Stavely who was engineer to the Leicester Navigation Company.

In 1832 Edward went to America and John was appointed the canal company's engineer. His experience of railway work began in 1832 when he was employed on surveys of the Leicester Swannington Railway. In 1835 under Mr Vignoles he was employed on the Midland Counties Railway and again in 1845 in surveying the South Midland Railway. During surveying the Leicester Hitchin branch in 1852, he was seized with a paralytic stroke, while in Charles Liddell's office. He recovered and was able to resume work in 1853. In 1857 he was appointed resident engineer to the Midland Railway Company becoming Engineer-in-Chief in 1858. After completion of the Settle and Carlisle Railway, he went with the other officials to inspect the line before it opened and was said to have exclaimed "Finis coronat opus" (the end crowns the work) when he reached Carlisle. The Midland directors presented him with a handsome gift, and made him consulting Engineer to the company. The 1871 the census records his family as John 58, his wife Agnes 64, son John 31, and daughters Julia 21, and Bertha 18. He died at his house at Barrow-upon-Soar in June 1879.

Cumberland and Westmorland Advertiser, 10 December 1872

STEAM EXCAVATOR

Within the last few days, Messrs. Benton and Woodiwiss, the contractors for No 2 section of the Settle and Carlisle Railway, have obtained a new and somewhat novel piece of machinery, patented by Messrs. Story and Lynde, the engineers in charge of the section in question. It is nothing less than a 'steam navvy', constructed by Messrs Fairbairn, of Manchester and somewhat like a travelling crane, with a large moveable pick at the end of the 'jib', which is worked up and down direct from a piston. We understand the design of the 'excavator' is new, and some interests felt as to its working power. It is at present on trial in a cutting close to where the Kirkby Stephen Station will be, and if successful will do much to obviate the difficulties into which contractors are thrown by scarcity of men.

Sir William Fairbairn (1789-1874) was a native of Scotland – the family moved to Newcastle where William was apprenticed to a millwright. There he met George Stephenson and developed an interest in steam engines. After making several early inventions, including a steam excavator, a sausage machine and a nail-maker he moved to Manchester in 1813. He was also a pioneer of

Intake Embankment, above, was intended to have a viaduct at this site, but this was abandoned and earth was tipped for a year before a solid foundation was found. The culverted embankment was started in 1870 and completed in 1875. Photograph author's collection.

iron shipbuilding. Initially the parts were prefabricated in his Manchester works but he later opened a shipyard in Millwall. Apart from his role in mechanical engineering, Fairbairn is remembered for his pioneering design of bridges and multi-storey buildings. He collaborated in the construction of the Conway and Britannia Tubular bridges in Wales and built hundreds of lesser structures.
Cumberland and Westmorland Advertiser, 31 Decemr 1872

APPLEBY BOXING DAY

It has always been the custom of the official staff of mechanics, engaged under Mr Joseph Firbank, the contractor for the Appleby section of the Settle and Carlisle Extension Railway, to celebrate their Christmas festivities by dining together on Boxing Day; and in what ever part of the world they have located they have always kept up a family interchange at this festive season. On Thursday afternoon about 30 mechanics in the various departments sat down to a sumptuous dinner, at the Commercial Hotel, which was got up by subscription, through the energy of Mr C Holmes and Mr Thomas Coldwell, jun. After discussing the good things so profusely provided by Mrs Longrigg, the health of the contractor, Mr Firbank was proposed, amid rapturous applause. The health's of Mr Throstle, the manager and his sons were given by the vice-chairman. Mr Greenway and others alternately proposed Mr Cruwys, Mr Austin, Mr C. Firbank, Mr J. B. Firbank, the locomotive foreman, Mr William Firbank, the working-men, Mechanics, and others… the pleasant meeting was brought to a close at an early hour.

Chapter Five
1873

Cumberland and Westmorland Advertiser, 7 January 1873

ACCIDENT AT CROSBY GARRET

A navvy, named Stafford, met with a serious accident on Tuesday last, in the rock cutting near Crosby Garrett. The unfortunate man was working on a ledge, about eight feet high, by the side of the cutting, when some rock fell on his head, and knocked him to the bottom. Medical assistance was immediately procured, when it was found his skull was fractured, and he now lies in a precarious state.

Cumberland and Westmorland Advertiser, 7 January 1873

ACCIDENT AT ORMSIDE

On Tuesday last, a serious accident occurred to a man named John Payne, at the Ormside viaduct on the new railway. It appears that Payne and another man were raising by means of a travelling crane about two tons of lime. When raised to the proper height, Payne's companion let the handle on his side go before the crane was locked or 'spragged', and the consequence was that the lime went down again, and the handle held by Payne was forced round with such velocity that he was struck on the arm, which was broken in several places, and he also received a severe blow on the head. He was brought to Appleby, where he is being attended by Dr Armstrong. His injuries are of a very serious nature.

Cumberland and Westmorland Advertiser 1 February 1873

DISCOVERY OF HUMAN REMAINS AT CROSBY GARRETT

On Thursday last, as Frank Gilby and his gang of men were working in a cutting near Crosby Garrett, on the Settle and Carlisle Railway, they exhumed the remains of two persons. Although evidently long entombed, the bones were in a good state of preservation, and were those of adult persons. They were buried about four feet below the surface and at some distance from each other. How the remains came there is a mystery, the most probable conjecture being that they were the victims of some foul deed in times when robbery and murder were rife in the land. What may give a colouring of probability to this is that the persons had been buried in a doubled-up position, as the manner in which the bones lay indicated.

The Penrith Observer, 18 February 1873

SETTLE AND CARLISLE RAILWAY
COMPLETION OF THE HELM
TUNNEL NEAR APPLEBY.

On Wednesday afternoon last the ceremony of fixing the last brick in the above tunnel was performed by Mr W. S. Fulton, of the Cumberland Union Bank, Appleby, in the presence of a large number of officials and workmen, assisted by Mr Drage, Mr Throstle, Dr Dinwoodie, Mr Chris Firbank, Mr J Whitehead, Mr J Cruwys, and other gentlemen. The tunnel, which is about 600 yards long, was brilliantly lighted up for the occasion, which gave a pleasing effect to the general outline of the work. A stage being erected in the centre, around which the company assembled. Mr Fulton proceeded with trowel in hand to the top, and having fixed the brick in the aperture, amid cheers, intimated the completion of the

Helm Tunnel. After a short pause Mr Fulton again stood forward and said, 'This work that was begun some time ago with such promise of success, in regard to labour and otherwise and which, has been continued amid all the complications of strikes and enhanced prices of labour and materials in the times in which we live, has this day been practically finished by the ceremony of inserting the key brick in this large and important undertaking... He would therefore content himself by expressing a hope that the remainder of Mr Firbanks large contract may be finished in as satisfactory and efficient manner as the tunnel at the Helm.'

Mr Drage, the company engineer, who responded said it was nearly two years since the first stone was laid in Helm Tunnel, and it was gratifying to be able to say that it had been completed hitherto without loss of life or any serious accident to any one connected with the works. It might therefore be regarded as an exception to the general rule that a work of such magnitude should have been thus far completed without witnessing any of those painful incidents which are of such frequent occurrence in similar large undertakings. There was also much satisfaction in mentioning that nothing of a very disastrous nature had happened to the work whilst carrying it out, which was chiefly to be attributed to the

efficient means employed by the contractor, and he also thought that special thanks were due to Messrs Price and Kirby, who were so assiduous in its superintendence. He further complimented the general workmen, who had laboured so hard and diligently…

After a few remarks from Mr C Firbank and Mr J Whithead, the gentlemen present after viewing the tunnel, returned to Appleby, where an excellent dinner was provided at the King's Head Hotel, and a pleasant and agreeable evening brought the days events to a close.

The Kings Head Hotel was in Bridge Street and kept by Sarah Rigg. Dr Frederick Dinwoodie, MRC's Surgeon practiced in the Market Place. William Scott Fulton of the Cumberland Union Bank also in the Market Place – source the Post Office Directory 1873.

Cumberland and Westmorland Advertiser, 8 February 1873

THE SETTLE AND CARLISLE LINE

In their report just issued, the directors of the Midland Railway Company say:- The anticipated progress upon all new works has not been realised, from the great loss of time occasioned by rain. All the works have been retarded to a very serious extent. On the Settle and Carlisle all possible progress has been made under adverse circumstances; the works are now well under control, and the more difficult portions in good position for completion…

Cumberland and Westmorland Advertiser, 25 March 1873

MIDLAND RAILWAY

Messers. Benton and Woodiwiss, the contractors for the making of this line from Dent Head to Kirkby Stephen, requiring the services of a locomotive engine for earth work, received one by rail at Sedbergh, on Monday last, named the 'Lorne', which was conveyed to Garsdale Head by about twenty horses. One or two slight mishaps occurred on the road, owing to the great weight of the engine, but by the patience and perseverance of the men in charge they were overcome without much difficulty.

(see appendix A)

Leeds Mercury, 21 April 1873

A MAN 27 HOURS IN A WELL

On Thursday afternoon the inhabitants of Sedbergh town were thrown into a state of alarm by the rumour that a workman, named Lindsay, engaged in doing something at the bottom of a well, 12 yards deep, was buried alive by the sides falling in upon him. The man had gone down a ladder for the purpose of fixing a stay on which a pump was to rest. The walls of the well gave way as he was ascending, and he had only got about two yards up the ladder when he was completely covered by stone and soil, which so effectually filled up the well that only a portion of five feet deep at the top was not closed. A couple of navvies engaged on the Settle and Carlisle Railway had been at the Police Court, and their aid was at once sought. They proved to be experts at mining, and went at once about the task of extracting the poor man with business like despatch. They worked till three on Friday morning, when they were relieved by a fresh set who had been sent for from the tunnel works in Garsdale.

About seven on Friday morning the navvies managed to get the head and shoulders of the unfortunate man bare, and gave him food and drink. The task of relieving him had so far succeeded and nearly all his body was at length uncovered, when it was discovered that his feet were fast in the ladder, and as the men were working to remove the impediment a fresh slip of earth and stones took place, which delayed the final accomplishment of the task for some hours. The whole of the well had to be lined with wood in regular tunnel style, and the adjoining houses had to be propped to prevent them giving way. During the afternoon of Friday the poor man slept in his uncomfortable position for an hour and a half, whilst the navvies worked round him. An attempt was made to convey water to him by means of a pipe, but that did not succeed. At length, about five on Friday afternoon, the poor man was extricated, and a feeling of relief was experienced when he was brought to the surface alive, terribly bruised, internally and externally, but with no bones broken. The navvies came in for a full share of admiration, which took a tangible form when the work was happily accomplished. A subscription was opened for them, and most liberally responded to. The unfortunate man was conveyed home on a stretcher.

Lancaster Gazette, 26 April 1873

John Lindsay whose entombment in an old well was reported… we are sorry to say sunk under the effects of the injuries received, and died on Tuesday last.

Cumberland and Westmorland Advertiser, 5 May 1873

FATAL ACCIDENT AT LANGWATHBY

A fatality of a painful and serious nature occurred to a man named Joseph Bewley, upon the Settle and Carlisle Railway, now in the course of construction, near Langwathby, on Saturday last. Whilst employed in filling wagons a large mass of solid earth became suddenly detached from the breast of the adjoining cutting, and fell upon him. His thigh was broken, and he was also severely injured internally. Dr Williamson, the railway medical attendant, being at Carlisle on important business, a messenger was dispatched for Dr Macgregor, of Penrith, who arrived at Langwathby with as little delay as possible, and at once reduced the fracture of the limb, and did all that medical skill could suggest to relieve the unfortunate man's suffering, which were most intense. Notwithstanding all the care and attention bestowed he never rallied, but gradually sank, and expired at four o'clock the following morning. The deceased, who was 24 years old, has left a young wife and child to mourn his sad and untimely end. He was the only son of Mathew and Elizabeth Bewley, of Langwathby, and his unassuming demeanour and steady habits had won him the respect of all classes. The melancholy event has cast quite a gloom over the whole village, where deceased had so long lived esteemed by all.

Yorkshire Post, 6 May 1873

TUNNEL MINERS wanted at Blea Moor Tunnel, Settle and Carlisle Railway No1 Contract. Wages 6s per day, Good lodgings immediately adjoining. Station, Ingleton via Leeds. Parties of ten men will be passed down. – Apply Alfred Terry, Midland Railway Offices, Settle.

The Newcastle Courant, 9 May 1873

An auction sale of heavy horses recently used by Mr John Bayliss, upon the Settle and Carlisle Railway, took place on Saturday, at Peel's Repository, Haymarket, Newcastle. The horses brought from £64 to £98 a piece. Mr Arthur T Crow was the auctioneer.

Penrith Observer, 13 May 1873

SAD ACCIDENT AT LANGWATHBY

Yesterday (Monday) evening, a labourer, named Foster, met with a very serious accident whilst working on the new line of railway near Langwathby. Foster, it appears, was attempting to leap upon an earth wagon in motion, and in doing so his foot slipped, and he fell to the ground, the wheel passing over his left leg and mangling it in a most shocking manner. Dr Masterton, of Penrith, was shortly afterwards in attendance, and rendered every possible assistance, but it is feared that a long time will elapse before the unfortunate man will be able to resume work.

The Liverpool Mercury, 14 May 1873

DESIRABLE VILLA RESIDENCE

At Lazonby, near Penrith, Cumberland, for Sale:- Picturesque locality, on the banks of the Eden, near Nunnery Walks. Convenient for the lakes and close by the Midland Station on the Settle and Carlisle Railway. Contains 13 rooms, with good cellars and water supply, nagged yard, coach house, stable, hay loft, fowl home, etc., large garden and orchard. The site comprises ½ an acre of land thereabouts. Is equally well adapted for a large boarding school, hotel, or private residence. Built nine years ago. Will be sold with or without the above ½ acre of excellent arable and pasture land. If not disposed of privately the whole will be sold by auction at the Odd Fellows Hall, in Penrith, on Tuesday, the 27th instant, at Three o'clock p.m. Further particulars by applying to Mr Hindson, seed merchant, Barnsley, or solicitors, Messrs Arnison, Penrith.

An interesting advert for property pre-empting the opening of the Settle line.

Penrith Observer, 20 May 1873

ACCIDENT TO A NAVVY NEAR ORMSIDE

Yesterday (Monday) afternoon an accident occurred on the railway near Ormside, to a navvy, named John Tiffin. It appeared that Tiffin was at work on the line when a wagon came up and knocked him down. While he was on the ground the wheels passed over his leg, crushing it in a most shocking manner about the ankle. Last evening the injured man was removed to the Carlisle Infirmary.

The Leeds Mercury, 29 May 1873

STEALING WORK TOOLS AT SETTLE

John King, Thomas Walker, and Jim Parker, were charged before Mr J. Birkbeck (chairman) Mr C. Ingleby, and Mr H. Christie, on Tuesday, with stealing a quantity of shoemaker's tools from the person of Mr Richard Robinson. The prosecutor, it appears had come from Batty Green, on the Settle and Carlisle Railway on the Monday night previous and failing to procure lodgings, lay down in the street at Settle, when the prisoners, sometime after eleven at night, had found him and taken away his kit, containing a quantity of tools. The prosecutor gave information to the police immediately after the occurrence, and the prisoners were traced to a lodging-house in the town with the whole of the missing property in their possession. They were at once taken into custody and conveyed to the lock-up. The prisoners, who pleaded not guilty, were committed to the sessions for trial.

The Penrith Herald, 26 July 1873

ACCIDENT NEAR ARMATHWAITE

Shortly after six o'clock on the morning of the 17th inst., while some masons were working in the tunnel nearest to the village of Armathwaite, the scaffolding upon which the men were working, by some unforeseen and unavoidable cause, gave way, precipitating two men to a depth of about twenty feet, on whom a quantity of heavy stones fell, inflicting on both very severe injuries. The more seriously wounded of the two is a young man, the son of Mr William Nixon, farmer, of Armathwaite, who received very extensive wounds on the head, the skull being exposed in several places. Dr Allen of Armathwaite, surgeon to this line of railway, was quickly in attendance, and we are glad to learn, from recent inquiries, that through the unremitting attention and skill of that gentleman the unfortunate sufferers are progressing towards recovery.

The Penrith Herald, 2 August 1873

THE SETTLE AND CARLISLE RAILWAY
FROM DENT HEAD TO SMARDALE: MARVEL OF CIVILIZATION

It is not the object of this article to enter minutely into the details of the whole of that vast undertaking by which the Midland Railway Company will add another 80 miles to their present gigantic network of railways, nor is it intended to give a dry technical account that would be only understood by engineers and in others with whom the construction of railways is a daily business, but rather to give a general description sufficiently interesting to the public, who, as a rule, know very little of the difficulties that have to be overcome, and the energy and perseverance required to bestow on them the benefits accruing from the extended use of one of the latest marvels of civilization.

How many gentlemen rushing through the country at 60 miles an hour in a first class carriage, bestow as much as a passing thought on the labour that was expended on that narrow track of road that they whirl over in even a minute of time, little do they think how that portion of the line was constructed bit by bit by the combined efforts of thousands of their fellow creatures, some of whom have required almost a life-time of study and experience before they could contribute their mite of knowledge to the general undertaking. It may be the genius of one man who directs and sets the whole of the mighty machinery in motion, but he would be powerless unless the orders he issued to the many parts were thoroughly understood by them in all their many details, he may be as it were the governor that controls the whole machine, but unless every bolt, every little screw, were performing its proper duty, the machine would collapse, and every effort to make it move would but involve the destruction of every part.

Let them then ponder a little on these things, and the next time they arrive at their destination a few minutes late, there will be less grumbling, and they will feel more grateful to those hard working men who have conferred upon them such immense advantages over their ancestors of 50 years back. The Settle and Carlisle Railway which will give the Midland an interest in the Scots traffic, commences

Empty earth wagons being returned to be refilled on the Hull and Barnsley Railwa; similar earth wagons would have been used on the Settle and Carlisle Railway as referred to in May 1873 at Langwathby. Photograph courtesy of Hull Museum.

about a mile south of Settle by a junction with the Little North Western Railway, and branching off through the town of Settle, winds its way along the valley of the Ribble and passes near the villages of Horton and Selside. At twelve miles from the commencement it crosses the road between Ingleton and Hawes, and passing over a long viaduct enters a tunnel through a hill called Blea Moor, at a depth of nearly 400 feet below the surface. After traversing the tunnel for a mile and a quarter, it emerges in the Dent Valley and crosses the River Dee by means of another viaduct, it now gradually creeps up the side of the hill, and at 17¼ miles from the beginning the first contract ends.

BAD WEATHER

The second contract now begins, which we intend to describe more fully. This was let in September, 1869, to Messrs Benton and Woodiwiss, and is now being carried out by them. It is to be regretted that the works not only on this contract, but on all other parts of the line, are not in such forward state as was then anticipated, owing to several reasons, the chief of which are the unprecedented quantity of wet weather that was experienced during the years of 1871 and 1872, and the remarkably unsettled state of the labouring classes. Let us take for example the rainfall in two instances in the year 1872, viz, at the commencement of the contract at Dent Head, and at its termination near Kirkby Stephen, at both of which places rain gauges are kept and the result carefully recorded. At Dent Head there fell during 1872, 92 inches against the average of 68, and at Kirkby Stephen 60 against 37, an increase of from 35 to 60 per cent. This excessive amount of rainfall hindered the progress of the works in three ways, by first of all considerably reducing the number of working days per week; secondly, on that account driving the men off the work to other parts of the country where the weather was more settled; and thirdly, by the damage that it caused the cuttings, rendering the otherwise hard material so soft that it was totally unfit to be tipped into the banks, and it was on this account that several cuttings had to be stopped until liberated by the fine weather.

ARTEN GILL VIADUCT

This contract begins then at a place called Dent Head, in one of the wildest and most unfrequented part of the north of Yorkshire. All around there is nothing but uncultivated moor land, and vast hills seem to hem one in on every side. Taking then our start at this point let us walk north wards along the line. A few minutes walk over a heavy cutting brings us to what is now known as the Arten Gill Viaduct. This viaduct spans the stream below by means of eleven arches 45 feet wide, and the rails will be, when laid, 117 feet above the bed of the stream. It is being built of the same sort of stone, which, when cut and polished at Mr Nixon's marble works close by, ornaments so many of our fire places, and is known by the name Black or Dent marble. It is obtained from a quarry in the side of the hill close by, but at a lower level than the bottom of the viaduct, and has all to be lifted up by steam power in immense blocks, some weighing several tons. Great difficulty has been experienced in obtaining a firm foundation for several piers, owing to the great depth that they had to be sunk, in some cases as much as 55 feet. It would be impossible in loose ground like that met here, to keep the sides from falling in, without supporting them in some way or other, and to look down one of these foundations, ready for putting in the masonry, it seems one confused mass of timber and strutting. Light delicate looking staging has been erected on both sides of the viaduct, on the top of which runs the steam grab used for raising the stones. A serious mishap occurred to the grab a short time back while lowering a heavy stone, which is done by means of a brake; from some cause the driver was not able to control it, and the stone in its decent knocked away part of the staging, and the whole machine was precipitated into the beck below.

THE VALE OF DENT

Soon after leaving Arten Gill, we come to a small occupation bridge at which great difficulty was experienced in obtaining a firm foundation; after sinking down 30 feet it was found necessary to build it

Arten Gill Viaduct before the arches were turned. To the left of the picture the rail head embankment is approaching what would be the abutments of the viaduct (author's collection).

on piles that were driven 25 feet deeper into the ground. We now pass through a cutting containing 95,000 cubic yards, and for the next mile the work is comparatively light. A large culvert over Keld Beck is, however, well worth going down the bank to see. Owing to the very sidelong ground, it was found necessary to build this culvert in steps, and the water pouring over them forms a cascade of 20 or 30 breaks, and has a very pretty effect.

At this stream, just above the line an enormous quarry hole has been excavated, from which stone for all the bridges and culverts about here has been obtained. The view from this point is really beautiful. Quite a birds-eye view is obtained of the Vale of Dent, nearly 500 feet below, now sparkling in the sunlight and now losing itself among some cluster of trees, winds the River Dee, while first on one side, then the other, is the road that leads to Sedbergh. No busy smoking town is to be seen close or in the distance, nothing but the greenest of green fields, speckled over with lazy herds of cattle, while here and there lie the homesteads, whose inhabitants are imbued with that simplicity that life in these rural solitudes alone can give. This valley is not, however, always a scene of peace and quaintness. In July 1870, there swept along it one of the most terrific storms that had occurred for many years. A thunder storm caused the river to swell so suddenly, that a wave of several feet in height came rushing not only along the bed of the river, but also along the road, with resistless force, carrying everything before it. Nearly all the bridges were carried away, and two or three unfortunate people were drowned.

DECENDING INTO BLACK MOSS TUNNEL

A short distance further on we come to a cutting of which 150,000 cubic yards, across the middle of which runs the coal road, the only accessible road between the valleys of Garsdale and Dent, a terribly steep and rugged road that rises to a height of nearly 2000 feet above the level of the sea. After passing through the cutting we come to a large embankment across Cow Gill, containing 166,000 cubic yards of filling. The line crosses this gill at a very sharp angle, and at a height of 80 feet above the stream. A culvert, ten feet wide, has been built in the bottom, and is by far the longest on the contract, being 540 feet from one end to the other. The arch is Gothic or pointed at the top, on account of the enormous weight it will have to carry. The masonry is of a very substantial nature.

Great difficulty seems to be experienced in forming the bank, owing to the sidelong ground, a large wall, 40 feet high, comprised of a rough stone, is being formed right across the low side to keep it from slipping away altogether. After toiling up the steep side of this ravine, we come to a small opening in the side of the hill, which is a temporary heading, leading into Black Moss Tunnel (now known as Rise Hill). This tunnel is one of the greatest undertakings of the line being through solid limestone, at a depth of 170 feet below the surface. As there is not much done at this heading we will get on to the top of the tunnel, as far as the first shaft, and taking our places in the iron skip, at a given signal to the engine driver we are rapidly lowered into the depths below. To one unaccustomed to such travelling, the sudden falling through space produces quite a giddy sensation and involuntarily we clutch the chain by which we are suspended.

We soon arrive at the bottom, owing to the sudden change from light to almost perfect darkness. Candles are, however, given to each of us, and following our leader, we carefully pick our way to that part where the men are working. When one's eye get more accustomed to the light what a wonderful place it seems. Solid rock above, below, and on each side, what an enormous amount of labour must have been expended in forming this subterraneous passage 26 feet wide and 20 feet high, at such a depth below the ground. After a long walk we arrive at the face, where we see some thirty or forty miners hard at work, whose occupation consists in drilling holes in the rock, which are afterwards charged with gunpowder and exploded. These men work in couples, one who holds the drill or jumper and slightly alters the position of its cutting edge after every stroke, and the other who by repeated blows of a hammer forces it into the rock. Great stalwart men are these miners, who seem to wield their heavy hammers with ease, and bring them down on the drill with tremendous force, the sharp clink of each blow betraying to even an inexperienced ear the hardness of the material that is being worked.

Contrary to our expectations, the air seemed to be very good, but that we are told has only been the case since an opening has been made into the other shaft, through which a constant current of fresh air is passing. On wending our way back, we were surprised to hear that it will be necessary to line the tunnel with masonry. The rock is so full of cracks that it is found impossible to excavate it to the shape required, and in many places large pieces have come down and left the roof quite flat for 20 feet. Arching is therefore going to be thrown across the top.

It is not a pleasant thought to think that 170 feet of solid earth lies between us and the sky, and it was a feeling of relief that we were drawn up into the fresh air. A quarter of a mile further on we came to the other shaft, but as the work is the same here as what we have already seen, we decided not to go down. This tunnel is one of the busy workshops of the line, huts, sheds, and storerooms, have been built on every side, and a temporary village of 350 inhabitants has been erected 1300 feet above sea level. As there is no road to this place, a tramway has been laid to the turnpike road, 600 yards distant, up which all materials required have to be drawn by a rope, worked by steam power. Just as we were leaving we were alarmed at hearing several heavy explosions, and feel the ground shake beneath our feet, but our fears are dissipated on being told that it was only the men firing the charges in the pit below…

GARSDALE AND HAWES BRANCH

We have by means of this tunnel left the Dent Valley and now arrive in Garsdale. After a short walk during which we pass over a deep ravine where great difficulty was experienced in forming a bank, although a wall containing 6000 tons of stone was built across the low side, we meet a small engine puffing along with a train of wagons at its tail, and waiting where they are detached, we examine the permanent way, which seems of a most substantial nature. The chairs are particularly heavy, weighing 42 lbs each, and have a large bearing surface on the sleeper. The rails, which are made of steel, weigh 85 lbs to the yard; and not being intended to reverse nearly all the metal is in the head, which gives them a very heavy appearance.

Mounting up the steps of the locomotive, we take our place against the driver, and the next mile is traversed in a very easy and expeditious method. We now arrive at the junction of the Hawes Branch, a branch to the town of Hawes, six miles distant. Messrs Benton and Woodiwiss are also constructing this branch, making a total length of 23 miles of this particular railway in their hands. This represents, however, only a small portion of the work that they are at present carrying out; besides the Liverpool and Manchester Railway, 40 miles long, they are constructing several very important lines in the Midland counties, The Hawes branch is not yet in a forward state, as all exertions are being made to get the main line completed as soon as possible.

We now come to a heavy bank, 50 feet high containing over a quarter of a million cubic yards of filling, and thinking it strange that the ground where the bank is to be tipped should have been removed for a depth of several feet, we learn that this has been done because the peat which forms a regular bog would not carry so deep a bank. Evidence of this was pointed out to us, where the bank had been tipped on the original surface the peat had heaved out on both sides and risen to a height of fifteen feet. We notice preparations being made for another viaduct of six arches being built here. Under this bank runs the turnpike road between Sedbergh and Hawes, the bridge spanning the road being a very fine and massive structure.

We now come to a cutting which has been the bugbear of the contract, containing 215,000 cubic yards of earth, and having a depth of 66 feet. A want of sufficient labour has been the cause of the works about here being in a backward state, although every effort has been made to induce the men to stop. Comfortable huts have been erected close by, which have not been more than half filled, and higher wages have been given here than on any other part of the line. It being supposed that a want of amusement was the cause, a reading room was built, which was well supplied with weekly and illustrated papers. As an instance of the unsettled state of the men, although 1300 is about the number employed on the contract, no less than 20,000 have passed through the contractor's books. On walking through the cutting, we could partly understand the cause of this; the strata through which it passes is known as boulder clay or glacial drift, a very stiff blue clay filled with stones, some of which are immense blocks,

Navvies working to construct a heading at Saunderton on the Great Central Railway in 1902. The same or very similar methods would have been used on the Settle and Carlisle some 30 years earlier in August 1873 at Black Moss (Rise Hill) tunnel. Photograph courtesy of Leicestershire Archives.

weighing several tons, all of which require to be broken into small fragments before they can be lifted into the wagons. The men must naturally prefer working in some easier material, such as is to be found in other parts of the country.

AIS GILL AND THE EDEN VALLEY

Two miles and a half further walking through several heavy cuttings, and we come to a cutting on Ais Gill moor, which is the summit of the railway, the rails being 1167 feet above the level of the sea. This cutting is composed entirely of soft peat, and as it is not fit to be put in the banks, it is being wheeled to one side of the line. A short distance from here on the right, three rivers take their source, the Eden, which flows into the sea below Carlisle and the Ure and Swale, which, after taking divergent routes in an easterly direction, join a few miles above York, and flow into the Humber. A stone with a Greek inscription, marks the source of the Eden, which, according to a date inscribed upon it, must have been erected recently.

We now enter the valley of the Eden and what is called in all old maps the 'Forest of Mallerstang', but few traces of a forest exist at the present day. The country is exceedingly wild and rugged, stone walls mark the divisions of the property, and all around is rough uncultivated common land. The few farmhouses that are in sight are just sufficient to remind us that the land is inhabited. From this summit the line now falls almost uninterruptedly to Carlisle, 1 in 100 being the ruling gradient; owing to the valley falling at a much more rapid rate, the line gradually creeps up the hill on the western side and soon attains a considerable elevation above the road which keeps by the river.

AIS GILL VIADUCT

A short distance further on we come to Ais Gill viaduct of four large arches, 65 feet high, upon which the masons were putting the finishing touches. Unlike what we meet with in towns, the work does not abound with tooled ashlar and moulded copings; everything is plain and rough, and therefore more economical, but it is not on this account less substantial, and its appearance is in our opinion more suited to the style of country it is built to accommodate. For the next three quarters of a mile the line has not been touched. Mounting up on to another locomotive, we are again accommodated with a ride, and passing over several bridges, we enter a heavy rock cutting through the mountain limestone. Strange as it may appear, we are told that had all the cuttings been of this material, instead of the boulder clay, the line would have been in a far more forward state than it is at the present. A bridge over a ravine, called Deep Gill, is worth going down the bank to see. It is half bridge and half culvert, the union between the two being effected in a very ingenious manner. The ground here is very sidelong, and great difficulty has been experienced in building the culverts which are very numerous. Owing to the great fall they have been built in steps with perpendicular drops, some of these drops as much as eighteen feet. The next mile and three quarters is still in its natural state, but hopes are entertained of having it completed by the end of the year.

BIRKET TUNNEL

We now come to another heavy cutting, composed of boulder clay, containing 131,000 cubic yards, which is being tipped partly to spoil and partly to bank. At the end of the cutting is the bank, which seems a considerable way off completion. It is estimated to contain 248,000 cubic yards of filling, but more than that quantity will have to be tipped into it before the permanent way is laid across it. It is 76 feet high, and as the ground is sidelong, the whole of the base has been benched and drained to render it firm. Another cutting containing 162,000 cubic yards, and we come to another tunnel under Birket Common. As this is only being worked from the north end, we walk across the top and enter at the open face. This, like the tunnel in Garsdale, is through solid limestone, but such is the different nature of the material, no difficulty is experienced in excavation of it to the shape required. The tunnel passes through what is called The Pennine Fault, the rock being thrown up till it is quite perpendicular. A small quantity of lead ore was discovered between the joints in the rock, but not sufficient quantities to render it profitable to work. We notice here a Berleigh rock drilling machine hard at work, being driven by compressed air, and, timing it carefully we saw a hole a foot deep drilled in five minutes. What a difference between this and manual labour, two men drilling by hand would take 40 minutes to do the same work. This tunnel is 428 yards long, and about half way through.

THE LAST FEW MILES

We now enter upon that part of the contract that is in the most forward state. From here to the termination, a distance of 4½ miles the cuttings are nearly completed, and this is owing to labour having been throughout more plentiful than in other parts, its proximity to the market town of Kirkby Stephen having been the attraction. A mile further on, the line passes through the Wharton Park Estates, and close by on the right is Wharton Hall the seat of the now extinct Dukes of Wharton, which is in a very fair state of preservation, and a good idea can be formed of what it once was.

SMARDALE VIADUCT

Another three quarters of a mile brings us to what will be the station for Kirkby Stephen. The town lies to the east of the line, about a mile and a half, but on account of the low level at which it is situated, it was not possible to bring the railway any nearer to it. Passing over the turnpike road between Sedbergh and Kirkby Stephen by means of a Girder Bridge, we enter another cutting, containing 85,000 cubic yards, which is rapidly approaching completion. We had pointed out to us an excavating machine, patented by two gentlemen connected with the railway, which is not now working, as it is only a trial machine, made to test the principal on which it acts. Diversity of opinion exists as to whether it can be rendered profitable.

After walking three quarters of a mile on the permanent way, we enter a heavy rock cutting, containing 160,000 cubic yards of excavation, through very hard limestone that required a deal of blasting. Another three quarters of a mile brings us to a viaduct that is highest on the railway – Smardale Viaduct consists of twelve arches, 45 feet span, and will be 145 feet from the parapet to the bottom of the foundations. It is being built of a grey limestone, quarried about half a mile higher up the stream. No better stone could have been obtained for the purpose, self bedded as it is; not much labour is required to bring it to the proper shape, and the immense blocks in which it can be worked render it well adapted for the construction of such narrow piers.

The greater part of the viaduct is within a few feet of springing level, and only a few weeks will elapse before the arching is commenced. We had been here shown us several specimens of the mortar with which the masonry is put together, and tested them severely by means of sharp blows. On no part of this contract has any thing approaching sand been found, and as no good sand could be obtained within any reasonable distance, it was, by the advice of the chief engineer, decided to use clay, burnt quite hard, and ground with lime in mortar mills, the result of which has proved eminently satisfactory.

AND SO TO CARLISLE

A short distance beyond here, the second contract ends, beyond which it is not our intention to proceed, but just simply to describe the route which the railway takes for the next 40 miles. From here to Carlisle the railway is let in two contracts, one of which, fifteen miles long, is let to Mr Joseph Firbank; and 24 miles long, to Mr John Bayliss. The works on these two contracts are not in a more forward state than on the others, similar difficulties as regards the weather and labour having been experienced. A short distance after leaving Smardale, the railway passes the village of Crosby Garrett, and after going through a tunnel at Helm, which is now completed, the River Eden is crossed for the first time at Ormside. A junction with the Eden Valley Railway is effected at Appleby, a short distance beyond which the line crosses over the railway, and, passing through the villages of Langwathby and Culgaith, enters a tunnel between five and six hundred yards long. After passing through Langwathby, the River Eden is again crossed by a viaduct of seven arches. The line then passes through Lazonby and enters Baron Wood, through which there are two tunnels, one 600 yards long and the other 300. After passing over a very heavy bank, the line runs near Armathwaite, and about eight miles further on it effects a junction with the North Eastern at Petteril Bridge.

This ramble along the works in progress has convinced us in what we had before suspected, viz., that railway making is no easy matter. On this contract which represents but a fourth part of the line, there will be, when completed, 45 cuttings containing 2¼ million cubic yards of excavation, two tunnels, whose combined length is 1540 yards; 4 viaducts, containing 33 arches of 45 feet span; 64 bridges, varying in width from 10 to 45 feet; 97 culverts, of all sizes from 2 to 10 feet, and a vast amount of other smaller works, such as draining fencing etc.

Joseph Firbank was born in 1819 at Bishop Auckland and at the age of seven joined his father down the mine. In 1840 he was working on the Bishop Auckland and Weardale branch of the Stockton and Darlington Railway. At 22 he took a sub-contract on the Woodhead Tunnel, from there he went to the York and Scarborough Railway and amassed enough capital to take a contract on the Nottingham and Lincoln line of the Midland Railway. He nearly lost everything on the Rugby to Market Harborough contract in 1848. In 1866 he was working on the Midland extension to St Pancras, London. He ended his contracting career on the Settle and Carlisle. He died aged 67 on the 29 June 1886 a J.P. and High Sheriff of Monmouthshire. He had seven sons Joseph, Charles, Christopher, Walter, Edward, Godfrey and William. It is probably his son Christopher that is mentioned in other parts of the text.

ENGINEERS AND NAVVIES

Mr John Crossley is the chief engineer, and we could not help admiring the manner in which by means of easy curves and gradients he had taken every advantage of the natural contour of the ground, and when it is considered that by these two methods, so many different lines might be obtained, it must be no easy matter to describe which will be the most economical, not only to construct, but to work, for who can say how many future generations.

Mr J. S. Story is the resident engineer, and Mr James Hay is the contractor's agent, on whom devolves the practical part of carrying out the works. Unlike the construction of a building or a large ship, when, by means of its compactness, the master can have the men working as it were beneath his eyes, the various gangs of men are here distributed over a length of 23 miles, and so no small amount of perception must be required to see that they are not only doing their duty while he is with them, but also during the time he has been away inspecting other parts.

The railway, as might be expected from the nature of the ground through which it passes, runs through a very sparsely populated country, and of course some special provisions had to be made for the accommodation of the numerous workers. To this end 116 temporary huts have been erected along the whole length, an inspection of some of which convinced us that for the personal comfort they might compare very favourably with the farm houses in the immediate vicinity. Navvies and miners, though usually considered a rough class of men, could not be induced to stop if, after a day's work, they were not lodged as comfortably as would satisfy others much higher in the social scale.

Of their moral condition it is not our intention to speak at present; they are not perhaps worse than other labouring men. It is well known that the more sober and steady the man, the better workman he makes, and to bring this about the directors have provided each contract with a Scripture Reader, whose duty is to visit the men in their own huts, and by precept and example, induce them to refrain from spending their earnings in a profitless manner. That this has borne good fruit might be easily shown, but there yet remains a deal to be done in this direction. To better the condition of the labouring classes is a work, than which there can be none more noble, and as such we recommend it to gentlemen of influence and position who seek some field in which their labour, however slight, may not prove in vain.

The Bradford Observer, 4 September 1873

THREE PERSONS KILLED

A terrible accident happened on Monday evening, at Garsdale, near Sedbergh, on the works of the Settle and Carlisle railway. A tramway laid down from the top to the bottom of a hill for the purpose of raising material, and small wagons are raised and lowered upon it by a wire rope worked by a stationary engine on the summit. The people living in huts at the top of the hill are accustomed to use the tramway in order to get up and down. On Monday evening eleven persons were descending in the three trucks when the pin connecting the rope with the train broke just as the wagons got to the steepest part of the incline, and the train descended with fearful velocity.

One of the men managed to check the speed of the train by blocking the wheels of one of the trucks, and nine of the passengers got out, only one of them being injured. Unfortunately two married women, aged 26 and 30, were unable to escape. The trucks continued to descend on the incline for a time, but presently went off, and the two women were thrown out, dashed against the stone, and killed on the spot. Nor was this the only fatal result, for just before the train started a man while drunk was descending the incline, and had laid himself down to rest with his head on the rails. A little girl, seeing his danger, tried to rouse him, but could not, and the train went over his head, killing him instantly. It is said that the rope had been pronounced unsafe and was about to be removed, but the accident appears not to have been caused by the breaking of the rope, but by the giving way of the connection between it and the trucks.

The Penrith Herald, 11 October 1873

FATAL ACCIDENT AT CROSBY GARRETT

A man named John Watson, who has been employed for some time as a labourer in the contractor's workshop on the Settle and Carlisle railway, at Crosby Garrett, met with an accident on Saturday last which caused his death. He was riding from Grisburn in a truck attached to a locomotive. And when near Crosby Garrett, had fallen upon the line and a loaded water tank passed over him. No one observed the accident, and it was not till the train stopped, that Aaron Jones, the driver, missed him. The poor fellow was quite dead when found. An inquest was held on Tuesday afternoon at the Fleece Inn, before G. R. Thompson, Esq., coroner, when a verdict of 'accidental death' was returned. The unfortunate man was about 28 years of age, and is supposed to belong to the neighbourhood of Bradford, in Yorkshire.

The Lancaster Gazette, 1 November 1873

ACCIDENT AT GARSDALE

On Wednesday the 22 ult., Raygill-in-Garsdale was the scene of another accident of a very distressing nature, and which might easily have proved fatal. Two trucks were being drawn up the hill, the foremost laden with baskets of provisions, etc., and the hindermost was filled with men, and a number of others got on the first one. Some of these feeling their position on the baskets unsafe were getting off while the trucks were in motion, when one of the number, a boy of fourteen, fell off at the back, and the wheels of the second truck passed over his thighs, making a most fearful gash, and cutting the flesh open, but strange, to say, breaking no bones. The men in the engine house finding that something was wrong by the motion of the trucks, of which one at any rate had run off the line, stopped the engine, thereby preventing further mischief. Mr Eaglestone, the doctor, happened to be in the engine shed, so assistance was promptly secured, the wound stitched up, and we hear that the boy is progressing favourably.

The Lancaster Gazette, 15 November 1873

FATAL ACCIDENT: An accident which terminated fatally, happened on Friday last to a young man, named William Henry Spencer, a resident of Settle, and employed on the new station ground of the Settle and Carlisle Railway. Whilst engaged in his ordinary occupation he by some means got between the buffers of some of the wagons and was severely crushed. He was conveyed to his home, but only survived a few hours. An inquest was held on the following evening at the Commercial Hotel, by Mr Brown the coroner, when a verdict of 'accidental death' was returned.

The Penrith Herald, 29 November 1873.

BOY CRUSHED TO DEATH AT CULGAITH

On Saturday last a boy named Edward Fitzpatrick, eleven years of age, met with an accident which resulted in his death. He was employed at the brick works in connection with the Settle and Carlisle Railway extension, and whilst oiling the machinery he made a remark to another boy engaged upon the work. His companion threw a piece of clay at him, and in stepping to one side to avoid it, he stepped too close to the machinery, by which he was caught, and dragged in amongst the wheels. His loud shrieks speedily brought assistance; the machinery was stopped but not until his body had been mutilated in a shocking manner. Surgical aid was procured, but it was of no avail, the injuries internally and externally, which he had received being so extensive that he succumbed to their effects at six o'clock the same evening. At the inquest, which was held on Monday before Mr J. Carrick deputy coroner, it transpired that the boy had every half-hour to pass around the machinery, and in one place only 21 inches space intervened between the embankment and the engine. This the jury considered extremely dangerous, and Mr Bayliss, jun., the son of the contractor, who was present, promised that in future the machinery should be properly fenced off and persons attending it protected from a similar casualty. The jury returned a verdict of 'accidental death'.

Chapter Six
1874

Penrith Observer, 10 February 1874

DASTARDLY TRICK ON THE SETTLE AND CARLISLE RAILWAY

During the night of Friday week a dastardly crime was perpetrated on the Settle and Carlisle Railway, at the Eden Viaduct, near Lazonby. At that point there is a siding, in which were standing some empty wagons. One of these was unhooked by some person or persons, and either pushed or allowed to run upon the permanent way as far as Eden Lacy, where it was left standing. Next morning, about half-past six o'clock, two carriages pushed from behind by an engine, were conveying the men to their work, on the line, and the driver being unable to see the obstruction the train came in contact with the standing wagon. The latter was knocked over, and the first carriage was thrown off the rails, but very fortunately none of the men it contained were hurt. So far the police have been unable to fix the crime upon anybody.

Penrith Observer, 14 April 1874

THE CROSBY GARRETT RAILWAY TUNNEL

To commemorate the laying of the last brick in the Crosby Garrett tunnel on the Settle and Carlisle Railway (No 3 Contract), which had been performed by William Richardson, Esq., of the Villa, Crosby Garrett, a number of the workmen were, the other day, entertained to dinner at Mr Tyson's the Black Hotel, Kirkby Stephen. This is the last of the two great tunnels which have been completed on this section, the other being one at the Helm, which was completed last year. Both of them have been carried out by Mr George Kirby and Mr Fletcher. The entire length of Crosby Garrett tunnel is 180 yards, and it consists of limestone rock and a mixture of flint of the hardest kind.

Penrith Observer, 5 May 1874

ACCIDENT AT LANGWATHBY

On the evening of Saturday last Teddy Marston, a railway labourer was walking along the road leading to his lodgings, when, no doubt accidentally, his leg was doubled under him, and he fell, breaking both bones of the limb a little above the ankle. Dr Macgregor attended the sufferer in the course of the evening, and set the fractured leg.

Penrith Observer, 5 May 1874

MEMORIAL STONE AT LANGWATHBY

An instance of the genuine sympathy which exists among railway labourers, not with standing the rough exterior by which they are characterised, has been brought to light at Langwathby. It will be remembered that within the past few months three navvies have lost their lives under very lamentable circumstances. John Mead and John Smith were both drowned in the River Eden, and John d'Boo, a Frenchman, died after a short illness. The kind-hearted navvies on the Langwathby Sub-section, of the Settle and Carlisle Railway have, at their own cost, erected in the churchyard at Langwathby, a beautiful grave stone to the memory of their departed companions. It is of Grey Park Spring Stone, and is the work of Mr Norman, Duke Street, in this town.

Lancaster Gazette, 9 May 1874

FATAL ACCIDENT

A fatality of a painful nature occurred to a man named Joseph Bewley, upon the Settle and Carlisle Railway, now in course of construction, near Langwathby, on Saturday last. Whilst employed in filling wagons a large mass of solid earth became suddenly detached from the breast of an adjoining cutting, and fell upon him. His thigh was broken, and he was also severely injured internally. Dr Williamson, the railway medical attendant, being at Carlisle on important business, a messenger was dispatched for Dr Macgregor, of Penrith, who arrived at Langwathby with as little delay as possible, and at once reduced the fracture of the limb, and did all that medical skill could suggest to relive the unfortunate man's sufferings, which were most intense. Notwithstanding all the care and attention bestowed he never rallied, but gradually sunk, and expired at four o'clock the following morning.

Penrith Herald, 9 May 1874

BASE INGRATITUDE

A few weeks ago we stated that a large number of agricultural labourers from the south had migrated to this neighbourhood to work on the Settle and Carlisle Railway. From what we have learned, we understand that the men came from Norfolk, where they had been in receipt of some 14s a week wages. Their railway fare was kindly paid by Mr Throssle, the manager at 27s per week. On Monday last, however, after a fortnight's work, a number of the men 'jacked up' and proceeded to another contract where they were able to make 1s 6d a week or 3d per day higher wages.

Penrith Observer, 19 May 1874

SHOCKING FATAL ACCIDENT IN WESTMORLAND

Yesterday (Monday) a miner, named Caleb James, employed at Birkett Tunnel, Mallerstang, died from injuries received while extracting a charge of dynamite which had not exploded. Another man, his mate, was seriously injured. It appears that the two men, after drilling a hole in the rock, stemmed it with dynamite, but the fire failing to ignite it, they again attempted to drill the same hole, when the dynamite exploded, killing James, and knocking out the eye of the other man, and inflicted such injuries on the other eye that it is thought he will be rendered totally blind. Dr Allan, from Kirkby Stephen, rendered medical assistance.

Penrith Observer, 19 May 1874

SAD ACCIDENT ON THE SETTLE AND CARLISLE RAILWAY

A boy, named Hind, about fourteen years of age, son of a labourer residing at Appleby, met with a serious accident yesterday evening. He was employed on the embankment behind The Friary, as a 'nipper', and his duty was to sprag the wagons before tipping them on the bank. In getting away, after uncoupling one, he stumbled, and in some way or other got under the wheel. The wagon was laden, and stood on his leg until it was discovered and put back by a person of the name of William Coal, who was then engaged as tipper. His right leg was found to be crushed almost to pieces. He was at once taken to Dr Dinwoodie, who bound up the leg, and he was removed by the 6 pm train to Carlisle Infirmary.

Cumberland and Westmorland Advertiser, 26 May 1874

ROBBERY AT KIRKBY STEPHEN

On Wednesday last, a miner, named Edward Jennings, also known as 'Shipley Ned' was brought before the Rev. Dr. Simpson at Kirkby Stephen, on a charge of stealing a purse containing £31 in gold, from the person of George Smith, striker, Birkett Huts. It appeared that on Tuesday, while Smith was lying asleep and intoxicated in the Fountains Inn at Kirkby Stephen, Jennings took the liberty of searching his pockets, and abstracting the purse and money. His operations were witnessed by Margaret Sedgwick and Elizabeth Atkinson, and he was apprehended the same day by Sergeant Hutchinson, in a public house at Ravenstonedale. Jennings was committed for trial at the next quarter sessions. None of the stolen money has been recovered.

Newcastle Courant, 14 August 1874

MURDEROUS ASSAULT UPON A SUSPECTED WITCH

At Leeds Assizes, on Saturday, before Baron Amphlett, a navvy named Abbot was indicted for maliciously wounding Ellen Bowers. Prosecutrix is a lodging house keeper on the Settle and Carlisle Extension Railway, her hut being at Blackmoor Tunnel, near Garsdale, Sedburgh. As prosecutrix, who is exceedingly stout, weighing nearly 20 stone, and who looked as unlike a witch as it is possible to imagine, was getting dinner ready for her lodgers on the 18 July, the prisoner, who had been sitting in the hut, went to the fireplace, took up a formidable looking poker, and with both hands dealt Mrs Bowers four blows with it, felling her to the ground, and inflicting several serious injuries on her head, from which it was apprehended erysipelas might supervene. Prisoner, who had been drinking for a fortnight, shouted out at the time to the other inmates of the hut that prosecutrix had bewitched him and his two pigs, and he afterwards expressed his regret that he had not succeeded in killing the witch. After his Lordship had said it was difficult to conceive that any man in the nineteenth century could believe that any old woman possessed the power to bewitch him or his pigs, the jury found the prisoner guilty of maliciously wounding. His Lordship said the circumstances were so peculiar he should take time to consider his sentence.

Blea Moor tunnel is 2629 yards long and took five years to build between 1870 and 1875. Work took place from sixteen faces and seven shafts, the tunnel has a depth of up to 500 feet.

Penrith Observer, 1 September 1874

SAD ACCIDENT

On Wednesday last an inquest was held before G. R. Thompson, Esq., in a hut at Smardale, touching the death of a ganger, named John Richardson, 33 years of age, who was employed at Smardale Viaduct. It appears that on Monday week a number of men, under the superintendence of deceased, were engaged in removing a large beam, by means of a crane, from one gantry, or bogie-way, to another they were forming some feet higher, and it seems that Richardson, in order to ease the beam from its position, applied an iron lever which slipped, causing the poor fellow to fall a distance of 45 feet upon stones below. Death ensuing a very short time afterwards. A verdict was returned of 'accidental death.' The deceased leaves a wife and a large family to mourn his loss.

Leeds Mercury, 19 September 1874

YORKSHIRE RAMBLES
SETTLE-BATTY GREEN–BLEA MOOR–DENT HEAD–DENT DALE

The station at Settle has been commenced, and few railway stations will have such noble outlook as there is from this place... up comes the panting locomotive, drawing loaded trucks and a kind of miniature Pullman car, minus the cushions, but with gangway at either end. We mount, Mr Williams, the obliging and attentive foreman, takes charge of the brake, and the little locomotive, one of, Manning

View across Smardale Viaduct showing the fields fenced ready for the new railway and spoil being tipped to form the approach embankment. Photograph author's collection.

Wardle and Co's (of Leeds) handy tank engines, puffs up Ribblesdale the accent being about 1 in 100… we pull up at Salt Lake, and are politely told that we can go no farther on the van. Mounting the engine we are carried forwards to Batty Green. We have passed through deep cuttings, where there are nearly vertical beds of clay slate having seen that the line is substantially constructed, station houses in course of erection, and evidences of completion on every hand, have heard 'shots' fired in succession as the quarry men blew up the hard limestone…

THE NAVVY CAMP

But here we are at Railway Hotel, in the navvy village of Batty Green, a congregation of wooden, white-washed huts and more substantial buildings. We have previously passed huts of this kind on the route, temporary erections for the work people and their families, but Batty Green, with the outlying places, which have been christened Salt Lake, Sebastopol, Jerusalem, and Jericho, appears to be the metropolis of this portion of the line. There are Sunday and day schools, a mission house, library, post office, and an hospital at Batty Green. It is impossible to go forward, as the wind is blowing fresh and rain descending in torrents, so we accept the kind invitation of Messrs. Burgoyne and Cocks, purveyors for Batty Green, and are hospitably entertained at dinner in their cosy dining room. Their store is something like what we could expect to find in the back woods of America. They appear to sell everything. They are butchers, bakers, hosiers, drapers, clothing the navvies and their families as well as feeding them; their 'establishment' is a rambling place, but everything is of the best, and the boots and clothing they show are such as will stand the hard work and the bad weather…

MEETING A NAVVY

Again on a little tank locomotive, we are conveyed along a dreary cutting, through a short tunnel, over which a stream known as Force Gill is carried. The rain descends in torrents, miniature waterfalls rush down the rocky sides of the cutting, and the mouth of Blea Moor tunnel is gained. There is water everywhere, and it is impossible to conceive more arduous work than the stalwart navvies have to encounter in this dreariest of places – but are cheerful. Look at Charley, as he is familiarly called! He stands on a jutting crag, strong in limb, rotund in person, with a jolly fat face, his coat thrown lightly and gracefully over his broad shoulders, his cap resting on his bushy dark hair, while his weather beaten face is irradiated with smiles, and his bright eyes twinkle knowingly as he answers questions addressed to him. How easy is his attitude, and how contented he stands, with his brawny brown arms, covered with an undergrowth of hair, exposed to the elbows, as the rain falls heavily. Then there is the 'walking ganger,' active and alert, plodding over the stones and through the water, clad in a waterproof, with strong boots on his feet, and the brim of his hat turned down to allow the rain to run off. He is prompt and firm in his orders, his countenance betrays the arduous nature of his duties, but there is not the least trace of a smile; for a smile, we are told, is dangerous where navies are concerned, but even he unbends to Charley as he gives him orders respecting the rails, for Charley is a clever workman, and therefore to be trusted.

THE TUNNEL

Passing underneath overhanging rocks, a candle, with a piece of clay for a candlestick, is placed in our hands, we enter the tunnel, and find that it is arched. The tunnel is nearly 2,600 yard long, and 500 feet below the surface in the deepest part. Seven shafts were sunk to enable the 'muck' as it is called, to be conveyed away. The strata is limestone, gritstone, and shale, and although hard enough to require blasting, the tunnel has had to be lined with brick arching. The level of the rails in the centre is 1,151½ feet above sea level, a rising of barely 1 in 100 from the junction with the Midland Railway beyond Settle. The headings in every case met correctly, showing the excellence of the surveying.

The arching is well advanced, but there is still a quantity of stone to be removed before both lines of permanent rails can be laid. It was a rough walk through the tunnel, although, for nearly the whole distance, men were at work with lighted candles. Here were a score of men engaged, in gangs of three, one holding an iron bar, and the others striking the iron with heavy hammers, forming holes in the rock for blasting. The clangour of the hammers, the dim forms of the men, and the weird light, formed a singular scene.

A rush of waters is heard, there is a gleam of light, and, peeping up a round orifice, we see daylight dimly, amid a cloud of falling water. Our candles go out, we stumble forward, and come upon a cosy hut, with a pleasant fire, while a little further on is a comfortable stable, where a couple of fat ponies are feeding; next we pass a fine grey horse, champing his bit and standing in the darkness as content as if he were under the canopy of heaven.

Here are the bricklayers at work, building the walls for arching, there is a man pounding away at the hard rock with a heavy bar of iron, the sweat standing in thick beads on his grimy face, while another is laying the permanent way. Now we descend into an excavation, climb up the face of the rock, pass through a narrow orifice, and again descend to the tunnel level; here are tall scaffolds, with branching

Spoil heaps at Blea Moor tunnel seen from a railway carriage window. Even after all the intervening years these heaps have not fully grassed over. Photograph author's collection.

arms, to enable the miners to bring down the rock from the top and sides of the tunnel, and load the 'muck' into wagons to be carried away to the tip. The tunnel is hot, fusty, and smells damp, indeed it is now very wet, but will be comparatively dry when the drains are made to take away the water.

A miner tells us that it is comfortable working in this tunnel compared with the tin mines of Cornwall, from which he has come, and he is content with both his labour and his pay. A broad blue light is seen ahead, and after floundering through a miry way, the end of the tunnel is reached, and we find ourselves at Dent Head… Everyone has been very obliging but the men were all 'dry' and we had to pass several tollgates, where a sixpence was the 'open sesame'. An agreeable blacksmith found some soap, and a wash was needful after our experience of the toil and trouble that men have to undergo in the trying labour of tunnelling.

'We can now see through the 'spectacles' of the powerful little engine which is drawing us, that we are approaching the mouth of what may perhaps be more strictly called the 'covered way' that leads to the famous Blea Moor Tunnel. It was intended to make the entrance some distance farther north but eventually it was thought safer in order to avoid any slipping of earth down the mountain or down the sides of the cutting, which would have been nearly 100 feet deep to cover in the cutting, and in effect to commence the tunnel 400 yards father south.

'We are now in the tunnel. Nothing is to be seen but the lamp, which our engineer has just lit, dangling from the roof, and throwing its bull's eye light on the tunnel wall. Nothing is to be heard but the roar of our puffing snorting little engine, and the hollow reverberation of the mighty cavern. Onward we go, beneath a mountain, which rises 500 feet above our heads; when suddenly some sharp shrill whistles are sounded, the speed is slackened, and we find ourselves slowly moving among groups of scores of men with flickering lights and candles stuck on end on the projecting crags of the rocky tunnel sides.

'For a moment we pause. 'What's up?' shouts a voice and some answer inarticulate to us, is returned.

The steam is turned on; again we move forward into the thick black night; other whistles follow; other lights glimmer and gleam; another group of workmen is passed, looking, by the red light of their fire, a picture fit for Rembrandt; and at last, not unwilling, we emerge into the sweet bright light of heaven…'

Williams.

Penrith Observer, 20 October 1874

ACCIDENT AT BIRKETT TUNNEL

A sad accident occurred on Friday last to two miners employed in Birkett Tunnel, near Kirkby Stephen. It appears that the men employed on the night shift had left a charging of dynamite unfired, and these men being ignorant of it, struck a bar into the hole, when an explosion immediately took place. One man's face was very much injured, and the arms of the other man were seriously shatter. We understand they are both doing well.

'After a long walk, we arrive at the face, where we see some 30 or 40 miners hard at work, whose occupation consists of drilling holes in the rock, which are afterwards charged with gunpowder and exploded. These men work in couples; one holds the drill, or jumper, and slightly alters the position of its cutting edge after every stroke, and the other, by repeated blows of a hammer, forces it into the rock. Great stalwart men are these miners, who seem to wield heavy hammers with ease, and bring them down on the drill with tremendous force, the sharp click of each blow betraying to even an experienced ear the hardness of the material which is being worked…

'When a hole is made the safety fuse is put in which is a long string, and is composed of some explosive material covered with canvas. It is very tough, and when lighted burns gradually. The hole is then charged with gunpowder, about a pint, or two 'tots' as they are called, being usually enough, but sometimes four 'tots' are used in a shot. The fuse is put in first, then comes the powder, and lastly the 'tamping', as it is called, which is the material that is rammed in to fill up the hole When a hole is drilled a stone is put upon it until other holes are ready The men retreat, some times 100 yards away, and the shots are fired by a man appointed for that service. It was he who also puts the powder in…' Williams

Penrith Observer, 3 November 1874

SAD ACCIDENT NEAR CULGAITH

On Friday last, a railway labourer was knocked down and run over by an earth wagon on the new line of railway near Culgaith. Both his legs were broken and crushed; and the poor fellow had to submit to the trying ordeal of being brought to Penrith, where he had to remain for nearly three hours before he could be removed to Carlisle Infirmary. His sufferings were intense; and he frequently wished he might die.

Penrith Observer, 10 November 1874

FATAL ACCIDENT ON THE MIDLAND RAILWAY

On Friday afternoon an inquest was held in the Infirmary, Carlisle, on the body of a man named Muncey. The deceased was employed feeding a mortar mill on the Settle and Carlisle Railway, at Culgaith, and it appears was knocked down and run over by a wagon on the 30th ult. He was at once taken to the Infirmary, where he died about eleven o'clock on Wednesday night. The jury returned a verdict of 'accidental death.' Adding an expression of opinion that in such cases the removal of one so injured to any great distance is to be reprehended, and that the mortar mill was too near the line.

Lancaster Gazette, 21 November 1874

EMBEZZLEMENT ON THE SETTLE AND CARLISLE RAILWAY

At the County Police Court, Carlisle, on Saturday, Fredrick Armitage, of Southport, time keeper on the No 4 contract (Carlisle) section of the Settle and Carlisle (Midland) Railway was charged with embezzling the money of his employers, Messers Bayliss, the contractors for the formation of that section of the new Settle and Carlisle railway. Mr Wannop was for the prosecution, and Mr Ostell for the defence.

From the statement of the prosecuting solicitor, and from the evidence of Mr John Bayliss, it appeared that Armitage was engaged as time keeper by Mr Bayliss on the 22 October. The situation is one of great trust, in as much as on this contract alone from £12,000 to £15,000 per month pass through the hands of the pay clerks and time keepers. Prisoner received 35s per week, and it soon appeared that out of this sum he had engaged a man named Thornton, a storekeeper, at the rate of 24s a week to assist him in his work of keeping his books. Part of the prisoner's duty was to keep the time of the men, part to 'sub' them (i.e. give them subsistence money), and part to give them pay off tickets, showing the balance due to them on pay day. There were between thirty and forty distinct cases to which the prisoner had falsified his accounts, but only one was gone into. It was the case of a man named Burke, who had worked six days and earned 24s. Armitage, however, actually 'subbed' him to the extent of 24s-6d and then his books claimed credit for paying £2 2s 6d thus obtaining 18s for himself. He now pleaded guilty, and was sentenced to six months imprisonment with hard labour.

'Contractors William Eckersley and John Bayliss had undertaken works for the Midland Railway between 1862 and 1870, they were contracted for the final length of contract No 4 to Petteril Bridge, Carlisle. The engineers were John Allen, and Samuel S. Paine. The two agents were J. Lambert and S. Williams. In 1871 the partnership was dissolved and Bayliss carried on to complete the work himself although Eckersley was not exonerated from the contract.

'When a contract was taken, the contractor would employ an agent who would superintend the entire work. This agent would have under him sub agents, who were in charge of eight or nine miles of the line. Under these was a time keeper for every couple of miles, who kept a record of time worked by every man in his section, the work was let to gangers who employed the men. The time keeper would report every Saturday to the sub agent the hours worked up to the Friday night, so the men would be paid on the Saturday…' *The Railway Navvies*

Penrith Observer, 24 November 1874

AWFULLY SUDDEN DEATH ON THE MIDLAND RAILWAY

On Tuesday afternoon last a workman named William Bulman, 49 years of age, died suddenly on the Midland Railway, near the New Inn works. He was formerly a servant with Mr. Robert Thomlinson, of Hill Ends, and is brother of Mr Bulman, of Lowthian Gill. Deceased went to his work apparently in his usual heath and spirits on Tuesday morning and continued on the line until the afternoon, when he was seized with a fit of coughing, causing the rupture of a blood vessel, which discharged itself through the mouth and nose, and ended in the poor man's death a few minutes afterwards.

(also see October 1870 and map)

Leicester Chronicle & Leicester Mercury, 5 December 1874

TOWN HALL

Saturday before W. Bowmar, Esq.

Deserter – William Marston was charged with being a deserter. PC Johnson said the prisoner surrendered himself to him at the police station, and said he was a deserter from H.M.S. *Duncan*, having deserted in July 1873. Defendant told him that since he deserted he had been on board two merchant vessels, but for the last four months he had been working on the Settle and Carlisle Railway. Remanded for the Admiralty to be communicated with.

Cumberland and Westmorland Advertiser, 22 December 1874

ROBBERY AT CROSBY GARRETT

One night a short time ago a tommy shop at Crosby Garrett was broken into by breaking a pane of glass in a back window, and a box of raisins, three or four bottles of sweets, and some oranges and apples, stolen therefrom. Information was given to the county police, and from inquiries made by Sergeant Hutchinson and Constable Lancaster, it appears that the keeper of the shop, John Bull, with his wife and family, had the previous day left, without stating they were going, leaving the place very insecurely fastened. The whole of the stolen property has been recovered, having been found by police concealed in an adjoining loft

Settle and Carlisle Railway platelayers at unknown location circa 1910, photograph courtesy of the Lazonby History Society. On investigation I think this photograph was taken at Lazonby, the track curving to the right as it leaves Lazonby Station towards Armathwaite. Also the trees in the background surround Lazonby Hall, they are still visible today from the platform. The crane in the goods yard appears on the Midland Railway Survey of 1911 published in 'Structures of the Settle and Carlisle Railway'. They carried the same tools as James Stansfield would have had in February 1890 at Culgaith. 'The Penrith Herald' in January 1916 reported: "Mr. Alexander Taylor, a widower in his 70s, lived in Kirkoswald and worked as a ganger on the railway at Lazonby. He set off home on Thursday 30th December in the evening with pains in his chest. He fell over twice in Lazonby, but refused to rest, and died on Eden Bridge. The post-mortem found heart failure and an inflamed right lung."

Chapter Seven
1875

The Penrith Herald, 9 January 1875

The Midland works at Appleby will be on an extensive scale. The station will be parallel with the Eden Valley station, at the distance of almost 300 yards. The foundations of the station were laid and workmen had just begun to lay the foundations of the goods station. Sidings on the south of the station for cattle and other goods, will extend a mile and a half. Not far from the station, on the north side, workmen were laying rails for a junction with the Eden line. From the station northwards, there is an immense embankment called Battlebarrow Embankment. At Battlebarrow, in 1281, Lord Clifford, Percy, and Vesey founded a White Friary, the site of which is now occupied by a gentleman's neat mansion called The Friary. Not far from the Friary, St Leonards Hospital once stood as a home for lepers. This home of the afflicted, like Shap Abbey, to which it had been given by John de Veteripont, passed from its original purpose under the reign of Henry the VII. A farmhouse now marks the spot where it once stood. The extreme height of Battlebarrow Embankment is 42 feet, and its cubical contents are 553,000 yards. In the centre of the bank there is a one arch skew bridge, with heavy retaining walls to sustain the pressure of the super incumbent earth, It is a piece of massive masonry containing 6,000 cubic yards. The arch is lined in brick with stone arch quoins. The stone was brought from Dufton quarries, a distance of two and a half miles.

Cumberland and Westmorland Advertiser, 19 January 1875

FATAL RAILWAY ACCIDENT NEAR CARLISLE

On Thursday, shortly before mid-day, a labourer, named John Beaty, who resided at 6 Collingwood Street, Denton Holme, met with a fatal accident near Carlisle. The deceased was employed on the Settle and Carlisle extension of the Midland Railway, and on Thursday morning he was engaged emptying ballast at Durran Hill, when an engine, of which he had no warning, struck the adjoining wagon to that in which he was and thus caused him to fall to the ground. The result was that the front wheel of the second wagon passed over him killing him instantaneously.

The Penrith Herald, 23 January 1875

NEWBIGGIN

A small country village of great antiquity, is situated a little in the south of where No 4 Contract begins. The neighbourhood is so thickly wooded that the village was not visible from the site of the station…
   …The first work of importance on No 4 contract is Crowdundle Viaduct. Which is a little on the north of Newbiggin. The viaduct, which is built of excellent freestone, consists of four arches, and it is 270 feet in length and 48 feet in height. The viaduct crosses the Crowdundle Beck, which divides the two counties of Westmorland and Cumberland. The beck on the north runs at the foot of a very steep wooded bank where Park Wood cutting commences. This is the first wood the new line passes through from the Settle Junction. The cutting is 572 yards in length and 70 feet in its deepest place. The material excavated was 207,000 cubic yards. Over the north end of the cutting there is a one arch stone bridge which on account of its loftiness had a very imposing appearance. It surpasses all the bridges on the line for its high elevation. The viaduct cutting and bridge were finished. The wood through which the line passes abounds in oak trees, and on the west side of it stands an ancient mansion, called from the fruit of those

trees Acorn Bank. Here the Crowdundle Beck makes a large curve and sweeps beneath the Acorn Bank, which is on the Westmorland side of the stream…

Crowdundle Beck Viaduct on the Settle and Carlisle Railway under construction. The arches have been turned on the wooden formers. Waiting for the deck and parapet walls to be finished and the embankment to reach the retaining wall. Photograph courtesy of Cumbria Railway Association.

WASTE BANK TUNNEL

On the north side of Culgaith tunnel Eden River makes a fine turn towards the new line, and for some distance skirts it on the west. From the tunnel there is a lengthy cutting, which is open on the Eden side, and bounded by a lofty wooded bank on the east. At the north end of the cutting there is Waste Bank Tunnel, which is 154 yards in length and 61 feet in depth. It was the difficulty of finding a place to deposit excavated matter which rendered it preferable to tunnel Waste Bank to making a cutting. In passing on the line towards Langwathby, one had a splendid view of Eamont as it came from the west to mingle its crystal flow with that of the Eden…

CULGAITH TUNNEL

The next heavy work to Park Wood Cutting is Culgaith Tunnel. It is 600 yards in length, and 101 feet below the surface of the hill it passes through. It was turned in brick and faced with blue brick quoins. The tunnel was all but finished. Culgaith is a small agricultural village situated on a hill on the east side of the line…

LANGWATHBY

At Langwathby there is a cutting 770 yards in length and 41 feet in depth. Its cubical contents are 129,000 yards. About a mile beyond Langwathby there is a fine viaduct of seven arches. Its length is 430 feet, and its height 35 feet. Its cubical contents are 9,000 yards. The station was in progress…

At Salkeld there is an embankment 660 yards in length and 40 feet in height. Its cubical contents are

120,000 yards. This embankment was finished. The Eden River or Salkeld Viaduct, which was nearly completed, consists of seven arches. Its length is 430 feet, its height 45 feet, and its cubical contents 9,000 yards. At this point the line crosses the Eden for the last time…

The house at Acorn Bank dates back to the times of the Knights Templar. The house and estate was sold by Henry VIII to Thomas Dalston in 1543. Thomas gave the house to his son Christopher, it was reconstructed by his descendent John and his wife Lucy Dalston between 1674 and 1690 and again in the 1740s. The property passed down the female line through the Nortons (1771), Edmonsons (1796) and the Boazmans (1808). In the 1920s the property was bought by Dorothy Una Ratcliffe and Noel McGregor Phillips who substantially renovated the house, she donated it to the National Trust in 1950. During the Second World War the Birmingham Railway Carriage and Wagon Repair Company of Smethwick relocated their offices into the house with some of the staff lodging in the house while others lived at Appleby.

Lancaster Gazette, 13 February 1875

FATAL ACCIDENT ON THE SETTLE AND CARLISLE RAILWAY

An accident of a fatal nature occurred at Bleamoor Tunnel on Friday, the 5th inst., to a tunneller called John Thompson. It appears that the deceased was, contrary to order, drawing some dynamite from a hole, when it exploded, blowing the right side of his face and head and hand off and killing him instantly. The body was taken to the hospital at Batty Green to await an inquest, which was held at the Welcome Hotel Inn, on Monday the 8th instant, before T P Brown Esq., deputy coroner. The jury returned a verdict of 'accidentally killed'.

Lancaster Gazette, 20 February 1875

FOUND DEAD

Henry Bachelor, about 22 years of age, was found dead on the Settle and Carlisle Railway near Sebastopol, Bleamoor, on Monday last. It appears that he was never seen alive after about 12 o'clock at noon on Sunday, the day previous, when he went to his lodgings at Mr Lirke's, and asked for a bird which he had there, but as he was drunk his landlord refused to give it to him, when he went away and was not again seen alive. About seven o'clock on Monday morning he was found lying on his face on the railway quite dead. There were no marks upon him except a small bruise on his forehead, which it was thought was obtained by his falling. An inquest was held at the Railway Inn, Batty Green, on Tuesday before Mr T P Brown, deputy coroner, when the jury returned a verdict of 'Found Dead'.

Cumberland and Westmorland Advertiser, 2 March 1875

PROJECTED NEW RAILWAY STATION AT APPLEBY

It is stated that the Midland and North Eastern Railway companies have decided to erect a passenger station at Appleby which will meet the requirements of both. A loop will connect the North Eastern Railway with the Midland at the north and south approaches. This arrangement will prove advantages to both companies, and it will be appreciated by passengers.

Bradford Observer, 31 March 1875

A FATAL PRIZE FIGHT

John Atkins (30) labourer, pleaded guilty to the manslaughter of William Williams, at Dent, on the 9 August last. Mr Fenwick was for the prosecution, and Mr Campbell Foster defended the prisoner. The parties had quarrelled, both being employed as navvies on the Settle and Carlisle Railway, and had gone into a field to fight, the result being that Williams received a bad injury in a fair 'stand-up' fight. Sentence was four weeks imprisonment, prisoner having been some time in goal.

Penrith Herald, 3 April 1875

ACCIDENT NEAR ORMSIDE

On Sunday evening an accident happened to a young man of the name of John McKay, a mason, employed on the Midland Railway extension. He was returning from Ormside along with several companions, and had to cross a deep gill on a plank, near to the quarry, from which he lost his footing and fell a height of fifteen feet, or more, and broke his thigh. It was nearly a couple of hours before his companions were able to release him from his perilous position.

Penrith Observer, 6 April 1875

MAN KILLED ON THE RAILWAY

On Thursday, the 1st inst, an inquest was held at Moorcock, before G R Thompson, Esq., coroner, on the body of James Bell, a navvy, who was found lying across the line on the night of the 30th ult., having been run over both legs and otherwise mutilated by the engines working this part of the line during the night. From the evidence of the witnesses it appears that the unfortunate man had been working for some time near the Incline Huts, Mallerstang, and for several days previous to the accident had been on the 'spree'. Robert Blakey said he was with the deceased on the night of the 30th ult., and left him within thirty yards of where he was found. He must have been stupefied with drink and laid down to sleep across the metals. Bell was one of the civilest men on the line. E Dent identified the body as that of her lodger. He left his lodgings about seven o'clock on the Tuesday night. J Adams fireman, said he discovered the body of the deceased by the light of his lamp, laying across the line just as they were about to run over him. Several engines appeared to have passed over him. The jury returned a verdict of 'accidentally killed.'

Penrith Herald 1 May 1875

THE SETTLE AND CARLISLE RAILWAY

The works connected with the formation of the Settle and Carlisle Extension of the Midland Railway are now approaching completion, and on Thursday the directors made a thorough inspection, commencing at Carlisle with the intention of passing through to Settle. The whole of the main line is not yet completed, but temporary girders would be constructed to enable the short train to pass over. Eight or nine of the directors of the Midland Railway, including the chairman, started from the Petteril Yard about nine o'clock, in two saloon carriages drawn by a pretty little engine, and were accompanied by Mr Bayliss, the contractor, and other officials connected with the railway. It is hoped the company will be enabled to open the line for goods traffic in the course of the autumn.

Penrith Herald, 8 May 1875

DINNER TO WORKMEN

On Thursday the 29th inst., Mr Walmsley, the contractor who, under Messrs Benton and Woodewiss, has built Smardale Viaduct provided his workmen and others (numbering about 70) with a very substantial dinner, to celebrate the completion of the viaduct, the directors having gone over that day in a saloon carriage in making their journey through the line from Carlisle to Settle. The dinner consisting of huge rounds of roast beef, legs of mutton, gigantic plum puddings, tarts, etc., washed down with a plentiful supply of beer or water, according to the Templar or Tippler proclivities of the guests, was served in one of the huts at the viaduct under Mrs Walmsley's superintendence, and amply testified to her proficiency as hostess. After all were satisfied (a work of time in some cases), and the cloths re-moved, Mr Gadsley took the chair, supported on his right by Mr Walmsley, and on the left by Mr Gudgin. After the usual loyal and patriotic toasts were honoured, the chairman proposed 'Success to the Midland Railway Company' and, in the course of his remarks, praised his company for the enterprise displayed by them in undertaking the formation of the Settle and Carlisle Railway, properly termed in navvy par-lance 'The Long Drag' and thus finding employment for very large numbers of workmen. The chairman concluded hoping that the company would find another Settle and Carlisle to make (A voice: 'They'll have a job.') After the toast had been duly honoured and responded to by Mr Gudginon behalf of the company, the chairman said he had a very pleasing duty to perform, which was to propose the toast of the evening, the health of their worthy host, who had struggled against numerous difficulties in carrying out this great work, the completion of which they had that evening met to commemorate. That viaduct, continued the chairman, was a work which any man might be proud of, and he had no doubt that years hence Mr Walmsley's children, and children's, children, might look with honest pride on it. That work would be an enduring monument of his skill and perseverance…

This article contains the first mention of the expression 'The Long Drag', the uphill climb to the summit of the line.

In 1878 Mr J. S. Storey was the surveyor for the county of Derbyshire. In 1882 a bridge was built across the Torrs, the valley where the river Sett joins the Goyt, to connect the two settlements of New Mills in Derbyshire and Newtown in Cheshire. It was reported that Mr Storey had consid-erable experience in bridge building gained while working for the Midland Railway (see 2 August 1873) The contractor was Mr M. W. Walmsley of Crumpsall near Manchester.

Cumberland and Westmorland Advertiser, 11 May 1875

A RAILWAY LABOURER KILLED

On Friday last, the 7th inst., an inquest was held before George Thompson Esq., at the Castle Inn, Mallerstang, on the body of John Green, railway labourer… James Clifford, of Birkett Huts, Mallerstang, railway labourer, 'But I knew the deceased, who was also a railway labourer, but I did not know whether he was married or single, nor his age. He had formerly been a master butcher in London. He left his lodgings, in my hut, about half past five o'clock on Wednesday evening, and I saw him come straight away to this inn. He was quite sober.' On Thursday morning an alarm was given that deceased was found dead on the railway. I went and found him lying in a culvert. He must, I think have been tipsy, and fallen over… He was about a quarter of a mile from the huts. It was a dark night and deceased must have missed his way… He might be about 45 years of age, he had been drinking heavily for some time past, but he had been working on the day in question. His death must have been immediate, but he might not have been very much injured if he had not struck the stone… The jury returned a verdict of 'Accidental death'.

Leeds Mercury, 25 May 1875

COMPLETION OF THE SETTLE AND CARLISLE RAILWAY

After five years hard work and immense outlay of capital, the making of this important new railway is now practically completed. Owing to the somewhat rough state in which portions of it remain, the line is not yet quite ready to be thrown open for ordinary traffic. The time for this is not far distant, as a train of saloon carriages has passed over the entire length of 72 miles from Carlisle to Settle. This news will be welcomed by the travelling public, and still more by shareholders, many of whom have been long impatient for some return from the enormous cost of the undertaking. Its real importance consist in giv-ing the Midland Company a direct and independent connection with the system of their Scots allies, the Glasgow and South Western, and North British Railway. This will at once effect a clear saving of the heavy rent amounting to about £70,000 or £80,000 per annum which the Midland directors hitherto had to pay for running powers over the Lancaster and Carlisle Railway. It will also enable a large share of through goods traffic to Leeds, Derby, Birmingham, etc., to be retained on the Midland main line, besides affording a more expeditious and straight route for passengers to or from the north.

In addition to these advantages that the new line will open up a district of country which has hitherto been but little known, contrasting strangely in the rugged grandeur at some points with the rich pasture lands of Craven, through which the traveller also passes. On account of the heavy cuttings through rock and the number of viaducts and tunnels that have to be made, the construction of the line proved exceptionally difficulty, even when divided as it has been into four sections, with separate staff attached to each. The first section, including 17¼ miles from Settle to Dent Valley, has been carried out not by separate contractors, like the other divisions, but by the Midland Railway Company themselves, for whom Mr Edgar O. Ferguson has acted as resident engineer, with Mr W. H. Ashwell as agent and manager. Under the general direction of these gentlemen, about 3,000 labourers have long been engaged with steady perseverance in overcoming natural difficulties which at times seemed hopeless and insurmountable. Now that the heavy work has been got over, all concerned may fairly be congratulated upon the substantial and thorough style in which it has been done.

At Settle itself the new line is sure to produce a change which will rather astonish some of the older inhabitants. The progress of works in the vicinity has already more or less disturbed the former repose of the streets, and ere long the place will be further enlivened by the arrival and departure of trains at a commodious new station in the village, instead of only at the old one, which is more than a mile distant. Well built cottages are already springing up in the immediate neighbourhood of the new station, and ere long still further improvements may no doubt be looked for, in keeping with the spirit of the times…

Leeds Mercury, 25 May 1875

For the purposes of the public sale of contractors plant, which commenced this forenoon, a special train was run from Leeds, stopping on the way at Shipley, Keighley, and Skipton. Upon their arrival at Settle the company (numbering about 200 passengers) found large quantities of working 'plant' arranged in no fewer than 1,200 lots on both sides of the line for a distance of nearly a mile from the new station. The collection, as may be supposed, was a heterogeneous one, including a locomotive, boilers, engines, upward 70 wagons, 400,000 bricks, nearly 400 tons of contractors rails, more than 100 tons of scrap iron and many tons of fire wood, as well as other articles less known to the general public, and variously described as 'Goliaths', 'overhead travellers', etc. The whole of this accumulation belonged to what is distinguished as the first contract, and its sale is expected to realise something like £10,000. The auctioneers are Messers Oliver and Son and Appleton of Leeds, who will continue the sale during the week. About 300 lots have been disposed of today and on the whole fair prices were realised. Amongst the first lots put up for the bid of purchasers was a large quantity of timber which had been used for huts of the now diminished navvy village of Batty Green. The attendance at the auction included buyers from Leeds, Bradford, Carlisle, Manchester, Liverpool, Birmingham, Ripon, Keighley, Bingley, Otley, Horsforth, and Derby.

Leeds Mercury, 29 May 1875

THE SETTLE AND CARLISLE RAILWAY: SALE OF CONTRACTORS PLANT

The extensive sale of contractors 'plant' used in making the first section of the Settle and Carlisle Railway was concluded yesterday, and has realised during the week about £12,000.

Yesterday's sale alone produced nearly £5,000, comprising several engines and valuable 'lots' at the Batty Green Viaduct and Bleamoor Tunnel. The company in attendance numbered between 200 and 300 gentlemen, who were conveyed to the scene of the sale in a special train from Settle. Amongst those present were Mr Wm. Firth, Leeds, Mr Kearsley, ex-Mayer of Ripon; Messers, Benton and Woodiwiss, who are the contractors for the second and fifth sections of the line; Messers Taylor and Thompson,

IMPROVED PORTABLE STEAM ENGINE.

The above Illustration represents our Improved Portable Steam Engine, which is constructed on the most approved principles, and made throughout of the best materials and workmanship; it is of great strength and durability, due regard being paid to portability.

Each Engine is supplied with Glass Water Gauge, Gauge Cocks, Blow-off Cock, Tallow Cock to Cylinder, Steam Indicator and Whistle, and provided with Waterproof Cover, Wrenches, Firing Tools, and all requisites.

Engines for exportation to countries where coal is scarce are made with enlarged fire boxes for burning wood, &c., and the chimney is provided with improved copper wire spark-catcher to prevent accident from fire.

Link-motion reversing gear can be attached to this Engine, for which an extra charge is made.

NOTE.—These Engines are also made with Steam-Jacketed Cylinders, Feed-Water Heater, and Patent Variable Expansion Eccentrics, whereby great economy in fuel is effected. The sizes and prices being as under :

Prices of Single-Cylinder Portable Engines, with Fittings Complete.				Prices of Double-Cylinder Portable Engines, with Fittings Complete.			
4 horse-power ..	£ 180	8 horse-power ..	£ 255	10 horse-power ..	£ 320	18 horse-power ..	£ 510
5 ,, ..	200	9 ,, ..	275	12 ,, ..	370	20 ,, ..	545
6 ,, ..	220	10 ,, ..	295	14 ,, ..	415	25 ,, ..	660
7 ,, ..	235	12 ,, ..	335	16 ,, ..	455	30 ,, ..	780

CHARLES POWIS AND CO.,
ENGINEERS,
MILLWALL PIER, LONDON, E. CITY OFFICES : 60, GRACECHURCH STREET, E.C.

contractors, Manchester and Normanton; Mr James Campbell, of Hunslet Engineering Company, Leeds; Mr Wardle, jun., of Messers Manning, Wardle, and Co., Leeds; Messers, Scott and Edwards, contractors, Melmerby; Mr Richards, Sunderland, and other buyers from a distance, including a few from Scotland.

As on former days, the sale was conducted by Messers Oliver, and Son, and Appleton, Leeds, whose management of the gigantic auction (including as it did no fewer than 1,200 lots) appeared to give general satisfaction, the whole having passed off without a hitch. Amongst the principle lots sold yesterday were three locomotives one by Manning Wardle and Co., with 12 inch cylinders, realising 720 guineas; the second by the same firm, 10 inch cylinders, for 440 guineas; and the third made by the Hunslet Engineering Company, with 10 inch cylinders, for 400 guineas; three winding engines for 200, 170, and 150 guineas respectively; three boilers realising from 100 to 140 guineas each; a travelling goliath, 82 guineas; a small size of Blakes patent stone crusher 105 guineas; portable steam engine, by Powis and Co., nine inch cylinder, 14 inch stroke, 182 guineas; circular saw bench, 48 inches, 48 guineas; and weigh bridge, 45 guineas. In a district so remote, and where casual labour is not plentiful, it proved a great convenience to purchasers that the Midland Railway Company, to whom the plant belonged, undertook the delivery of all goods except bricks, and in the case of firewood the ordinary freight was reduced.

William Frith, Leeds, Merchant and Inventor with patents to improve machinery in the coal industry. Henry Kearsley, Iron works Ripon, Mayor 1870-71, died 1878.
Scott & Edwards, Railway contractors, Wigan, responsible for the Mold & Denbigh Railway 1868, and the Brading & Bembridge Branch, Isle of Wight, also worked the branch under contract until 1898. Another visitor describes the line during this period of construction:

The pretty passenger station at Settle built of freestone and in Gothic style, was nearly finished, the walls of the spacious goods shed were almost ready to receive the roof and the commodious cottages hard by, for the company's servants, would soon be completed, but around were white washed wooden sheds, the temporary offices of the company's staff, and innumerable piles of contractors material, no longer needed but readily marked off in lots for the great clearance sale.

It is the dinner hour and a strange silence prevails through out the works. Navvies are taking their siesta on the great piled-up baulks of timber in various and grotesque attitudes, apparently sleeping… The locomotive that is to convey us has drawn with full steam up alongside the platform… We are ready, and in a minute our engine is puffing and snorting its way up the incline of 1 in 100. Leaving the stone built, cleanly houses and streets of Settle, we rise up a heavy embankment containing a quarter of a million cubic yards of earth and then enter a blue limestone cutting… We now pass the works of the Craven Lime Company… We now stop at a wooden tank (beyond Horton in Ribblesdale) to give our engine water…

Four miles from Settle we cross the turnpike that runs from Ingleton to Hawes and now the heaviest part of the works begins. Dwellings had been erected for 2,000 navvies who were to work on Ribblehead viaduct and Blea Moor tunnel. We may add that the principle owner of Blea Moor required the company to bury their telegraph wires in order to prevent injury to his grouse on the wing. This is the moorland town of Batty Green… Potters carts, drapers carts, milk carts, greengrocery carts, butchers and bakers carts, brewers drays and traps and horses for hire might all be found, besides numerous hawkers who plied their trade from hut to hut.

The company's offices, yards, stables, store room and shops occupied a large space of ground. There were also the shops of various trades people, the inevitable public houses, a neat looking hospital, a post office, a public library, a mission house, and a day and Sunday schools. But despite all these conventionalities the spot was frequently most desolate and bleak… all agreed they were in one of the wildest, windiest, coldest and dreariest localities in the world. The wind was so violent and piecing that for days together the bricklayers on the viaduct were unable to work simply from fear of being blown off… Through the dreadful Blea Moor tunnel and on into Dent dale where the inspection trip finished…

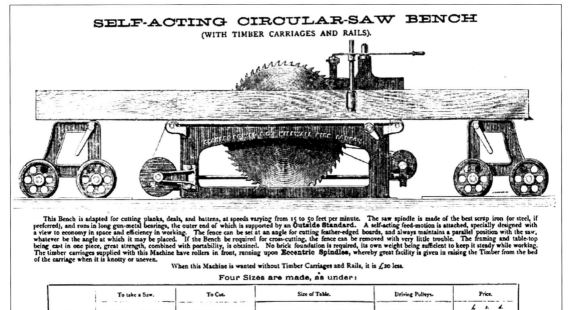

SELF-ACTING CIRCULAR-SAW BENCH
(WITH TIMBER CARRIAGES AND RAILS).

This Bench is adapted for cutting planks, deals, and battens, at speeds varying from 15 to 50 feet per minute. The saw spindle is made of the best scrap iron (or steel, if preferred), and runs in long gun-metal bearings, the outer end of which is supported by an **Outside Standard**. A self-acting feed-motion is attached, specially designed with a view to economy in space and efficiency in working. The fence can be set at an angle for cutting feather-edged boards, and always maintains a parallel position with the saw, whatever be the angle at which it may be placed. If the Bench be required for cross-cutting, the fence can be removed with very little trouble. The framing and table-top being cast in one piece, great strength, combined with portability, is obtained. No brick foundation is required, its own weight being sufficient to keep it steady while working. The timber carriages supplied with this Machine have rollers in front, running upon **Eccentric Spindles**, whereby great facility is given in raising the Timber from the bed of the carriage when it is knotty or uneven.

When this Machine is wanted without Timber Carriages and Rails, it is £20 less.

Four Sizes are made, as under:

	To take a Saw.	To Cut.	Size of Table.	Driving Pulleys.	Price. £ s. d.
No. 1	36 inches diameter	15 inches deep	5 feet 9 inches by 2 feet 9 inches	12 inches diameter	80 0 0
2	42 "	18 "	6 " 0 " 3 " 0 "	14 "	90 0 0
3	48 "	21 "	7 " 0 " 3 " 3 "	16 "	100 0 0
4	54 "	24 "	7 " 6 " 3 " 6 "	16 "	110 0 0

CHARLES POWIS AND CO.,
ENGINEERS, MILLWALL PIER, LONDON, E. City Offices: 60, GRACECHURCH STREET, E.C.

Above and page 85, Charles Powis and Co, Cyclops Works, Milwall Pier, London – steam engine and saw bench similar to those in the contractors plant sale list of May 1875,

We had been drawn up by engine No 568 (a Kirtley double-frame 0-6-0 built at Derby in 1870). The engine had gone and our carriage was to be run down the incline of fourteen miles by itself. In the morning when ascending we noticed that only the up line of the permanent way was in use, and we asked if there was any possibility of meeting a train coming down. 'Oh no!' said our engineer, 'There are only two other small engines on the road and they always cut out of the way when they see us coming.' So having been drawn back through the tunnel by one of the aforementioned little engines and started off at the other end of our decent, we trusted to the law of gravitation, the strength of our brake and the skill of our engineer. We can drop you down in 20 minutes he remarked and all we need add is, drop us down he did.   (This is also quoted in Williams' book)

Penrith Observer, 1 June 1875

RAILWAY ACCIDENT AT LANGWATHBY

On Tuesday morning last, while a fireman named Johnston was on an engine at Langwathby, he slipped off and fell beside the rails. One of his legs which lay across the rail was fearfully crushed, and on being removed to the Carlisle Infirmary, amputation had to be performed. He was a steady man and very attentive to his duties.

Penrith Observer, 1 June 1875

SHOCKING ACCIDENT AT KIRKBY STEPHEN

On Saturday last a melancholy and fatal accident occurred at the Midland Railway Station, Kirkby Stephen, by which a poor lad, named Robert Crewdson, (employed as a nipper at this station,) lost his life. It appears, from the evidence given at the inquest, that during the dinner hour a ganger named

Wilson was arranging some trucks in readiness for the men to start with after dinner, and was moving towards the trucks with the contractors small engine used for that purpose, when the lad Crewdson rushed in quickly to couple the wagons to the engine. This not being necessary, the fireman called to him to come out and in doing so he was caught by the engine which ran over his chest. As quickly as possible the engine was stopped, but life was quite extinct, the poor fellow being almost cut in two. He was picked up and conveyed home. And the inquest was held at the Pack Horse Inn yesterday, before G. R. Thompson, Esq., and the following gentlemen as jury:- Messrs J. B. Davis, George Steel, Thomas Brown, J. Scott, J. Buck, J. Parkinson, James Yare, N. Berry, John Shaw, Thomas Woof, John Garnett, and Richard Fawcett. The following evidence was taken.

William Smith Webster, engine driver, 'I saw deceased coming up to meet some wagons; both were in slow motion. When the wagons were about a yard apart from the engine deceased stepped in, as if to couple them. Robert Robinson shouted that no coupling was wanted. Deceased tried to get out, but fell and was run over by the first wheel of the engine. The second wheel rested on his body. The driver of the engine was on the opposite side to that upon which he entered.'

James Crewdson, clogger, Kirkby Stephen, said, 'Deceased was my son and was thirteen years of age on the 20 August last. He was employed on the Settle and Carlisle Railway under Phillip Aynes as a nipper, and had been working under him, about eighteen months or two years. On Saturday afternoon he was brought home, having been run over by an engine. The wheels seemed to have gone over his chest. His back was broken and his arm crushed entirely.'

Thomas Wilson, ganger, said, 'Deceased was employed under my charge. His duties were to take picks to the smithy and go messages. On Saturday last he was employed close to the station. About one o'clock I was dragging an engine and was on it I had seen deceased about ten minutes before.'

Robert Wilson stated that he saw the deceased go between the engine and the wagons, and shouted to him, 'Not to be coupled.' As he did so one of the engine wheels passed over him. he had hold of the chain to couple them, and had got on to the line on the opposite side of the driver. The jury returned a verdict of 'accidentally killed' no blame was attached to any one.

Leeds Mercury, 2 June 1875

THE SETTLE AND CARLISLE RAILWAY, DESCRIBED BY OUR OWN REPORTER

Although this important addition to our railway system is not yet available for regular traffic, a well filled excursion train has already passed over its first section. The excursionists, numbering nearly 300 gentlemen, were no doubt more bent upon business than pleasure, but pleased at the same time to find an opportunity when both could be so well combined. Their main object was to attend the public sale of contractors plant, which as was announced in Saturday's *Mercury*, has realised about £12,000. Let it not be supposed, however, that the travellers on the way thought only of auction bids and bargains. Most of the intending purchasers knew before starting what they wanted to buy, and therefore needed not to sacrifice time on the journey in the close study of dry catalogues. The prospect of cheap lots at the coming sale rather served to put everybody in better behaviour for admiring a region which many of the party then entered for the first time. As the course of the line may be equally new to many of our readers, and must be of interest to all who care for railway progress let us now briefly describe the works and the district through which they pass.

The line, which has been in course of construction fully five years, commences on the south side of Settle by a junction with the Midland Railway, 425 feet above the sea level. It is thence carried up the Ribblesdale and through the hills at its head to an elevation of 1,167 feet at Aisgath Moor; then descending to Carlisle, where it terminates 70 feet above the level of the sea. In its course through the hills and over the valleys there are many works of great magnitude, the line traversing some of the wildest, as well as tracts of the most picturesque beauty in the British Isles. The rugged grandeur of some of the portions further north forms a striking contrast to the rich pasture of the Craven grazing land, that the traveller leaves behind him after entering the southern end of the new line. The making of the new railway has been divided into four separate sections or contracts, the last of which is 17¼ miles in length, extending

FROM SETTLE JUNCTION TO INGLETON VALLEY: SETTLE STATION

The railway which is now so nearly completed commences by a junction, about a mile and a half south of Settle. At that point the main line has been slightly diverted in order to make a better curve and secure a straight road for through trains to Carlisle, as this will in future be the main route, the existing line to Lancaster being continued simply as a branch, although an important one. At the junction there will be a station where passengers can change from one train to another. With this view the platform walls, sidings, and signal box have already been erected.

Shortly after its start from this point, the line crosses the Skipton road by a fine skew girder bridge, 62 feet span passing on the left Auley House, the residence of Mr John Birbeck. It then enters a deep cutting through grit stone from which many of the bridges have been built, and crosses the turnpike road by another handsome arched bridge, approaching the mansion known as Lagfield recently occupied by Rev. Mr Swale, ex-chaplain to the British Embassy at Paris. A large quantity of earth has been removed on the west side of the line nearly opposite this estate to fill up the embankments.

The Settle Station ground has been raised to nearly the level of the rails, and makes a yard of considerable area- probably not less than ten acres. Within the space a commodious and well built station has been erected, which has the further advantage of a convenient road to the town, instead of being like the old one, more than a mile distant. From the excellence of the provision made here, and the number of stations placed at other points along the line it would appear that the Midland Company have been anxious not to overlook these claims for accommodation, even in thinly populated districts, which cannot be expected to develop very much traffic. The town of Settle nestles in the valley. The view of it from the front of the station is somewhat obstructed by houses and trees; but we can see Giggleswick with its grand scar, ancient church, and picturesque woody neighbourhood, whilst Ingleborough, Penygent, Pendle, and Fountains Fell raise their lofty heads towards the gathering clouds which seem to foreshadow wet weather. Even before our special train starts, rain begins to fall, but in light showers, which happily do not prevent enjoyment of the landscape through which we are shortly conveyed.

Rev Hogarth, J. Swale MA, JP, born Kendal. In 1881 he lived in Surrey and he was first incumbent of St Marys, Brompton.

THE CRAVEN LIME COMPANY

On leaving Settle the line crosses Kirkgate, one of the principle streets, by a viaduct of four arches 30 feet in span and 23 feet in height. Another viaduct spans the Giggleswick road and the pretty laid out grounds in front of Mrs George Hartley's house, with the bold cliff known as Castleberg forming an effective background. Passing thence along a high embankment which contains 250,000 cubic yards of earth, the line enters a slate-blue limestone cutting under a light girder bridge leading to the residence of Mr Hector Christie. The cutting itself is spanned at two points by 'flying' arches which spring out from the solid rock, and are about 42 feet in span.

The railway also passes Barrel Sykes, the residence of Mr G. W. Perfoat, and crosses Langcliff road by a neat bridge of the same, material as the viaduct. Here we come to within sight of the celebrated Winskill Crags at Willy Wood, presenting, like so many more of the hills grouped around, the quaint outlines which characterise the limestone region. Between the feet of this frowning eminence and the railway line, extensive kilns on the principle of Hoffman's patent have been constructed by the Craven Lime Company for the burning of bricks, tiles, pottery, cement, or lime. For the present the company are confining their attention almost exclusively to the burning of limestone, which is obtained in great abundance and of capital quality from the neighbouring crags.

In the immediate vicinity Mr T. Mugatroyd has commenced work suitable for fluxing iron stone. Both he and the Lime Company have for a considerable time past been, allowed to send off almost daily many loads of the lime and limestone, thus developing a class of traffic which will soon be further facilitated by the erection of a station at this point.

Hector Christie, JP, Lancliffe Mills, also Salford Manchester. Mr Lorenzo Christie bought Lancliffe Mills in 1861. The weaving looms were taken out and replaced with spinning and then doubling machinery. Mr Lorenzo Christie was followed by his son Hector until his death in 1915.

An almanac for 1876 mentions the Craven Lime Company and Mr Thomas Murgatroyd, both firms producing large quantities of lime and limestone. Murgatroyd first opened a quarry with the coming of the railway. In the 1876 April rate book for Stainforth he was paying rent and rates on land, quarry and tramway. By April 1877 he was paying for two lime kilns as well. Murgatroyd's quarry should properly be called the North Ribblesdale Limestone and Lime Works. Murgatroyd gave up the lease rather suddenly and can only have gone bankrupt. He continued his coal business into the next century, purchasing ten new railway wagons in 1904/5 finished in his red livery with the lettering Thomas Murgatroyd, Skipton.

Hoffman's continuous kiln was built in 1873 for the Craven Lime Company. Lime burning became a key local industry. The kiln was patented by Friedrich Hoffman in 1858. The kiln at Lancliffe had 22 chambers where limestone was continuously burnt in a circuit that took around six weeks to complete. The kiln and quarry closed in 1931.

TAITLANDS AND SHERIFF BROW

Leaving Willy Wood, we pass through a heavy cutting three-quarters of a mile in length, and in the middle of it, under Taitlands, there is a tunnel 120 yards long bringing us up to Stainforth, its waterfall and pretty village. At Sheriff Brow the line crosses the River Ribble twice within a short distance by a handsome bridge, one of which is remarkable for its great angle skew. They are neat and substantially built. Both consist of three arches, and they are built with ashlar quoins, with brick arches and block in course piers. For the greater security of persons who may have to walk on the line recesses have been left in the parapets of one of them. In order to avoid a cutting of considerable extent, and also an awkward bend in the line, the course of the river has been diverted at this point for 100 yards, and the rails now run over its original channel. After passing over the second bridge we are soon in another deep cutting, the strata of which is 'clay slate' with its 'beds' nearly vertical. The slate in this district is worked by Mr Ralph and others for paving slabs, landings, troughs, etc.

Taitlands was built between 1831 and 1862 by Thomas Joseph Redmayne a wealthy mill and quarry owner. In the 1845 railway mania Redmayne had connections with a number of railway schemes the Northumberland & Lancashire Junction Railway Co., Keighley, Halifax & Huddersfield Junction Railway and he was a director of the North Western Railway. In 1862 the house passed to his son Henry.

It was advertised in 1868 as, 'Taitlands near Settle. This desirable residence, situate in one of the most picturesque localities in Yorkshire, and comprising: entrance hall, dining, drawing, and breakfast rooms, eight bedrooms, besides man-servant's room and attic. Butler's pantry, good kitchens, scullery, and excellent cellars, will shortly be offered for sale by Public Auction.'

It was bought by Thomas Stackhouse whose family remained there until 1911 followed by Canon James Allen Wilson and Major A. C. Tempest. The house eventually became a Youth Hostel in 1942, passing back into private ownership in 2007. It is said that when the Settle and Carlisle was built because the tunnel under the north eastern corner of the site was only 40 feet below the house the family were moved out until construction had finished.

VIEWS FROM ELWORTH BRIDGE

Elworth Bridge has been rebuilt by the Midland Company on a new site, and on a much larger scale than the narrow ancient looking structure still standing a few yards distant which has hitherto served for crossing the river. The contrast between the two in such close proximity quite justifies the jocular note in Mr Wildman's local almanac, that here the traveller sees a good specimen of 'bridges ancient and modern', one to be admired for its strength and lightness, the other for its picturesque style. Along the side of the river is a long wall to protect the embankment from floods. After having passed Elworth Bridge we should have a good view of Penygent, but its summit, rising 2,273 feet above sea level, is now shrouded in mist. Passing next Mr Hammond's shooting box, we reach the village of Horton, with its curious old church. Here there will be a station, for which a siding, signal boxes, waiting shed, and platform have been provided. From this point, for a considerable distance we go through uncultivated moorland which has hitherto been good only for keeping a few sheep or shooting, but may perhaps be hereafter adopted to a larger extent for pasture. If the cost of drainage, etc., be not too great.

BLAKES PATENT STONE CRUSHER

Next we reach Selside (celebrated for its 'pot holes'), nestling on the slopes of Ingleborough, and here it is said there be held once a year a fair which was less remarkable for business than for the joviality with which country visitors entered into the festivities of the occasion. Eight good cottages have been erected by the company at Selside for the occupation of their servants, corresponding to six built near the station at Settle, and half a dozen more are provided at 'Salt Lake', the next noteworthy place at which we arrive. Nearly opposite the cottages there is a large quarry, from which thousands of tons of stone have been got. At the time of our visit work is still proceeding here under the charge of a good-natured portly 'ganger' who, with dimensions almost equal to those of the Claimant, seems to thrive thoroughly well, in spite of hard work and constant exposure to all sorts of weather. At the quarry, as well as at other points along the line, we find Blakes Patent Stone Crusher (belonging to the Mayor of Leeds) in active use and highly appreciated, some of the officials indeed, speaking of it as having proved almost invaluable in breaking hard stones for road purposes and permanent way. At Salt Lake there used to be a navvy village, which, however has recently been cleared away. Pressing onwards we come to another bridge, crossing the turnpike road to Ingleton, and then reach an embankment containing no less than 280,000 cubic yards of earth. This brings us within view of a huge viaduct and tunnel, still more remarkable than any we have yet passed; but before visiting these gigantic works, our party land at a strange little town consisting entirely of the wooden huts of railway labourers.

A VISIT TO THE NAVVY VILLAGE

The site of the village at which we have now arrived, was simply bleak moorland before the railway works commenced, not an inhabitant in it or within some distance. When the making of the new line was in full operation, the place numbered, however, between 500 and 600 people, mostly navvies, with their families. Even now, when the works are nearly finished, about half of that number still remain, residing in wooden huts covered externally with black felt. The village is situated on the Ingleton and Hawes road, between Ingleborough, Whernside, and Pennyghent.

It is sometimes called simply Batty Wife or Batty Wife Green; but we are assured by a local authority that the full and proper name is Batty Wife Hole. This name is said to have been taken from a legend which relates that, once upon a time, as the story tellers say, a man named Batty lived for years apart from his wife. At last the couple became reconciled and agreed to dwell together, appointing to meet each other one night at a field in which there happened to be a large hole full of water. The woman arrived first and waited some time; but her husband did not appear, so concluding that he had proved faithless she threw herself into the hole and was drowned. Almost immediately afterwards the unpunctual husband came and he, in turn, waited a considerable time at the rendezvous, but, of course no wife appeared. Eventually he too became impatient, and, strangely enough, sacrificed his own life by casting himself into the same place where she had so recently perished. This tragic story was told to me by Mr

Henry Hancock, the railway company missionary, who, however, seemed to be sceptical about its truth, and advises that it should at any rate be taken with a grain of salt.

From his hints and courteous guidance the visitor may indeed be soon satisfied that Batty Wife Hole, as it now exists, owes little to tradition all its interest being essentially modern. The worthy missionary himself appears well suited to his arduous work, being an elderly but active and wiry gentleman, kindly in manner, and withal not too proud to wear the stoutest of boots, expressly adapted for the rough and dirty roads over which he has often to trudge. He has been upward of eleven years in the companies service, the last three and a half of these spent in this remote neighbourhood. It is well that the company provides such services as he gives, and another circumstance which may be mentioned to their credit is that almost every week parcels of periodicals and newspapers are sent from headquarters for distribution amongst those engaged in the more distant parts of the work.

VISIT TO THE HOSPITAL

Whilst the auction sale goes on at the station yard. Mr Hancock kindly escorts 'our own reporter' over the village, greeted on every hand as he does so, with the hearty good word of the working folk, with all of whom he appears to be on the most friendly terms. Among the 'institutions' we find in the village are a mission house, schools, library, post office, hospital, and improvised hotel. The mission house will hold nearly 150 people, and has on many occasions been almost filled at the simple Sunday evening services. During the week, when the pastor is engaged visiting the hospital, or in domiciliary visitation over his wide district (which includes almost the whole of the first contract), the little chapel is used for a school, under the charge of a smart and competent governess. Occasionally it has also been used for concerts and other entertainments, with which musical friends from Settle have kindly enlivened long winter evenings in this remote place.

At the time of our visit the hospital was rather fuller than usual. Two or three men were in it suffering from injuries caused by a recent explosion of gunpowder or dynamite, and unfortunately our special train brought still another patient who was injured in the drive up from Settle. He was a labourer who, taking shelter from a shower under one of the bridges, fell asleep with his feet on the line. When the train came up, one of the iron guards in front of the engine caught his leg and, pushing it aside, saved him from being run over, but his foot was still so much hurt that he had to be conveyed in a cart to the hospital. In this case it was said the man was somewhat the worse for drink, and obviously he had his own recklessness to thank for the mishap, which narrowly escaped proving much more serious. In the case of such railway work, full of difficulty and danger a number of accidents have, of course happened, and some lives have been lost; but we are glad to learn that, as a rule, the men have been careful, well skilled, and tolerably well behaved. Sometimes, after a large consumption of beer, fights have sprung up among parties of the rougher workmen, in which case, we presume, it would be the function of the local police force, numbering only one man, to stand by and see fair play between combatants, there being no lockup in the village.

BRINGING PROVISIONS FOR THE NAVIES

One indispensible institution at Batty Wife is the store of Messrs Burgoyne and Cocks, the enterprising railway purveyors. This firm send provisions and almost every kind of goods to each of the navvy settlements along the first section of the line. At times this has proved exceedingly difficult work. Before the permanent line was available or any tramways laid, food had to be sent to the exiled workmen by a drove of donkeys. On account of the softness of the damp ground, the poor brutes often got 'bogged' the whole length of their legs, and had to be pulled out by horses with ropes to save them being buried alive. As the wheels of carts used also to sink, requiring sometimes that their cargo should be unloaded and carried on foot, it was found necessary in some parts to send the food in a box with upright shafts resting on the axle of two broad cylinders, which were rolled along by horses with flat boards attached to their hoofs.

Another difficulty was the weather, which is often extremely severe amongst these northern hills.

Often the wind sweeps fiercely up the Ingleton Valley; indeed, the bricklayers engaged on some of the more exposed viaducts have often had to give up work for a time lest they should be blown over. The water supply for Batty Wife was formerly obtained by the help of a kind of windmill; but one day the sails of the contrivance, although composed of steel iron, were blown to pieces by the violence of the wind, and now the water supply is conveyed by manual pumping into a raised tank, from which it descends in pipes by gravitation to the lower levels.

LIVING AT BATTY WIFE HOLE

The people of Batty Wife do not, however, by any means confine their drinking to water, if we may judge from the profusion of public houses amongst the huts in the main street. In many of the dwellings the domestic arrangements appear to be of somewhat rude nature; but in others there is every appearance of neatness and comfort. In one to which the latter description applies, a buxom cheerful wife, said she preferred her home at Batty Wife to living at Settle or even Leeds. With no little pride she showed a large illustrated Family Bible which she had just bought for nearly 30s, and evidently valued as a great bargain, especially considering the number of coloured pictures with which it was enriched. Such an incident sends us away with a pleasanter impression of the life at Batty Green than we might otherwise have had.

We pay a passing visit to the pastor's cot, neat but humble like those of his flock. It is distinguished only by a little wooden porch at the front door, like the doctor's house and one or two more, on what may be called the 'West End' of this little town. Batty Wife Hole may be described as the metropolis of the mountain communities (probably a dozen in number) which the railway has called into existence. Its life may be taken as typical of the whole. As the work approaches completion, the number and extent of these old villages diminish, until at last most of them probably will have disappeared. In talking with some of his parishioners, our good missionary becomes quite scornful at this prospect of the dispersion of his flock, and of the time when they must separate and scatter. Even here we find illustration of the truth that, be it ever so humble, there is no place like home. One or two of the more attached residents have got to feel so much at home in Batty Wife as to say that, come what may, they will remain hoping still to earn a living by the traffic which the new station and railway may bring to the place.

Already the work of dissolution has advanced in some of the other communities, as well as Salt Lake, which we have before mentioned. Until a few weeks ago, for instance, a navvy village, containing nearly 500 inhabitants, stood between Batty Green and the neighbouring viaduct which spans the water shed of the Ribble and of Little Dale Beck. It was called Sebastopol, and amongst the industries of the place were a large machine brick-making establishment, as well as mortar grinding mills, mixing sheds, etc., required in the erection of the viaduct. Now that great work is done, and the whole village has vanished like some airy fabric of a vision, leaving not a rack behind. Not far distant is a community known as Jericho, with 200 inhabitants. Over against Jericho we appropriately fine Jerusalem, which is, however, fast diminishing, having now only seven or eight huts, with not more than fifty inhabitants. Ere long this Yorkshire Jerusalem will have disappeared from the map, if, indeed geographers have ever had time to dignify it in their record surveys with a local habitation and a name.

FROM BATTY MOSS OR RIBBLE HEAD VIADUCT TO DENT HEAD

But now the auctioneers have finished their sale of engines, boilers, etc., at Batty Wife, so we hurry back and rejoin the company in time to go up with them in the special train to Bleamoor Tunnel. On the way we have first to pass over the Batty Moss Viaduct, which spans the valley leading to Ingleton, and is probably the largest work on the line. It consists of 24 arches, is 1,328 feet in length, and measures 100 feet in height to the level of the rails. It contains about 34,000 cubic yards of masonry, besides 300 cubic yards of concrete, upon six feet of which, laid upon the solid rock, nearly all the piers rest. The piers themselves, 23 in number, stand 45 feet apart, and most off them are thirteen feet at the base, and six feet at the spring of the arch. To give additional strength, as well as to add to the imposing appearance of the viaduct, which is certainly one of the finest in England, every sixth pier is 18 feet at the top instead of six feet. By adopting this arrangement the contractors were enabled to build six arches at one time instead of the whole twenty four, thereby saving both time and money. In order to obtain the foundation of rock, 25 feet of peat, clay and washings had to be penetrated. The piers and abutments, graceful in shape, are built of blue limestone, and the arches are in brick covered with boiling pitch and courses of stone. The views from the viaduct are magnificent, and we now see to advantage, the clouds having to some extent cleared away. Southward and eastward is Ribblesdale and Penyghent, with a long range of wild moorland. Blea Moor closes in the prospect northwards; Whernside shuts out the western view, but looking down the green slopes and craggy heights of Ingleton valley are seen, away in the distance, the brown sides of Burn Moor and the smiling green dale at its foot, while the giant form of Inglebrough, visible now in its grand proportions towers up on the south west.

BLEA MOOR TUNNEL

After crossing the lofty viaduct, where a stiff breeze is always blowing, we pass through some cuttings, one of which, although of soft material, has given at least as much trouble as any of the hard limestone cuttings on the contract. It was composed of boulder clay and a dead sand, which required blasting to excavate, but which, after exposure to the air and wet, ran to thin mud. This slipped out of the embankments and stuck to the tip wagons, often causing these to come bodily over the 'tip head' and damage greatly, besides the expense of getting the wagon again on the embankment some fifty feet high. Near this point the railway runs underneath a stream, called Force Gill, by means of a short tunnel 100 feet in length, on the top of which a trough is built, having stone run in with hot asphalted, to ensure its being watertight.

This gill has been the source of much trouble, carrying away temporary bridges and to some extent drowning the quarries during heavy rains. About 250 yards north of Force Gill we come to one of the most extensive pieces of tunnelling on the line. Blea Moor Tunnel, by which name this great excavation will hereafter be known, is 2,640 yards, or about 1½ miles in length; and in the deepest part 500 feet below the surface. Seven shafts, four of which will be permanent, were sunk to enable the excavated material to be conveyed away. The strata is limestone, grit stone, and shale, and although hard enough to require blasting. The tunnel has had to be lined with brick arching.

The level of the rails in the centre is 1,151½ feet above sea level, a rise of nearly 1 in 100 from the junction with the Midland Railway beyond Settle. The headings in every case met correctly, indeed within three inches, showing the excellence of the surveying, long as the distance was which had to be driven from each end. As illustrating the difficulty and cost of this great work, it may be mentioned that about £600 per annum, or £50 per month, had to be spent in candles alone for giving light to the workmen during the excavation of the tunnel.

On its southern side, sidings and a large water tank are being provided. A little beyond the tunnel is the viaduct at Dent Head, consisting of ten arches, 596 feet long, and 100 feet above Fell End Gill. At Dent Head a station is being provided. From this point the scenery around is highly picturesque. We are gladdened by the sight of the Dent Valley spreading away at our feet, with the River Dent roaring and foaming as it tossed and tumbled over masses of rock, forming a series of pretty waterfalls and cascades, the banks of the river bordered with trees.

Having now gone over the whole of the first section of the new line, a word of credit is due to all concerned for the excellent and substantial way in which the work has been carried out, despite many great difficulties. Unlike the other contracts, No1 has been carried out by the Midland Railway Company themselves, under the thoroughly competent charge of Mr Edgar O. Ferguson, resident engineer, and Mr W. H. Ashwell, as contractors agent.

Batty Moss viaduct is now more well known as Ribble Head viaduct.

CONTRACT No 2 DENT HEAD TO SCANDAL BECK

The second contract, a length of seventeen and a quarter miles, was let in September, 1869, to Messrs Benton and Woodiwiss, and commenced by them early the following year. During the five years the works have been carried on by them, the progress has at no time been rapid, but from reasons entirely beyond the control of the contractors. There can be no question that this contract has been one of the most difficult in the whole undertaking; for independently of the works themselves, which are quite as heavy as on any other part, the nature of the country through which it passes created difficulties, which were not to be met with, to the same extent elsewhere. The first of these was the materials of which the cuttings are composed, a very stiff blue clay filled with boulders, better known as the glacial drift. In dry weather it is so hard to work that it is only by blasting any progress can be made, and in wet weather it is so soft that it could hardly be kept in the wagons.

Indeed, so difficult was it found to excavate some of the cuttings that in two instances, after struggling for three and a half years, it was decided by the engineer to give up the attempt of clearing them out, and tunnels were driven through them. The banks also, which were composed of clay, could not carry their own weight when above a certain depth, and have slipped so much that in some cases the width at the bottom is about double what it was intended they should be. In two instances also the attempt to make them was given up, and viaducts were constructed in their place. The next difficulty was the great amount of rainfall that occurred during the past four years. This is partly owing to the high level at which the line is situated, nearly 1,200 feet above sea level, it having been found that the fall was greatest where the line was highest.

The country through which the contract passes is very wild and uncultivated, the population scarce, and no accommodation could be procured for the many men employed. That the country and its surroundings found no favour with the men may be inferred from the fact, that over 30,000 men have passed through the contractor's books since the commencement of the work. Everything has been done to induce them to settle down. Comfortable huts have been erected, and reading rooms, chapels, and schools have been built for their accommodation, but in vain. It is, of course, very difficult to get work done under these conditions. As soon as a gang was properly organised it was broken up by several of the men leaving, and cuttings which were working full swing one day were almost deserted the next. It was these difficulties that up to three months ago caused this contract to be behind the rest of the line; but aided by the fine weather that has been experienced this spring, the contractors have, regardless of expense, made such exertions, that it will be ready for opening at the same time as the other contracts.

THE RAILWAY IS ALMOST READY

Of course the line, though nearly ready for goods traffic, is far from being completed. The cuttings are nearly cut and the banks made, but owing to the nature of the material, it is natural to expect that some time will elapse before the cuttings can be called finished or the banks become quite settled. The viaducts will be completed in a week or two, and the bridges are so far forward that the finishing of them will prove no hindrance to the working of the goods traffic.

It is impossible to fix any time when the passenger trains will commence running, but every effort is being made to get them through by the end of the year, and as progress depends entirely on the weather, there will be no difficulty in doing this if it should prove a fine summer. Some idea may be formed of the difficult nature of the undertaking by the following figures.

On Contract No 2 alone there are 47 cuttings, containing 2¼ miles in cubic yards; five viaducts, whose combined length is half a mile, and from 145 to 50 feet deep; four tunnels, which would extend for over a mile if placed together, and in some places 140 feet below the surface; 65 road bridges, from ten feet to 50 feet span, and 100 culverts from two feet to ten feet wide, together with a vast amount of smaller work, such as fencing, draining, etc. The contract commences at Dent Head, where it joins No 1, and after traversing the Dent Valley for two miles it turns off to the right and by means of a long tunnel through Rise Hill it emerges on Garsdale. It then runs along this valley as far as the Moor Cock

Inn, where it turns northward, passes over Aisgill Moor, which is the summit of the line, the rails being, as we have said, no less than 1,167 feet above the level of the sea.

It then runs several miles down Mallerstang, which is the commencement of the valley of the Eden, but owing to the rapid rate at which the valley falls, the line skirts the hill on the western side and passed over the Birkett Fells. At seventeen miles from the commencement it crosses over the South Durham Railway by means of the Smardale Viaduct, and a few chains further on this contract ends and No 3 begins. The works on No 2 have been carried out under the superintendence of Mr J. Somes Story as resident engineer, and Mr James Hay the contractor's agent.

FROM CROSBY GARRETT TO CARLISLE

The third contract, for which Mr J. Drage is the resident engineer, is fifteen miles in length, extending from Crosby Garrett to Newbiggin. The viaducts and bridges are completed, and the other works are far advanced. The double line of permanent way will be laid through this week – there are five stations on the contract, viz., Crosby Garrett, Ormside, Appleby, Long Marton, and Newbiggin. The telegraph poles and wires are fixed from Carlisle to three miles south of Appleby. The first work of magnitude on the contract is Crosby Garrett Tunnel, which is through grit and limestone, mixed here and there with flint. After passing through a cutting 176 yards long and 65 feet deep we reach Crosby Garrett Viaduct. It is 270 feet in length and 53 feet high, consisting of six arches 38 feet span. More heavy cutting follows, and then High Gisburn Viaduct, also of six arches, after which Helen Tunnel is arrived at. This is one of the heaviest works on the contract, being 500 yards in length and 110 feet deep. The scenery above Appleby is charming, pasture, woods, meadows, and the moorlands gradually blending into the Pennine and Cumberland high hills and mountains. A lofty viaduct, 86 feet high, consisting of ten arches, carries the railway over that picturesque river, the Eden, and another viaduct, somewhat smaller, carries it over the Troutbeck.

VIADUCTS AND TUNNELS

The largest contract in No 4, which is 24 miles in length, extending from near Culgaith to Carlisle. The country through which it passes is beautiful, chiefly agricultural and splendidly wooded. The line follows the valley of the Eden, and in many places skirts the hills and cliffs close to the river. There are many heavy works on the contract, in viaducts, tunnels, cuttings, and embankments, of which we shall name only the most important. There is a viaduct at Crowdundle Beck, four arches 50 feet high, a long tunnel at Culgaith, 800 yards in length, and a 100 feet deep; and another tunnel 200 yards long, under West Bank. At Eden Lacy the line crosses the Eden on a viaduct, and south of Lazonby there is another tunnel 100 yards in length. There are two short tunnels in Eden Brow Wood, closely followed by the Armathwaite Viaduct, Drybeck Viaduct, and an enormous embankment containing 400,000 cubic yards of earth. On approaching Carlisle the new line joins the old Newcastle and Carlisle, now the North Eastern Railway, about half a mile from Citadel Station, which is now being enlarged considerably for the additional traffic. A six mile branch of the Settle and Carlisle railway is being made to Hawes from Moorcock; but this is being less hurried than the main line.

72 MILES OF RAILWAY

From the particulars already given it will be seen that many works of exceptional difficulty and magnitude have had to be undertaken in the construction of the new line. Within the length of 72 miles over which it extends, there are no fewer than fifteen viaducts, the arches varying in number from four to twenty four, the length in feet from 260 to 1,328, and the height from 35 feet at Settle to 130 feet at Smardale Viaduct.

The ten tunnels on the line range from 120 yards in length at Taitlands to 1,230 yards at Rise Hill, and 2,600 yards at Blea Moor, driven through limestone, gritstone, shale, flint, red marl, and red sandstone, whilst the depth of the tunnels from the surface varies from 40 feet at Taitlands to 500 feet at Blea Moor.

In addition to these heavy works there are, as we have stated, many deep cuttings, lofty embankments., and numerous bridges, inevitably bringing up the cost of the enterprise to an enormous figure. On the other side of the account, however, it must be remembered that the Midland Railway Company, by this direct and independent connection with their Scottish allies, the Glasgow and South Western and the North British Railways, will at once save something like £80,000 per annum, which has hitherto had to be paid as rent for running powers over the Lancaster and Carlisle Railway. There is also the chance of greatly increased traffic, with the certainty of improvised facilities and comfort for through passengers, whose patience has often been so sorely tried in the past by tedious delays and frequent changes in their journey between England and Scotland.

According to present arrangements, the entire length of the new line from Settle to Carlisle will be opened for goods traffic on the 1st August next. It is expected that it will be ready for passenger traffic four or five months later.

Penrith Observer, 15 June 1875

SMARDALE VIADUCT

On Tuesday last a very interesting ceremony in connection with the new line from Settle to Carlisle took place in the presence of a few spectators. Our readers are no doubt aware that the Midland line crosses what is known as Scandal Beck, near Smardale, by means of a viaduct consisting of twelve arches, 45 feet span. The length from end to end is 780 feet, and the depth from rail level to the surface of the stream is 128 feet.

The piers and arches are built of stone obtained from Park Gate quarries, a very durable limestone, and the ashlar and parapets are of the millstone grit from Lartington. In its construction no less than 60,000 tons of stone have had to be quarried, dressed, and put together. It was commenced in the autumn of 1870, thus requiring four and a half years for its construction.

It is a very noble looking structure, and considering the difficulties under which it has been carried out, reflects the highest credit on all concerned. As it was to be expected that the completion of so important a work should not be passed over without some ceremony, the contractors invited Mrs Crossley, the wife of the engineer under whose superintendence the whole of the works have been carried out, to lay the last stone. The company which assembled at the place at twelve consisted of Mr and Mrs Crossley, Mr Woodiwiss (the contractor), Mr and Miss Mason, Miss Jackson, and several gentlemen connected with the railway.

Mr Woodiwiss then, on behalf of himself and partner, in an appropriate speech, presented Mrs Crossley with a very elegant trowel, with which she adroitly prepared the bed of mortar. The stone, a massive block, six feet long was then lowered into its place, and Mrs Crossley tapped it with a mallet, and declared that it had been truly and properly laid. On the stone was cut the inscription: 'This last stone was laid by Agnes Crossley, 8th June 1875.'

After several hearty hurrahs from the workmen, three times three were given for Mrs Crossley. Some more cheering was given for the engineer, the contractor, and the sub-contractor; after which the party inspected the new works as far as Moor Cock where a substantial lunch was provided for them in one of the new cottages built by the company. That one of the heaviest pieces of work has thus been completed shows that the day is not far distant when the line will be open for goods traffic; and only a few months will elapse before passenger trains will commence running which, considering the efforts made by all connected with the works during the past five years, will prove as gratifying to them as to the public, for whose convenience the line has been constructed

Due to heavy rain in the summer of 1870 difficulties were experienced in October in laying the foundations of the viaduct in Scandale Beck. December produced more rain, but six of the piers were already at a height of nineteen feet, and 1,319 men were employed on the work. In January 1871 work stopped due to frost and by January 1872 a lack of workmen slowed down the construction and delayed completion.

Williams recalls an incident that took place near Smardale: 'In connection with the prosecution of these works in this district an alarming incident occurred. A party engaged on the line one evening returning from their duties, and, having a rough road to walk upon, and a good incline, it occurred to them (engineer like) that they could ride down the hill in a tip wagon. Accordingly they placed a plank as a seat across a wagon, and having armed themselves with a piece of timber called a 'sprag' to be used as a brake, they set off. Merrily they went along, and the excellence of the pace, which increased every moment, was unquestionable.

'At length they were approaching their journey's end, and as the line some distance forward was blocked with loaded trucks, it was thought wise that the speed should be reduced; and accordingly the brakes man leant over the side, and applied his sprag. A sudden blow, however, knocked it out of his hand; he jumped off to pick it up, but could not overtake the wagon. "And there we were," said an engineer, who was one of the party, "running down an incline of 1 in 100 at 20 or 30 miles an hour, with a 'dead-end' before us, blocked up, and going faster every minute."

'Mr Woodiwiss, the contractor, seized the plank on which the passengers had been sitting, and tried to sprag the wheels with it; but could not get it to act, till at last, by standing on the buffer behind, putting the plank between the frame of the wagon and the side of the wheel, and pressing it sideways, he managed to pull up the runaway truck just in time to prevent a perhaps fatal collision.'

Penrith Observer, 29 June 1875

ACCIDENT TO THE SCOTS EXPRESS

The Scots express, due in Leeds on Tuesday night at 5-5, met with a serious accident at Calverley Station, five miles from Leeds. It was proceeding at the usual speed, when it came in collision with a luggage train which was being shunted. The engine of the express was thrown off the line, and alighted on the turnpike road. Three or four carriages were smashed, and about a dozen passengers injured. One of the carriages struck contained a corpse, which was partially injured. The line was blocked for a considerable time. Mr Walmesley, an official under Mr Firbank, contractor for the Settle and Carlisle Railway, who was travelling with his wife and family in the carriage next to a composite one that was smashed, had two of his children slightly injured. They had come from Kirkby Stephen, in Westmorland, and were booked to Castleford.

Calverley was on the Leeds to Bradford line opened in 1847 and closed in 1968. Castleford was eleven miles south east of Leeds, on the Hallam to Pontefract line.

Penrith Observer, 6 July 1875

PRESENTATION AT SMARDALE

On Friday last, an interesting meeting was held at the Midland Railways School room, Smardale, for the purpose of presenting Miss Rudd, the teacher of the school, with a token of the regard of the parents and friends. The presentation was neatly and appropriately made by Mr Fletcher, the respected missionary, and consisted of a bible, beautifully bound in morocco and suitably inscribed, also a purse of money. After tea, a very interesting meeting was held, conducted also by Mr Fletcher.

The Lancaster Gazette, 17 July 1875

SETTLE

Petty Sessions Tuesday. Before C. Ingleby, and H. Christie, Esq., Assault. John Dagan, a railway labour, appeared in support of an information against David Plank, an employee on the new Settle and Carlisle

Railway who was charged with having assaulted the complainant on the 24 June last, in a railway truck at Willy Wood, near Lancliffe. The case had been adjourned to enable the defendant to appear along with a witness, and from whose statement it appeared that some 'larking' was being carried on with the complainant, but that there was no intention of injuring the complainant. The Bench, however, intimated that the 'larking' indulged in was very dangerous and ordered the defendant to pay a fine of 10s and 12s costs.

Penrith Observer, 27 July 1875

FATAL ACCIDENT AT MOORCOCK

On Tuesday week a serious accident befell a young Scotsman, named John Smith, of Inverness, who was working as a mason at Moorcock viaduct. He fell a distance of twenty feet, and hit his head on a quantity of stones. He was picked up insensible, never regained consciousness, and died on the Monday following. An inquest was held on the body before the North Riding coroner and a jury. Verdict 'Accidental death'.

The Bradford Observer, 29 July 1875

THE SETTLE AND CARLISLE RAILWAY

Thursday evening witnessed the influx of about 100 railway employees, consisting of station masters, goods porters, pointsmen, etc., into Skipton from various parts of the country, who had been summoned from their various posts to work the new line between Settle and Carlisle. Each of the inns and hotels in the town had its complement of strangers, who created some little curiosity among the inhabitants. They were all conveyed to their respective new quarters by a special train early yesterday morning. About thirty of the men were destined for Carlisle Station. The first goods train over the new line will leave Leeds on Monday next, after which the goods traffic will be regularly continued.

Penrith Observer, 3 August 1875

OPENING OF THE SETTLE AND CARLISLE RAILWAY

The formal opening of the Settle and Carlisle (Midland) extension took place yesterday (Monday), for goods traffic only. On Sunday eight powerful engines passed over the entire length from Settle to Carlisle. One of the engines, to which a saloon carriage was attached, conveyed a number of directors and officials, the latter taking their respective stations on the route to be in readiness to assume their duties. The line was put to a severe test throughout. Five powerful engines, attached together, each over forty tons, went first, and the other three followed at intervals. The first arrived at Appleby Station at twelve o'clock; the other two coupled together, with a number of vans, at half past one; and the last, with the directors, at three o'clock, and proceeded thence to Carlisle. On Monday the first train of goods wagons from Carlisle passed the station at Appleby at twelve o'clock. All passed off well and without any accident. There is still a great deal of work to be done on the first and second sections before the line will be ready for passenger traffic, which is not likely to take place before the end of the year at least.

The Penrith Herald, 7 August 1875

SETTLE AND CARLISLE RAILWAY

On Monday the formal opening of the Settle and Carlisle (Midland) extension line took place, the traffic, meantime, being confined to goods. On Sunday, eight powerful engines passed over the entire length from Settle to Carlisle, and a saloon carriage, which was attached to one of the engines, contained a number of directors and officials. The line went through the usual severe test, but answered quite satisfactorily all that was expected, the first train of goods wagons, a very lengthy one, from Carlisle passing the station at Appleby about twelve o'clock. We are glad to record that no mishap occurred.

Much work will, we understand require to be done before the line will be ready for passenger traffic, and it is yet a matter of uncertainty whether or not the public will receive any personnel benefit from the new line this year.

The Penrith Herald, 21 August 1875

A LUGGAGE TRAIN DOWN AN EMBANKMENT

An accident of a very serious nature, though happily unattended with injury to life or limb, occurred on Sunday afternoon last, on the new portion of the Midland Railway, near to the village of Culgaith. A heavily laden goods train, consisting of an engine and about thirty trucks, was travelling on the down line north, and had just emerged from Mr Crackanthorpe's wood near Newbiggin, and was rapidly proceeding to the tunnel near Culgaith. It would appear, however, that a portion of the line between these two points had not become thoroughly consolidated, and we are informed that the driver of a previous goods train found it vibrate in an unsteady manner, at this place, and on reaching Carlisle reported it as such, but there was not enough time to get information conveyed before the next train followed.

There must however, have been some negligence, if the information be correct, that from the same cause a bale of wool fell off a truck when passing the same place a few days before. When the train to which the accident occurred reached the portion of the line over Mr W. Lancaster's cattle creep, the engine and tender and four trucks went safely on, but the succeeding twenty trucks ran off the line, down the embankment into Mr Lancaster's land, seriously damaging the cattle creep in their erratic course. Strange to say, the three last trucks and the van also remained on the line, so that neither driver nor stoker nor guard were imperilled. The carriages, however, which went off the line were piled one upon another, the metals were bent as if they were but pieces of pin wire, and the sleepers were torn up in every direction.

The contents of the trucks which seemed of a valuable character, were strewn on all sides, mirrors, sideboards, hats, baskets of fruit, biscuit tins and all manner of goods being heaped together in strange confusion. The loss to the company under these circumstances must be very considerable. After the accident occurred, the news of it was soon known far and wide, and hundreds of people from the surrounding district inspected the scene during the afternoon and evening. By Wednesday last, most of the debris was cleared away, and traffic resumed. We only hope that the accident is no augury of the future, and that it may be long before we have a second one to record.

The Northern Echo, 30 August 1875

NEVER LIVE WITH A MOTHER-IN-LAW

On Friday morning a young man, 30 years of age a platelayer on the Settle and Carlisle Railway hanged himself on a post in a public drying ground in Carlisle. Before doing so, he wrote with a piece of chalk on a neighbouring wall the following message:- 'I take the pleasure of riting these few lines if it will be a warning to all young men and never live with a mother-in-law. Now I end my miserable life.'

The Penrith Herald, 11 September 1875

ACCIDENT AT CROSBY GARRETT STATION

On Monday last an accident, our correspondent informs us, occurred at the Crosby Garrett Railway Station, of a rather serious nature. An assistant guard, while engaged in uncoupling the brake van, it being in motion at the time, missed his foot and fell across the rails, the van passed over his left foot. The poor man was almost without it. He was immediately conveyed to the Infirmary at Carlisle. It is to be hoped that this will prove a caution to others engaged in this work not to transgress the rules by uncoupling while trains are in motion.

A station master and family at an unknown location on the Settle and Carlisle line. Station staff were moved to their new posts in July 1875 ready for the line to open to passenger traffic. Photograph courtesy of Cumbria Railway Association.

Cumberland and Westmorland Advertiser, 14 September 1875

ACCIDENT ON THE MIDLAND RAILWAY

On Monday week an unfortunate accident happened in the Crosby Garrett Station yard to a brakesman, named Charles Sherry, employed in ballasting the line. He was in the act of greasing the wheels of his van, having his left foot upon one of the rails, when the engine gave a sharp click forward, causing the wheel of the van to pass obliquely over the fore part of his foot. Since his removal to the Carlisle Infirmary, he had his foot amputated, and is doing as well as can be expected.

Penrith Observer, 19 October 1875

SCAFFOLD ACCIDENT AT LANGWATHBY

On Thursday last the rope supporting a scaffold used in the erection of the new railway station at Longwathby, gave way, and three of the workmen fell a distance of fifteen feet. Two of the men caught hold of the loose cross stones in the wall and dragged them along with them. Jos. Storey had his shoulder fractured, and the other two labourers were shaken.

Stations at Scotby, Cumwhinton, Armathwaite, Lazonby, Little Salkeld, Langwathby, Culgaith and Cotehill were built by local builder George Black of Cecil Street, Carlisle, who established a building firm in 1832

Penrith Observer, 12 October 1875

SETTLE AND CARLISLE RAILWAY

This great undertaking is fast being completed, and the company ought to be well repaid for making a line devoid of sharp gradients and small curves, through what may be called generally a pretty rough country. Some of the stations are nearly finished, and the station master's houses are rapidly progressing, and the line is gradually assuming a settled appearance. Warehouses for goods, and cottages for porters and signalmen, are also being built near to the various stations.

Although the line is only opened for goods traffic, as yet, it seems almost everywhere throughout this part of the country at least, to be ready for either kind of traffic. In some parts it has already the appearance of an old line, in places where the way has got firmly fixed in the ballast, the slopes of the cuttings and embankments covered with grass, and the arches of those bridges that span it blackened with smoke. Where the line runs parallel with the Pennine range, the long black looking, slowly running goods trains, seen from a distance standing out in rather dim relief against the fells, might be compared to monster reptiles crawling along their bases.

To those who knew parts of the country which the line passes previous to the line being made, the change will, in many instances, be remarkable. There may be some who, like Wordsworth, think that railways mar a landscape on account of their rigidity; but if a large and handsome residence, formed chiefly of right lines, be considered a striking and pleasing feature in landscape, may not a noble viaduct or long grass covered embankment be equally attractive? In some instances their presence undoubtedly enhances the beauty of the natural scenery.

Well, I suppose the world does not move any quicker now than when Galileo first said it did move; but the mind of man does and nowadays, when a new mode of applying an old force comes to light it is rapidly developed and improved, and sometimes as rapidly becomes obsolete and is succeeded by something better. The railway system, which has become so extensive in this country and abroad, is only fifty years old; and who can say that in fifty more it will not be supplanted by another method of locomotion in the same manner as it superseded canals and coaches. Its very history, at some distant epoch, may be lost, and the geologist of the future coming on the railway formation may vainly seek for the cause of so remarkable a phenomenon.   W. T. Watson

Cumberland and Westmorland Advertiser, 7 December 1875

FATAL RAILWAY ACCIDENT

On Thursday evening Dr Elliot, city coroner, held an inquest at the Infirmary, Carlisle, on the body of a man named Thomas Larthey, aged 33 years. Larthey lived at Bleatarn, Westmorland, and on Tuesday last was working as a labourer on the Midland Railway, at Grisburn, near Ormside. While crossing the line as a dirt wagon was coming up, though he had been warned not to do so, his foot slipped and he fell, and before he could recover his feet the wagon passed over one of his legs. Dr Dinwoodie, of Appleby, was summoned, and after dressing Larthey's wounds ordered his immediate removal to the Infirmary Carlisle. Larthey was admitted at half past seven, two hours afterwards the injured limb was amputated, and after that the man died. The jury returned a verdict of 'Accidental death' and expressed an opinion that it was not proper to bring any man so seriously injured as Larthey a distance of 37 miles.

Chapter Eight
1876

The Lancaster Gazette, 15 January 1876

MAN KILLED ON THE MIDLAND RAILWAY

On Thursday morning a man named David Carty was found lying dead by the side of the line near to Scotby, on the Settle and Carlisle Railway. The deceased lived in Carlisle, and leaves a wife and four young children. He was employed as a brick burner for Mr Bayliss, the contractor, and it is supposed that he was knocked down by a passing train, as his head is severely crushed, which was the cause of death.

Carty lived at Blain's Yard, Annetwell Street, Carlisle – *Penrith Observer.*

Cumberland and Westmorland Advertiser, 18 January 1876

SMASH ON THE SETTLE AND CARLISLE RAILWAY

On Friday evening, between 4 and 5 o'clock, an express goods train from Leeds to Carlisle broke down immediately after passing the points at the Ormside Station. The train, which consisted of 30 wagons was near the large viaduct, which spans the River Eden, one of the largest on the route from Settle to Carlisle, when a wagon broke down within a few yards of the bridge, on the highest part of the embankment, and tore up the down line for nearly 200 yards. It is presumed that the tire of the third wagon from the engine broke, and with that the couplings gave way. The whole of the remainder of the train ran off the line, tearing up the metals and sleepers which were broken and twisted into various shapes. Eight of the carriages (wagons) were thrown on the up line, which was completely blocked. Information of the accident was soon forwarded to the station at Appleby, and a telegram was despatched to Hawes, where the break down gang were engaged. By half past seven the same evening a large number of workmen arrived, under the superintendence, of Mr Whitaker, Mr Whitby, and Mr Goodman; whilst on the Appleby side Mr Throsle, agent for Mr Firbank, the contractor, despatched a number of men to assist in clearing the line, which was accomplished before midnight. Fortunately no one was injured, and beyond the damage done to the permanent way on the down line, the loss to the company will not be of a serious character. Had the wagons fallen the other way undoubtedly they would all have rolled down the embankment, and the damage would have been considerable.

The Penrith Herald, 26 February 1876

A BOY KILLED NEAR LAZONBY

On Wednesday week, an accident occurred on the Settle and Carlisle branch of the Midland Railway, near Lazonby. It appears that an errand boy, named Robert Askins, twelve years of age, in the service of Mr Bayliss, contractor, left Lazonby about half past one o'clock on Wednesday, and went along the railway in the direction of Langwathby, where he had been instructed to deliver a letter. On reaching Eden Viaduct the boy, who was suffering from a sore foot, sat down on the railway, and took off one of his clogs, when a special goods train came up from Langwathby, with the engine running tender first. The day was exceedingly wild and windy; and there being a curve in the line near the viaduct, the engine driver was unable to observe any obstruction in front; whilst the boy, owing to the violence of the wind, was unable to hear the train until it was close upon him; but it was then impossible for him to escape, and he was run over and killed. His body was found about half an hour afterwards by the driver of another engine, and conveyed to Lazonby, where it was examined by Dr Dudley, who found a large fracture upon the left temple, the left arm and right leg broken, and the body otherwise mutilated. Death must have been instantaneous. Information was given to the coroner, but no inquest was ordered.

Cumberland and Westmorland Advertiser, 29 February 1876

THE SETTLE AND CARLISLE RAILWAY

We have already reported that the new line will be opened for passenger traffic on the 1st of May. At the meeting of the Midland Company, on Tuesday, the chairman stated that of the £700,000 of capital expended during the past year on lines in the course of construction, the Settle and Carlisle line had absorbed £264,000. The expenditure on that line had very much exceeded the estimate, but after the contracts were let the price of labour and material rose so rapidly, and the difficulties of the work were found to be so enormous, that the directors felt bound largely to assist the contractors, who would otherwise have been ruined. Up to the present time the sum of £3,330,000 had been spent upon the line, and a further sum of £17,600 was required, making altogether £3,467,000 for 72 miles of double line and eight miles of single line. They were applying in the present session of Parliament for powers to raise a further sum of £158,000 to complete the works. The works were extremely substantial, being well executed. The whole has from end to end been laid with steel rails, and there was not a more perfect railway in the world.

Penrith Observer, 29 February 1876

ANOTHER RAILWAY ACCIDENT NEAR LAZONBY

One day last week an accident, which might have been attended with serious results, occurred on the Settle and Carlisle Railway, near Lazonby. It appears that a ballast train was being taken along the line, when one of the wagons, containing 28 workmen, was overturned. Fortunately the train was just starting, or the result might have been serious. We are glad to learn that no one was seriously injured, though one man had face cuts, and another was bruised about the arm.

Cumberland and Westmorland Advertiser, 7 March 1876

APPLEBY

The opening of the Settle and Carlisle extension of the Midland Railway for local traffic, took place on Wednesday last. Most of the principle officials have taken their stations along the line. Mr John Pearson, wine and spirit merchant, etc., received the first mineral consignment at the Appleby Station, consisting of several trucks of lime, which was supplied through the agency of Mr Walter Couzens, of the New Midland Railway Hotel, Clifford Street, representative of the Craven Lime Co.

Cumberland and Westmorland Advertiser, 7 March 1876

SAD ACCIDENT ON THE SETTLE AND CARLISLE RAILWAY

On Friday afternoon a labourer of the name of William Betts, met with a sad accident on the line between Crosby Garrett and Griseburn. He was returning from the former place where he had been to receive his pay, and was walking on the line. The day was unusually stormy and boisterous, and when about half way between the places, he was knocked down from behind, or rather, as is supposed, blown down off the line by the stormy wind, which prevailed, when in the act of looking round, at a place where there is a sharp curve. He had fallen into the four foot, and the supposition is that he was struck on the head when lying by the fire box of the engine. The whole train passed over him, and he laid for some time until he was observed by the driver of a goods train going in the other direction, who reported it at the next station. He was brought to Appleby, and lodged at the Midland Hotel, adjoining the station, where he was attended by Dr Armstrong, and Dr Herd… He was a young man about 26 years of age and is a native of Norfolk. The medical gentlemen have but little hope of his recovery… the poor man died yesterday. An inquest will probably be held tomorrow.

Penrith Observer, 14 March 1876

IMPORTANT PURCHASE OF LAND BY THE MIDLAND RAILWAY COMPANY

We understand that the Midland Railway Company last week purchased a large quantity of land at Lazonby on which, it is believed, they propose to erect extensive engine works. This step, we understand, has been resorted to in consequence of the enormous price of land about Carlisle. Should this prove to be correct and we have reliable authority for the statement, Lazonby may at some not far distant day become a second Crewe.

(also reported in *The Huddersfield Chronicle*, 25 March 1876)

Penrith Observer, 21 March 1876

IMPORTANT PURCHASE OF LAND AT LAZONBY

We have authority to state that Mr William Heskett, of Plumpton Hall, acting on behalf of Mr Dalrymple Maclean of Lazonby Hall, and Mr Douglas, has sold to the Midland Railway Company 15 acres of land situate at Lazonby, on which we believe the company propose to erect extensive new engine works. Negotiations are still proceeding to enable the company to acquire more land at the same place. Should the works turn out to be as extensive as it is stated they will be, the fell-side village of Lazonby and Kirkoswald will be surprisingly metamorphosed in a few years. *Carlisle Patriot.*

In 1871 the Midland Railway Chairman Mr Allport, Crossby and Johnson reported engine facilities at Lazonby, a 12,000 gallon water tank with pumping engine and a cottage for a man in attendance. There are two Midland Railway marker posts almost opposite the Joiners Public House, Lazonby, they may have been the site of the proposed pumping station. A water tower was eventually built on the up side of the line at the northern end of the platform and water was pumped from a beck 200 yards north of the tower also on the up side of the line.

The Penrith Herald, 25 March 1876.

FATAL RAILWAY ACCIDENT NEAR ARMATHWAITE

On Tuesday a fatal accident occurred to a platelayer on the Settle and Carlisle Railway, named George Richardson, aged 50 years, who lived at Armathwaite. He was working on the up line in Barron Wood, when a train from Carlisle approached on the same line, Richardson stepped upon the down line, and still looking at the train going up did not notice an engine coming down. There is a curve at that place and the driver of the down engine did not see Richardson until close upon him, and when he whistled failed to make the warning heard, probably in consequence of the noise made by the up train. The result was that Richardson was knocked down, run over, and killed on the spot, An inquest was not considered necessary.

Yorkshire Post and Leeds Intelligencer, 10 April 1876

SETTLE AND CARLISLE RAILWAY

To Contractors, Colliery Owners, Builders, Brick Manufacturers, Quarry Men, and Others.
   Extensive sale of Contractors Plant.
   Mr Arthur T Crow has received instructions from John Bayliss Esq., who has now completed his

contract on the Settle and Carlisle Railway to sell by public auction at the Petteril Bridge Yard, Carlisle, on Tuesday and Wednesday, April the Eleventh and Twelfth 1876: The whole of his valuable Plant and Materials, comprising contractors rails, 100 three-yard earth wagons, 5 locomotives engines, by Manning Wardle & Co, Leeds; 4 portable steam engines, combined steam engines and mortar mills, steam pumps, Scotch and quarry cranes, carts, timber drags, dobbin carts, several travelling cranes, brickyard plant complete, principally by Messers Bradley & Craven; metal presses, trollies, incline winding gear, turntables, bridge centres, quarry and smiths tools, cart shaft and trace gears, scaffold poles and boards, and a large quantity of hut scantling and boards, planks, battens, barrows, prop wood, sleepers, firewood, 200 tons of scrap iron and metal, horse and hand chaff machine and a great quantity of contractors general tools, stores, and materials of every description.

Catalogues will be issued in due course, which may be obtained from the Contractors Office, Carlisle or the office of the Auctioneer, Manor House , Sunderland.

N.B. The Midland London and North Western, North Eastern, and all Scotch Railways have direct communication with the sidings into Petteril Bridge Yard, Carlisle.

Manor House Sunderland, 8 March 1876

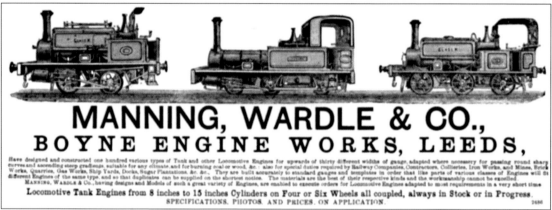

This advert from 'Engineering' 1880, illustrates two possible engines that were sold in the contractors' sale. The locomotive on the left of the picture is a Class H built with twelve inch cylinders and three feet wheels. The locomotive on the right is a Class K built in 1875 and dispatched to Benton and Woodwiss one of the congtracors for the Settle to Carlisle line in 1876 for use at Melton Mowbray. It had twelve inch cylinders and three foot one and three eighth inch wheels.

The Penrith Herald, 15 April 1876

MR CRACKENTHORPE AND HIS OLD OAKS

Whilst surveying for the Settle and Carlisle line, the engineers came across Mr Crackanthorpe, of New-biggin Hall. 'May I enquire,' said he, 'in what you are engaged on my property here?' 'We are surveying for a new line.' 'A new line! Where to and from?' 'From Settle to Carlisle.' 'And which way is it to go in this direction?' 'Through that wood.' 'What! Through my wood, my old oak wood, that no one has touched a bough of for years and years?' shouted Mr Crackenthorpe, indignantly. He would not hear of such an act of desecration for a long time, and finally only reconciled to it by the entities of Mr Allport. At his interview with the latter he said, 'Well there's one condition I have now to make.' 'You have only to name it, sir, and it shall be attended to,' was the reply. It is that you spare me the largest and finest oak in my wood.' 'Certainly.' ' Do you know what I want it for?' continued the proprietor. 'No sir; but whatever you want it for it shall be saved.' 'Well,' said Mr Crackanthorpe, good naturedly, 'it's to hang you and all the engineers of the Midland Railway upon, for daring to come here at all.'

From *The Midland Railway Its rise and Progress* by F. S. Williams.

William Crackenthorpe was in favour of the Eden Valley Railway, and was at the cutting of the first sod on 28 July 1858. He was also a director of that line. The Crackenthorpes of Newbiggin Hall were also part owners of Crodundle Quarry along with Culgaith Parish. Red sandstone from this quarry was used to build Newbiggin or Crodundle Viaduct and the tunnels in the Culgaith area etc. Although Crackenthorpe complained about his trees it appears he could have profited in other ways from the Midland Railway.

Manning Wardle, H Lovatt No. 2, 0-6-OST on the Great Central.
Photograph courtesy of Leicestershire Archives.

Herepath's Journal, 15 April 1876

This new route to Scotland will be opened for passenger traffic on 1st May next, and a new and efficient service of express and fast trains will be established. A morning and night express train will be run between St Pancras, Edinburgh and Glasgow, with Pullman cars attached. Express trains will also run to and from Bristol, Bath, Gloucester and Birmingham , in connection with the through service between London and Scotland, and likewise between Liverpool, Manchester, and stations on the Lancashire and Yorkshire line and Skipton in connection with the through service via the new route.

Manchester Courier, 26 April 1876

THE OPENING OF THE SETTLE AND CARLISLE RAILWAY

In connection with the opening of the Settle and Carlisle Railway, which is to take place on Monday, the Midland Railway Company will give an opportunity to travellers between London and Edinburgh the choice of travelling in an improved English coach and a Pullman car. The directors of the Midland Company, while anxious to develop the traffic upon their system to its utmost extent, are not, as is well known unmindful of the convenience of the public, and the opening of the new line between Settle and Carlisle, the delay in the completion of which has formed the subject of much discussion at the half yearly meetings of the company for some years past will be marked by the introduction of a new carriage, which is, in point of arrangement, a compromise between the English and American principles.

Two of the new carriages left the works of the Ashbury Carriage Company Limited yesterday, en route to London, and their trial, for ease and safety, will be tested on the line between Manchester and Derby. The carriages, constructed to carry 58 passengers each, 18 first class and 40 third class, are 54 feet long and 8 feet wide with eight compartments, composed of three first class each of these being 7 feet 3 inches long; four third class, 5 feet 11¼ inches; and a compartment for passengers luggage, 7 feet 3 inches. The internal width is 7 feet 6 inches, and the height at sides 6 feet 4 inches; the doorways are 6 feet high. The carriages have a raised part (or roof) in the centre 4 feet wide, running the whole length, similar to the Pullman Palace Cars, for the purpose of giving increased light, the internal height in the centre of the carriage from floor to this raised roof being 8 feet 4½ inches. Ventilators and lights are placed in this raised part at the sides.

The interior of the first class compartments is sumptuously fitted, the seats and backs are trimmed in rich dark blue cloth, finished with broad lace, French Merino curtains of the same colour to the quarter lights, silk hat-cords, and parcel nets being placed on either side and above the trimmings upwards they are artistically panelled in sycamore, bordered with birds-eye maple and a profusion of rich gilt mouldings, and each seat is arranged by arm-rests for three persons.

These arm-rests are hinged to turn back at will, giving a seat the full width of carriage for reclining.

Midland 3rd class dining car.

Midland 1st class dining saloon.

A lamp supported in the roof from a brass ring of chaste design gives light over the whole compartment. The seats of the third-class are padded and covered with striped repp, having parcel nets above. The backs and sides of these compartments are painted and grained oak, and above the parcel nets handsomely decorated with painting to represent panels, of similar design to the first class.

The carriages are supported on two six-wheeled bogies placed 36 feet apart. The weight is carried at each bogie by sixteen elliptical springs placed traverseley on swing beams and four strong spiral springs between the bogie frames and the side beams. A buffer composed of Spencer cylindrical springs with a stroke of three inches is placed central in the frames at each end of the carriage the head being shaped for radiation. The draw gear is continuous, arranged with joints, sufficient space being allowed in the bearers it passes through for radiation also. The wheels are Mansell's patent, three feet seven inches diameter with Bessemer steel tyres and axels. Westinghouse's patent continuous brake acting on four wheels of each bogie is attached to the carriages.

The body panels of these carriages are Honduras mahogany, and the framing best American oak; the undercarriage is also of oak of the same quality, the side soles being plated on the outside with angle iron nine inches by four inches by half an inch thick; the side plates of the bogies are of best Staffordshire iron, half inch thick, with oak pieces three inches thick between. The body of these carriages is painted in rich crimson lake, picked out with black and gold, and fine lined in vermillion. The under carriage and bogies are painted and picked out in the same colour, and fine lined with chrome yellow. They have been manufactured for the Midland Company by the Ashbury Carriage Company Limited.

Midland 1st class sleeping carriage.

The Lancaster Gazette, 29 April 1876

THE SETTLE AND CARLISLE LINE

On Thursday, an empty train of passenger carriages and Pullman cars was run on the Midland line from Leeds to Carlisle. The distance was done in two hours and three quarters between Leeds and Carlisle, stopping a quarter of an hour at Skipton.

(This must have been a test train run before the public service started)

The York Herald, 1 May 1876

THE OPENING OF THE SETTLE AND CARLISLE RAILWAY

Today one of the greatest railway works of recent years is to be fully opened for passenger traffic, the vast line by which the Midland Railway will be extended north, and its trains will run from London to Glasgow…

It is ten years since the line was projected and the first sod was cut about 1869; in August, 1875 the line was open for goods traffic, and, now that the permanency of the works has been proved, and the substantial stations have been erected, the full use of the line has begun, and Midland directors, share-holders and officials may be congratulated on the removal of the line from the non-productive to the productive portions of their expended capital.

The Sheffield & Rotherham Independent, 2 May 1876

Though the line was opened for passenger traffic today, the first train then, was not actually the first that had passed over the line, inasmuch as the Carl Rosa Opera Company had gone over it the previous day, on their way from Sheffield to Scotland.

The opera company was formed by Carl August Nicolas Rosa in 1871 and their first performance was in 1873 at the Princess's Theatre, London.

Penrith Observer, 2 May 1876

THE NEW MIDLAND RAILWAY

Yesterday (Monday) the new line of railway between Settle and Carlisle was opened for passenger traffic under the most favourable auspices. The weather, though cold, was not unfavourable, and at different points along the route the greatest interest was manifested in the event. The line opens out for communication with large centres of industry a wide extent of country which hitherto has not been reached by any railway. The new line was projected about ten years ago, and the first sod was cut in 1869. It is 72 miles in length, was opened for goods traffic in August last, and has cost about £3,000,000. There can be little doubt that the new line will divert a considerable amount of traffic which would otherwise have been conveyed along the London and North Western Railway, and will, at the same time add materially to the railway facilities of such towns as Appleby and Kirkby Stephen.

LANGWATHBY, LAZONBY. ETC.

At Langwathby, Lazonby and other villages along the route crowds of villagers and others assembled to witness the passenger trains run to and fro. Great enthusiasm was manifested.

Lazonby School Log:- 29 April 1875. Several children absent this morning with leave to see the first carriages go up the New Railway. 1st May 1875 holiday for the first passenger trains on the railway.

KIRKBY STEPHEN

The opening of the extension from Settle to Carlisle passed off today (Monday) with considerable eclat. There were considerable number of local passengers by the different trains, which ran in tolerably good time. The extension to this town is likely to open up the Leeds and Bradford district, the saving of time in reaching these points being some three hours.

CARLISLE

At Carlisle yesterday the Citadel Station was crowded with people anxious to witness the arrival and departure of the several trains. The service arranged for embraces eight trains each way daily. The fastest train is the 10-30 a.m. train from London arriving at Carlisle at 6-25 and at Glasgow at 9-15. There is a night express leaving London at 9-15 arriving at Carlisle at 5-4. No trains leave Carlisle on Sundays. An immense number of people, including many of the directors, availed themselves of the opportunity for an outing. All passed off in a most satisfactory manner.

APPLEBY

At Appleby the demonstration was probably on a larger scale than at any other place, the size of the town considered, as the new branch will confer very considerable advantages upon the trade of the town and neighbourhood. The event was marked by considerable animation, businesses being to a great extent suspended. Sports were also indulged in. A fuller report for which we had arranged had not reached us when we went to press. The first sod on the south junction which will connect the Midland and Eden Valley lines was cut on Wednesday last. The link will be nearly half a mile in length, and when completed will form a traffic medium between the two lines over the respective stations.

The Northern Echo, 3 May 1876

…Another notable fact is that the new line, which will, for the most part be crossed by expresses running at forty miles an hour, without stopping once between Carlisle and Skipton, will have the best arrangements yet devised for the safety of traffic. It is, of course, worked on the block system, with interlocking points and levers, and an ingenious contrivance prevents the wires ever becoming slack. There is only one level crossing on the whole route, and it is worked by interlocking levers from a signal box. [There are infact two level crossings!] Every signal man is appraised by electricity as to whether lamps are burning in the distant signals. The same care has been bestowed upon the rolling stock. Every carriage is fitted with a continuous air brake, acting on eight wheels of every carriage, which would enable the fastest and heaviest train to be brought up in 250 yards. The carriages themselves mark an era in passenger traffic. They are eighteen yards long, and each contains seven compartment and a luggage van. They are lighted not only from the sides but from the top, which rises in the centre, and has side lights, The carriages are supported on two six wheel bogies, which are so contrived that the motion is almost imperceptible. Every passenger can communicate at once with the guard, and driver as well as the guards can apply the brake. Besides these carriages, Pullman sleeping cars are provided for those who travel by night…

The Leicester Chronicle, 6 May 1876

A Sheffield contemporary in its issue of Saturday last, 29 April 1876, remarks:- *Finis coronat opus*, was the ejaculation of Mr Crossley, the engineer, on reaching Carlisle, when he accompanied the Construction and Works Committee of the Midland Directors in the final inspection of the Settle and Carlisle line, preparatory to its opening on Monday next. It was an interesting party. There was Mr. Ellis (of Leicester), chairman, son of the notable John Ellis, who took the reins when they fell from the hands of king Hudson, and inaugurated the policy that saved the Midland system. There was the veteran Sir Isaac Morley, who rocked the cradle of more than one of our local lines. There was Mr Allport, among railway managers A1, after 45 years' experience combining the enterprise of youth with the wisdom of age. There was Mr Carter, who for many years had charge of all the Midland bills in Parliament, and of whom it is said he never lost a bill. And there was Mr Thompson, the vice chairman, Mr Mappin and Mr Thomas, directors, Mr Crossley, the late engineer, Mr Johnson and his successor Mr Saunders, the architect, Mr Gratton and several others, officials or visitors. A contentment prevailed, mixed with quiet pride, among those who could especially say the day crowned their work.

The new Venus Pullman car was used on Tuesday and Wednesday by the directors in their inspection of the line. Its beauty, the perfection of its appointments, and its comforts were the theme of every tongue…

On Tuesday, the object of Mr Ellis, the chairman, with the officials, Mr Alport, Mr Johnston, Mr Saunders, Mr Gratton, and others went to see the line and they denied themselves the luxurious Pullman drawing- oom and the commodious saloon carriage, and took their seats in a cattle truck, roughly fitted with benches for the purpose. There, in appropriate wrappings and in close fitting caps, with nothing to obstruct their view of the line as the train ran on, as well as of the country, to right and left, or behind, as they were enabled to appreciate the glories of the land and sky, the ranges of mighty mountains, intersected by wild gorges or divided by lovely valleys, through which ran the rivers and their tributaries streamlets and rills, in a way denied to those travelling in any closed carriages. We do not recommend open trucks for entire journeys, amid all hazards of weather, or without adequate wrappings. But in summer time, each train had a truck attached to which passengers might betake themselves, if they chose, during parts of the journey, we believe the glorious scenery of the Yorkshire Wolds and dales, of the Westmorland mountains, and the wild Cumberland fells would be increasingly attractive.

Above the Smith family, left to right, Stephen, Mary Jane, Elizabeth, Herbert, William, Farnk. William Smith was signalman at Armathwaite between 1903 and 1910. The present signal box dates from 1899 and was decommissioned in 1983. Photograph courtesy of Armathwaite Signal box collection.

Below a typical gang of platelayers with their tools circa 1899, relaying track at Carlisle. Photograph courtesy of Cumbrian Libraries Image Bank.

Above a Johnson 0-6-0 goods engine fitted with a snowplough at Durran Hill shed. 120 of these engines were built for the opening of the Settle to Carlisle railway, photograph courtesy of Cumbria Railway Association.

Below, Carlisle Citadel Station cira 1912 showing bay platforms now used by the Settle and Carlisle trains. Photograph courtesy of Lens of Sutton.

Above, Langwathby Station circa 1912, photograph courtesy of Lens of Sutton.
Below, Lazonby and Kirkoswald Station circa 1900 before development occurred on the fields be-
hind. The Midland Hotel (formerly the Crown and Thistle) stands behind the running in board.
The station was originally only called Lazonby, the name changing to Lazonby and Kirkoswald in
July 1895. Photograph courtesy of the Lazonby History Society.

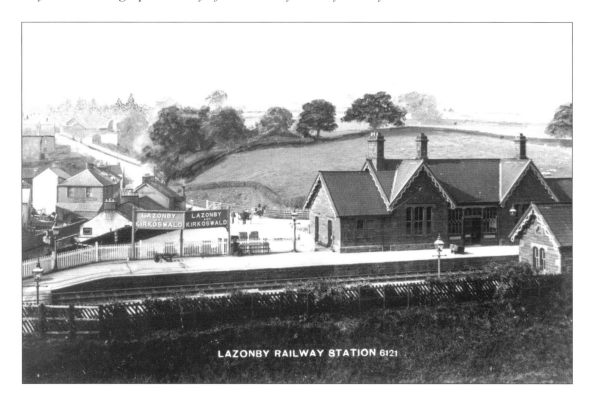

Above, Settle and Carlisle railway entering Carlisle circa 1907. Durran Hill sheds and sidings on the left and on the right Durran Hill Junction signal box. The Carlisle to Newcastle line runs in on the far right behind the signal box. Photograph courtesy of Cumbria Railway Association.

Below, Hawes station circa 1912 with Midland Railway trucks in the siding. Photograph courtesy of Lens of Sutton.

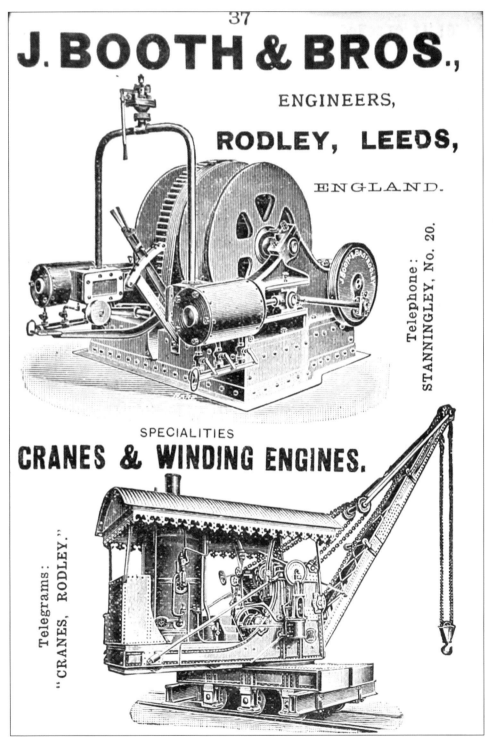

Winding engines were used at the top of vertical shafts to lower men and materials, then extract the waste rock. The shafts were sunk down to rail level from where horizontal headings were driven to form the tunnel. The cranes would be used to lift building materials on to the partially built viaducts.

The two photographs on these pages are of men working in the Greenside Mine, Glenridding, Cumbria. They show the way that the shot holes were hand drilled and the later use of a power drill, in a very similar way to the drilling in Black Moss Tunnel. Both photographs by kind permission of the Beamish Museum.

Gravestone at Langwathby Churchyard erected by fellow navvies for John Mead who died 23 April 1873, John De'Boo died 21 February 1874 and John Smith died in March 1874. Photograph author's collection.

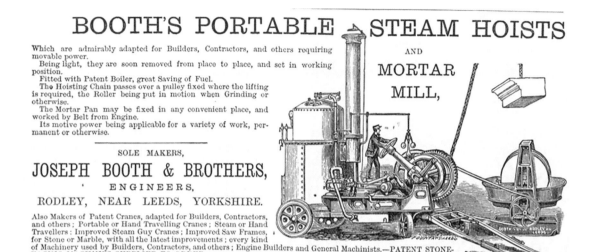

Steam driven mortar mills were used by the contractors at various locations along the route of the new railway. Joseph Booth set up his crane making business in 1847 at the Union Foundry next to the Leeds and Liverpool Canal. In 1855 the firm passed to his son Joseph, and was called Joseph Booth & Bros. They made Goliath cranes, portable steam hoists and winding engines, all equipment that would have been used by contractors building the Settle-Carlisle Railway.

The Hunsley Engine Company was founded in 1864 at Jack Lane, Leeds. The first engine was built in 1865, a standard 0-6-0 saddle tank for Brassey and Ballard Railway Civil Engineering contractors. In 1870 they went on to build narrow guage engines for the slate quarries in Wales. The engine sold in the contractors sale could have been of either guage as there was a tramway at Ribblehead.

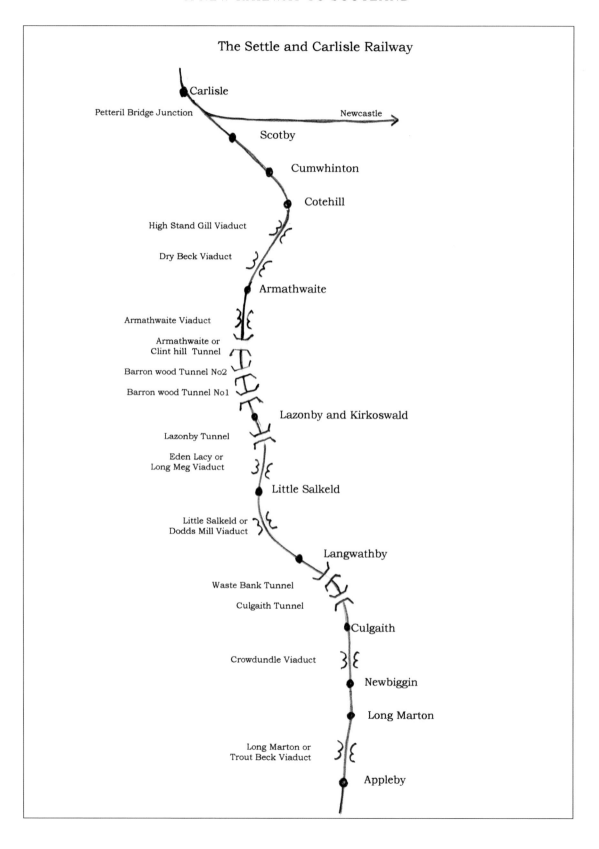

The Settle and Carlisle Railway

A NEW RAILWAY TO SCOTLAND

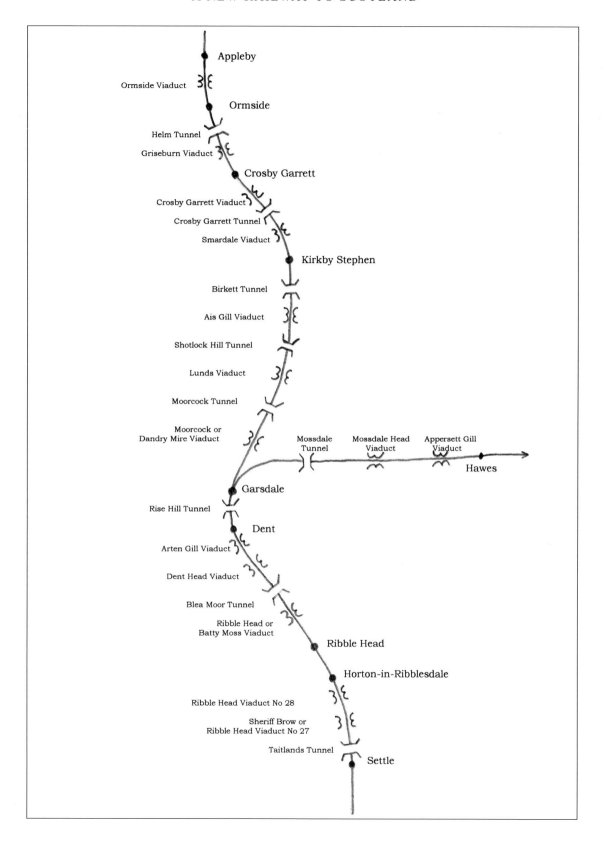

Close up view of contractor's locomotive on Sheriff Brow Viaduct (pictured on page 45).
Photograph courtesy of J. Shevelan.

Penrith Observer, 9 May 1876

OPENING OF THE SETTLE & CARLISLE RAILWAY

On the 1st May Appleby was truly *en fête*. The sports and gala provided by Mr Walter Couzens, of the Midland Railway Hotel, in commemoration of the above event, were such as to cause an immense concourse of people to assemble from all parts of the country, many hailing from distances. The day although cold was fine. The church bells rang out merry peals, and at an early hour the strains of the well known band of the Royal Westmorland Militia led the holiday makers to the field near the Midland, where the gala was to be held. The multitude of 'Bonny Belles' who were soon tripping the light fantastic toe in unison with the merry notes of the band, brought vividly before the minds eye the inspiriting scenes which were wont to be annually enacted on May-day throughout our Merry England in the halcyon days of yore, whilst the athletic contests provided for the lusty youths lent an attraction to the day's proceedings which far exceeded anything of the kind ever witnessed in Appleby. Banners and bannerettes floated from every available point in the vicinity of the station, and the creature comforts disposed from a large marquee left nothing wanting to render the enjoyment of the pleasure seekers complete…

The Midland Express passing Armathwaite Station and a group of platelayers. The train is headed by a Kirtly 800 class No 817 built by Nelson in 1870, rebuilt by Johnson in 1876, and renumbered 50 in 1907. Photograph courtesy of D. Joy.

Penrith Observer, 30 May 1876

SAD ACCIDENT ON THE SETTLE AND CARLISLE RAILWAY

On Friday afternoon a person of the name John Carrah, employed on the line as a labourer, was seriously injured at Long Marton, about three miles from Appleby Station. He was engaged removing some soil, which had been emptied from a ballast wagon, which for the time had been detached from the others. The driver, without observing him, backed the train to have the wagon replaced, when Carrah was struck by the buffers, and knocked down, and one or two wheels passed over one of his legs and an arm, mangling the latter close to the shoulder, and crushing his leg severely. He was removed by the next train to the infirmary at Carlisle, where his left arm was amputated. He lingered in great agony up to Saturday evening… He was a native of Dufton, near Appleby, and was well known in the neighbourhood as a peaceable and industrious man. He was 39 years of age, and leaves a widow, but no family. An inquest was held before Dr Elliott, at Carlisle, yesterday, when a verdict of 'accidental death' was returned.

The Penrith Herald, 3 June 1876

FATAL ACCIDENT ON THE NEW MIDLAND LINE

On Monday an inquest was held at the Carlisle Infirmary before Dr Elliot, city coroner, and a jury of whom Mr Thomas Jackson was foreman, touching on the death of a man named John Currah, who died at the Infirmary on Sunday. Deceased, who was 30 years of age, and resided at Dufton, was a platelayer on the Midland line, and on Friday last, about 10 o'clock, was in a ballast wagon, comprising part of a train which was put on a siding at Long Marton station to allow the morning express to pass. While the wagons were being removed from the siding on to the main line the driver of the engine observed a manure wagon on the adjoining rails close to the points and in such a position that if he ran up to it his engine would invariably have come in contact with it. To avoid a collision, he shut off steam and brought the train as rapidly as possible to a stop, which however, jerked Currah out of the wagon. He fell within the four foot, and his arm being on the rail, the wagon moved backwards for two or three feet, crushing his arm severely and otherwise injuring him. He was immediately placed in the guard's van, and removed to the infirmary, where his arm was amputated, but succumbed to the injuries he had sustained. It was stated in evidence that if the engine driver had not opportunely observed the manure wagon, a serious mishap might have occurred. Several jurymen thought the servants were to blame for leaving the wagon so near to the points, but the Coroner remarked that the wagon might have moved a foot or two farther than the servants had intended. No blame was attached to the company servants, and a verdict of 'accidental death' was returned.

Penrith Observer, 20 June 1876

ACCIDENT ON THE MIDLAND RAILWAY

On Tuesday night an accident occurred on the Midland Railway near Armathwaite. Just after the 6-5pm goods train from Carlisle had passed Armathwaite, an axle of a Glasgow and South Western wagon containing pig iron broke and threw four wagons off the rails. The driver, perceiving what had occurred, shut off steam and pulled up, just in time to escape catching the abutment of a bridge which crosses over the line. The up main line was blocked upwards of four hours, and trains from Carlisle had to be worked on the down line between Armathwaite and Lazonby. Mr Goodman, with the break-down men, which are stationed at Carlisle, was speedily there, and commenced to clear the line. Fortunately the permanent way was not damaged beyond a few chairs being broken. The rolling stock was very little the worse.

Penrith Observer, 27 June 1876

LANDSLIP ON THE NEW MIDLAND RAILWAY

On Saturday night an extensive landslip occurred on the Midland Railway, near to Kirkby Stephen Station. The slip had been impending for some time, and the rain on Saturday carried away many tons of earth from the embankment upon which the up line of rails is laid. A gang of 100 workmen were very soon on the spot, but reparation of the damage was not completed until three o'clock on Sunday afternoon.

There was another big landslip on the line. At the curve of the Eden just before High Stand Gill a landslip took place, and five acres of ground began to move; the space between the line and the river blew up, unable to resist the pressure of the embankment, and slid down towards the water. It had been known at the outset that this spot would be troublesome, and it had been said that no railway could be carried here. But Crossley took the line across the slope, and, though the incline of the bank was 200ft form top to bottom, and the bank slipped and carried with it trees forty or fifty years old for a distance of 150ft, driving the river sideways into the next parish, the difficulty was overcome. (*Our Home Railways,* Gordon, 1910)

This embankment lasted until 2016 when engineers found that heavy rain had made it unstable and 500,000 tons of earth moved towards the river again. This has been remedied by building an inverted bridge to carry the line that is expected to last another 150 years.

Penrith Observer, 11 July 1876

FATAL ACCIDENT ON THE MIDLAND RAILWAY

On Wednesday evening a man named Thomas Garner was accidently killed on this line, close to Appleby Station. Deceased, who was 58 years of age, has been for upwards of 30 years in the employment of Mr Firbank, railway contractor, as general foreman. He had latterly been engaged in superintending the construction of the loop line which is to connect the Midland with the Eden Valley section of the North Eastern Railway, and he was in the habit of walking on a portion of the Midland main line in going to and from his duties. At the time when the fatality occurred, he was on his way home when the down express which runs through Appleby (without stopping) at 5-48pm, ran over him. The driver of the express seeing that Garner was in a dangerous position, immediately applied the brakes, and gave the danger signal. The deceased, however, who had been for some time past severely afflicted with rheumatism, unfortunately failed to get clear of the rails, and the train passed over him, when he received such injuries as resulted in almost instantaneous death. An inquest on the body was held on Thursday at the Midland Hotel, Appleby, before Mr George R Thompson, coroner, when the above facts having been given in evidence, the jury returned a verdict of 'accidental death'. We understand that Mr Firbank had recently awarded a life pension to Garner for his long and faithful service, and he was only awaiting the completion of the short loop line upon which he was engaged prior to retiring from active labour.

Penrith Observer, 18 July 1876

FATAL RAILWAY ACCIDENT

Yesterday afternoon Dr Elliot, city coroner, held an inquest at the Infirmary, on view of the body of George Mann, nineteen years of age, who was employed as a shunter by the Midland Railway Company, and who was so severely injured on Saturday night while attempting to uncouple some wagons while in motion, at Petteril Bridge Yard, Carlisle, that he died on Sunday afternoon. The evidence went to show that deceased tried to uncouple the wagons though warned not to do so by the foreman until they came to a stand still. A verdict of 'Accidental killed' was returned, the jury recommended that the rules regarding the uncoupling of wagons be more strictly enforced by the company.

The Penrith Herald, 12 August 1876

A MAN KILLED AT LAZONBY

On Tuesday morning, about six o'clock, James Lowther, potter, of Penrith, aged 58 years, was killed by a train at Lazonby. He was employed as a labourer, and was going to his work at a ballast siding, and was walking upon the line when a goods train came up. The driver, seeing some men on the line, commenced to whistle. Although several of the men called to the deceased, he did not seem to heed them until the train was too near, and the poor fellow was killed instantaneously. An inquest was held at the Crown and Thistle Inn, when a verdict in accordance with the above facts was returned.

The Midland Hotel was originally the Crown and Thistle Inn.

Penrith Observer, 15 August 1876

STRIKE OF WORKMEN ON THE SETTLE AND CARLISLE RAILWAY

On Friday a number of workmen engaged on this section of the Midland route were paid off at the various stations from Newbiggin to Griseburn. Those whose services were retained were informed, as the pay van arrived at the intermediate stations, that their pay was reduced, 8d. per day, from 4s 4d. to 3s 8d., representing a loss to the men of 4s. per week. The workmen having had no official intimation of the change refused to submit to this reduction or accept the proffered terms, and consequently they struck in a body. In this state of affairs an official, who was passing in one of the fast through trains, was stopped at Appleby. Ultimately the men were ordered to resume work on the old terms.

The Manchester Guardian, 16 August 1876

RAILWAY ACCIDENTS
ALARMING ACCIDENT ON THE SETTLE AND CARLISLE LINE

Carlisle Tuesday.

This morning, about one o'clock, a serious and destructive accident occurred on the Settle and Carlisle section of the Midland Railway, near Ormside station, 33¼ miles south of Carlisle. The Midland night express from Scotland, to which Pullman cars are attached, is now divided into two sections along this part of the line, so as to better accommodate the Edinburgh and Glasgow passenger traffic. The Edinburgh section leaves Carlisle eight minutes after midnight.

On Monday night it was an unusually light train, consisting of engine and tender and six vehicles, two of which were guards brake vans, one Pullman car, placed near the front of the train, a Midland 'bogie' composite carriage, a Midland ordinary composite, and a North British composite. The train was due to pass Ormside Station, at which it does not stop, about one o'clock in the morning.

About that hour the signalman at Ormside received a telegram from Crosby Garrett, the next station further south, that a goods train had divided. This goods train was travelling from Bradford to Carlisle, and consisted of about 30 trucks laden with miscellaneous goods. The couplings had broken or come loose between Kirkby Stephen and Crosby Garrett, and as the line at this part is upon an incline towards the north, the second section, consisting of about three quarters of the train, followed the first, and the engine driver had not discovered what had happened. The signalman at Crosby Garrett, however appears to have noticed that the goods train was travelling in two divisions, and he signalled that effect to Ormside, where the signalman put up his lamps and semaphore against the goods train, and at the same time signalled 'caution' to the express train which he knew was nearly due.

The driver of the goods train, on reaching the distance signal at Ormside, and finding it against him naturally slackened his train; and at this moment the broken off section of his train, which had acquired great momentum while travelling down the incline, dashed with fearful force into the front section of the train at a point between the distant and home signal. The crash was tremendous. Large trucks were hurled across the line, fouling the 'six foot' and the up line to London, while others were projected to the other side of the line.

At the critical moment the express from Carlisle arrived. In obedience to the signal it was travelling at 'caution' speed; but it ran into the wrecked goods train with a fearful crash. None of the express vehicles was thrown of the line; but the carriages sustained a great amount of damage. First after the engine and tender came the guards van. The side of this was completely dashed out, and the guard, named

Barber, a North British guard, was afterwards removed from the van insensible. He now lies at the Midland Hotel at Appleby in a precarious condition. Next came the Pullman car, whose massive build stood it in good stead in withstanding the shock of the collision. One corner was smashed in and the panels along one side were grazed and some of them dinted in by coming into collision with portions of the goods wagons, while one window at the north end was broken.

Other of the carriages received serious damage, but happily only two passengers were injured. They were Mr John Larbrey, 26, Phillip Lane, London, who had his feet hurt; and Mr J. W. Crabtree, Woodstreet, London whose head was cut and bleeding. Both were able however, to resume their journey. Another gentleman whose name could not be ascertained, remained all night at the neighbouring clergyman's house, but after a sleep seemed all right.

No other passengers complained of being hurt. The express train, as we have said, never left the metals, but fourteen goods wagons were thrown off the road. A breakdown gang from Carlisle, under the direction of Mr Goodman, were soon on the spot; but it was five hours before the lines were cleared, and at mid-day today the passenger carriages were still in a siding and many of the broken trucks lying tumbled one on top of the other by the line side of the railway.

Sheffield and Rotherham Independent, 22 August 1876

ANOTHER ACCIDENT ON THE SETTLE AND CARLISLE RAILWAY

Between nine and ten o'clock on Saturday night an accident, which might have caused loss of life but for the prompt attention of the officials, occurred near Carlisle. A goods train running from Skipton to Carlisle came into collision with another train at Durran Hill sidings, situate about half a mile south of Carlisle. Both up and down lines were fouled, but the passenger trains were not very much delayed, as they were piloted through the goods sidings, and were steered clear of the scene of the accident.

The Penrith Herald, 16 September 1876

THE LATE RAILWAY ACCIDENT NEAR APPLEBY

Colonel Rich's report on the accident that occurred on the 15 August, near Ormside Station has been issued. He says the accident was caused by the mistakes of the signalman on duty at Ormside Station. He was perfectly aware of the regulations, and the only reason he gives for disregarding them is that he lost his presence of mind at the time.

Sheffield and Rotherham Independent, 2 October 1876

OPENING OF NEW RAILWAY STATION

The new station at Settle Junction on the Settle and Carlisle section of the Midland Railway will be opened shortly, and the old station will be utilised only for the receipt and disposal of mineral and other heavy traffic for and from Barrow-in-Furness way, and stations in the south. The new Ambergate Junction station will, it is anticipated, be ready for opening in the course of a few weeks.

Cumberland and Westmorland Advertiser, 3 October 1876

FATAL ACCIDENT AT ARMATHWAITE

On Thursday, a platelayer, named Lawrence Stanton, in the employment of the Midland Railway Company, was killed near Armathwaite Station. From the information we have been able to gather, it appears that deceased had while working stepped aside on one line to allow a train to pass on the other, and while standing was killed by an express train which came up at the time unobserved by him. Stanton was about 63 years of age. He leaves a widow and family.

Sheffield and Rotherham Independent, 13 November 1876

FALL OF TUNNEL ROOF

A portion of the roof of the Barron Wood Tunnel near Armathwaite, on the Settle and Carlisle Railway gave way on Friday night, the debris fouling one of the main lines. The trains, however, to and from Scotland suffered no delay.

The Barron Wood Tunnel No1 is 207 yards long and was in built 1870-73. The No2 tunnel is 251 yards long and was built in 1871-73.

Sheffield and Rotherham Independent, 29 December 1876

LANDSLIP ON THE SETTLE AND CARLISLE RAILWAY

Late on Wednesday night, a rather serious land slip occurred on the Settle and Carlisle line, between Hawes Junction and Rise Hill Station, and nothing was known of the fact until one of the passenger trains had with difficulty passed the spot. The 8-15 pm passenger train, Carlisle to Leeds, ran well up to the advertised time as far as Hawes Junction, but shortly after leaving that station it ran over a quantity of debris, the result of a land slip, and the passengers sustained a severe shaking. Fortunately, the engine and carriages kept the metals, or the consequence might have been disastrous. Some of the carriage steps were wrenched away and broken. The train, after a considerable time, resumed its course southwards.

Staff at Lazonby Station in 1910 looking towards Lazonby tunnel photograph courtesy of the Friends of the Settle-Carlisle Line. Mr Richardson (on the left) started his career at Ormside then moved to Long Marton as a lamp man one of his duties was to look after the signal lamps on Long Marton viaduct. From there he moved again to Newbiggin and then to Lazonby before becoming leading porter at Langwathby in 1911.

Chapter Nine
1877

Bradford Daily Telegraph, 1 January 1877

LANDSLIP ON THE SETTLE AND CARLISLE RAILWAY

Late on Wednesday night, a rather serious landslip occurred on the Settle and Carlisle line, between Hawes Junction and Rise Hill stations, and nothing was known of the fact until one of the passenger trains had with difficulty passed the spot. The 8-15 p.m. passenger train, Carlisle to Leeds, ran well up to the advertised time as far as Hawes Junction, but shortly after leaving the station it ran over a quantity of debris, the result of a landslip, and the passengers sustained a severe shaking. Fortunately, the engine and carriages kept the metals, or the consequences might have been disastrous. Some of the carriage steps were wrenched away and broken. The train, after a considerable time, resumed its course southwards.

Penrith Observer, 2 January 1877

MIDLAND RAILWAY COMPANY

To the editor of the *Penrith Observer,*   27 December 1876

Dear Sir,

Allow me, through the medium of your columns, to bring before the notice of the public what I consider a piece of arbitrary and tyrannical conduct on the part of the Midland Railway Co., or their officials. About the middle of December I ordered two trucks of coals from a colliery office at Skipton, to be delivered at Crosby Garrett Station, with the intention of distributing them amongst the poor of this village before Christmas Day. The coals were duly despatched, and reached Crosby Garrett on Thursday, the 14th instant. On hearing of their arrival I, at once, made arrangements for a number of carts to remove them, when to my utter surprise, I found that the station master at Crosby Garrett had received orders to detain them for further instructions, for no other reason that I can conceive except that the coals were not ordered through their appointed agent.

This was to me a great disappointment, as well as a serious hardship to the poor to whom the coals would have been a most invaluable benefit during this rigorous weather. Nothing was done in the matter for a whole week, after which as no tidings reached me as to permission to remove the coals, I wrote to the goods manager at Derby, who then sent a telegram conveying leave to unload. Now, can any readers inform me if the Midland Railway Company have any right to prevent the unloading of coals (more then any other species of goods) consigned to any person, when they have reached their destination? This company has always possessed the reputation in the eyes of the public of being a very accommodating company, but the above specimen of their behaviour is calculated very speedily to disabuse people's minds of such a notion. This is not a solitary instance, for I have heard of similar complaints being made, and I cannot but think it bad policy on the part of the company, inasmuch as such treatment will inevitably drive people to procure their coals elsewhere. I have ,on several former occasions had coals conveyed to stations on the line of either companies, who readily afford every facility for their immediate removal.

I am, dear sir, yours truly,

Thomas Hutton, Soulby, Brough, Penrith.

Cumberland and Westmorland Advertiser, 9 January 1877

TRAINS SNOWED UP ON THE SETTLE LINE

The Pullman express and the night express due at Sheffield at 12-30 and 4 o'clock respectively on Thursday morning arrived at 10 a.m., joined together, having with a number of other trains, been stuck fast in various snow drifts. The worst of these was at a bleak place called Rose Hill, on the Settle and Carlisle section. At this place the tremendous gale drifted the snow on Wednesday to a depth of fifteen feet or more. The 5-20 p.m. train from Carlisle on Wednesday ran into this and stuck fast, the snow being carriage high. The telegraph wires, including those working the block system, being broken down, great alarm existed lest the other trains should run into this, but by dint of careful working accidents were averted. The 4 p.m. from Glasgow and Edinburgh and the night Pullman also got fast. The passengers state that the snowfall and the violence of the gale were tremendous. They say the wires were everywhere down, and that for miles at a stretch the country was under water.

Penrith Observer, 9 January 1877

SMARDALE VIADUCT MIDLAND RAILWAY

We understand that the foundations of this splendid viaduct are in such a state that the structure is being watched day and night.

Penrith Observer, 16 January 1877

SMARDALE VIADUCT

We are requested to state that a Kirkby Stephen correspondent was in error in stating that the foundation of this viaduct had given way. The viaduct is quite safe, and in no way dangerous.

Northwich Guardian, 27 January 1877

SERIOUS ACCIDENT ON THE SETTLE AND CARLISLE RAILWAY

A serious accident occurred on Tuesday morning on the Settle and Carlisle Railway, resulting in an immense destruction of rolling stock and considerable injuries to an engine driver, guard, and stoker. By some means part of a heavily-laden goods train became detached, and, running into the other part with great violence, threw a dozen wagons off the rails shivering them into splinters. Large quantities of valuable goods were thrown on the permanent way. The driver was fearfully shaken and slightly cut, and the guard and stoker less seriously.

Penrith Observer, 30 January 1877

ACCIDENT ON THE SETTLE AND CARLISLE RAILWAY
SAD DEATH OF AN OLD MAN

On Saturday afternoon an inquest was held at the railway station, Newbiggin, near Temple Sowerby, before Geo. R. Thompson, Esq., coroner, on the body of Samuel Stanfield, an old man 66 years of age, who was employed as night watchman at Hale Bank Cutting. He was on his way to the place to resume his duties when he was caught by the 5-50 express train, when about 100 yards from the hut in which he watched the embankment, and killed.

Richard Metcalfe deposed. I am a farm servant living at Black Lesses. Last night (Friday), about 8 o'clock. I and Stephen Eggleston went up the Midland Railway to keep the deceased company for half and hour or so. he was engaged watching a slip in a cutting on the line, about a mile south of Newbiggin Station. When we got about 100 yards of the place we found him lying on the right hand side (south), clear of the rails. He was dead and cold. His stick was broken and lying by his side, and his lantern was

Many of the Settle and Carlisle tunnels were lined with brick as at Barron Wood in February 1877.
In this photograph of Saunderton tunnel around 1902, brick lining is taking place.
Photograph courtesy of Leicestershire Archives.

close by. They did not remove the body, but returned home and told Mr Burne, who immediately went with assistants and removed deceased to Newbiggin Railway Station. Deceased's left arm and right leg were broken. He had apparently been struck by the express, which passes the station at 5-50 pm.

Thomas Stanfield, son of the deceased, said his father had been employed as night watchman at the Hale Cutting since about July last. On the day of his death he left his home at Culgaith about 5 o'clock, to attend his duties. He was 66 years of age. The coroner commented on the fact of employing as railway night watchman an old man between 60 and 70 years of age.

The jury returned a verdict of 'Accidental death.' Deceased was an old and respected inhabitant of Culgaith, of steady and industrious habits.

The Penrith Herald, 3 Febuary 1877

SERIOUS ACCIDENT IN BARRON WOOD TUNNEL

On Tuesday morning an accident of a somewhat serious and alarming character occurred in one of the tunnels on the Settle and Carlisle Railway at Barron Wood, near Armathwaite. It has been thought advisable to case the tunnel with brick, and about a hundred men were employed at the work on scaffolds. Eight of the men were boring a hole in the rock for the purpose of blasting, when the cross pieces gave way and the scaffold fell, carrying with it to the ground six of the men who were upon it. Of these, four were thought to be so seriously injured that they were carried to the Carlisle Infirmary, but when they arrived there one was so little worse that his wounds were dressed, and he was allowed to depart. The other three remained. Two of them reside in Carlisle and the other at Settle. And one of them named Barnes is dangerously wounded, through his injuries are not necessarily mortal. Nearly all the timbers fell upon him, and though none of his limbs are broken it is feared his brain is hurt. The other two are less injured.

The *Penrith Observer* (6 February) named the injured men as, Irving and Arthur Barnes, one living in Botchergate and the other in Newtown, Carlisle, and William Rogers of Settle. A similar report in the *Nottinghamshire Guardian* of 2 February explains that the men were carrying out repair work to the November roof fall.

Cumberland and Westmorland Advertiser, 3 April 1877

THE MIDLAND RAILWAY

On Thursday last 400 men, chiefly ballast and rough gangs, were paid off from the Long Marton and Hawes Junction section. On the same day five wagons of a goods train were thrown off the rails near Hawes by the breaking of an axle, and the Pullman express was delayed for a considerable time.

Cumberland and Westmorland Advertiser, 17 April 1877

THE PULLMAN EXPRESS IN PERIL

On Saturday about two p.m. the Pullman express from Edinburgh to London was saved by the prompt application of the Westinghouse brake from a serious accident. On emerging from a tunnel on the Settle and Carlisle Railway, a broken down goods train was observed across the rails, and the driver had just time to pull up before reaching the damaged wagons.

Penrith Observer, 8 May 1877

NARROW ESCAPE OF A PULMAN TRAIN AT APPLEBY

On Friday last the up Pullman train, on the Midland line, which passes through Appleby about 1 a.m., had a narrow escape from what might have been a very serious catastrophe. On nearing the signal box at the northern junction with the North Eastern line the signalman on duty noticed a peculiar sound in the revolution of the wheels as the train passed by, and observed that one end of a Pullman car was leaning to one side. He at once telegraphed to the south junction to stop the train, and it was brought to a stand still with in forty yards after the appearance of the signal. On examining the train it was found that one of the wheels of a Pullman car was broken. Most of the passengers were in bed and asleep. After considerable delay the car was detached, and the other portion of the train proceeded on its journey. Had it not been for the promptitude displayed by the signalman an accident of a very serious nature might have resulted.

Penrith Observer, 22 May 1877

THE LATE NARROW ESCAPE OF A PULMAN TRAIN AT APPLEBY

The signalman through whose promptitude a Midland Pullman train was saved at Appleby, as detailed in our last week's issue, is Joseph Herbert, a well conducted and respectable man, who has been some years in the company's service. He has been highly complimented on all hands for his quickness of decision in stopping the train; and it is thought the company will recognise his vigilance by some substantial token of reward.

The Penrith Herald, 26 May 1877

FATAL ACCIDENT AT MOORCOCK

On Monday last, a young man named Rankin was killed on the Midland Railway at Moorcock. Whilst standing on the line he was knocked down and run over by two earth wagons which approached him unawares. An inquest was held on Wednesday, and a verdict of accidental death returned.

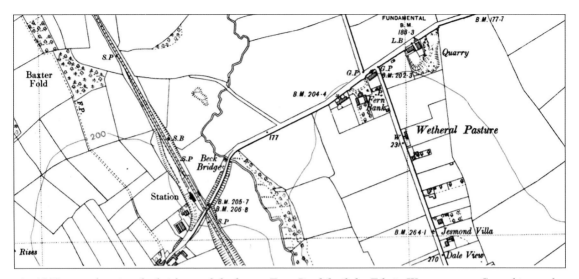

An 1898 map showing the bridge and the house Fern Bank built by Edwin Westerman at Cumwhinton described in October 1877 news report.

The work at Moorcock was being carried out on the Hawes extension, Contract No5. The resident engineer was Edward Newcome the contractor was Benton and Woodiwiss and the contractors agent was James Hay.

The Penrith Herald, 22 September 1877

THE RAILWAY ACCIDENT AT LAZONBY: THE COMPANY CENSURED

The enquiry touching the death of Mary Ann Matherson, 50 years of age, of Great Salkeld, near Penrith who sustained a fatal accident on the Midland Railway at Lazonby, on the 11th inst., was resumed before Dr Elliott, at the Cumberland Infirmary, on Monday. Mr Watson, of the firm of Messrs Dobinson and Watson, solicitors, Carlisle, attended on behalf of the representatives of the deceased, and Mr Young from the office of Messrs Beale, Marigold, and Beale, solicitors of Birmingham, watched the proceedings on behalf of the Midland Railway Company.

The examination and re-examination of witnesses lasted from two o'clock till about eight o'clock in the evening. As reported last week, the deceased travelled from Langwathby to Manchester by an excursion train, and on the return journey, according to the evidence of one of the railway officials with whom she conversed after the accident, she had slept a little, and passed the station at which she had intended to leave the train. On arriving at Lazonby, she attempted to get out of the carriage, but owing to some unexplained circumstance, she missed her footing and fell, and was crushed so severely by the train, which happened at the time to be moving away, that she succumbed the same day at the Cumberland Infirmary, whither she had been conveyed a short time after the accident.

The main question to which the jury's attention was directed was, as put by Mr Watson, whether deceased met her death by simple accident, or through the negligence of the railway company's servants. Miss Little, of Lazonby, said she saw the deceased on the foot board of a carriage at the latter end of the train, and her brother shouted to the porter when the poor women fell. There were three guards in charge of the train, and before it moved off, one of them, as usual, not seeing anything wrong gave the signal that all was right to the driver.

Joseph Garlick, porter at Lazonby, who at the time was acting as ticket collector, did not see any of the carriage doors open when the train moved off. When he lifted the woman up after the accident, she said, 'Oh, my poor bairns; oh that I had sat quietly in the train.' Mr Wescott, station master at Lazonby, stated that deceased, when carried into the station, was perfectly conscious, and told him that it was through her own fault that the accident occurred. The jury returned a verdict to the effect that deceased met with her death by falling from the footboard of a carriage in motion, and that her death was the result of negligence on the part of the railway company.

The Manchester Guardian, 5 October 1877

The following story is a court case concerning fraud perpetrated against the Midland Railway Company on the Settle and Carlisle line. As interesting as the case is, it also provides us with an insight into the organisation and operation of the Midland Railway in the 1870s. Edwin Westerman was appointed Superintendant of the Settle and Carlisle Railway at £180 per annum on the 15 January 1876. At the same time the Midland Railway Way and Works Committee took over contracts 1 and 3, and the whole of Bayliss's contracts along with the work men, their tools and huts.

Edwin Westerman, superintendent of permanent way on the Midland Railway, who lives at Wetheral, near Carlisle; Thomas Herrick, who lives on the same line, at Scotby, between Carlisle and Wetheral; John Lambert, station master at Cumwhinton, on the Midland Railway; and G. M. Tickle, brick maker and contractor Maryport, were brought before the magistrates at Carlisle yesterday, on charges arising out of recent discoveries made by the directors of the Midland Railway Company as to a series of frauds upon the company. Westerman was charged with stealing 4,000 bricks, the property of the Midland Railway Company, on the 29th of June last. Lambert was charged with aiding and abetting the fraud. Tickle was charged with stealing 5,000 bricks, the property of the company, and Lambert with aiding and abetting. Herrick was charged with stealing a large quantity of wood and 1,000 stones of hay all the property of the company.

Mr Beale and Mr Young (solicitors) appeared for the prosecution. Mr Bendle, Carlisle, defended Lambert; Mr Rannop, Carlisle, defended Westerman; Mr Errington, Carlisle, defended Herrick and Mr Tyson of Maryport, defended Tickle. An application was made to admit the prisoners to bail Mr Beale opposed it. He said that Westerman had made a clean breast of the whole thing and he was there now on his own confession. With regard the other prisoners, evidence had to be given against them by men working under them and also documentary testimony of subordinate officials, and it would be most dangerous to allow them to be out, where they must meet the persons who had to give evidence against them. The bench, after a short consultation decided to admit Tickle to bail of £200 Herrick to bail £50 they refused bail in the other cases.

FACTS OF THE CASE

Westerman recently built him self a house in the country at Wetheral, and one of the cases out of which the charges arise is with reference to the materials with which the house was built.

The facts of the case gleaned by our reporter (*Sheffield Telegraph*) who proceeded to Derby yesterday… ascertained that some days ago it became known to those who manage the Midland system that materials such as timber, bricks, etc. was being removed from the station of Cumwhinton on the Settle and Carlisle extension by certain of the employees, and was being used by them in the erection of houses with which the company had nothing whatever to do. Steps were at once taken to ascertain the extent to which the robbery had extended. An investigation committee held its sittings and on hearing the circumstances suspended one official, who is an inspector of permanent way in the locality where the depredations were committed…

One of the officials is said to have been building a house in doing which he used some of the company's bricks, and not even paid for the transport of others. It is stated that several other houses have been built with materials belonging to the company, but these can be taken possession of by the company, to whom the actual loss cannot be very serious.

The Manchester Guardian, 16 October 1877

THE CASE CONTINUES

The frauds on the Midland Railway Company:– At Carlisle yesterday, George Mason Tickle, Edwin Westerman, and Thomas Errick were again before magistrates on the charge of stealing a large number of bricks, some wheel barrows, wooden staging and other articles, the property of the Midland Railway Company. From the additional evidence given, it seemed that when Westerman was arrested he said he had been expecting the police officer, and inquired if Tickle was in custody, and if any proceedings were to be taken against Tickle's brother. In Errick's (permanent way inspector) possession was found a memorandum written by Westerman absolving him from all blame, saying that what he had done in any way had been to screen Westerman and Tickle, The prisoners reserved their defence and were committed to trail at the Manchester assizes.

HOUSE AND BRIDGE

A second case was then gone into. This was a charge against Westerman, Errick, and Lambert, station master at Cumwhiton, of conspiracy to defraud the company. Some time ago it seems the prisoner Westerman was building a house in the neighbourhood of Cumwhinton Station, and the counsel for the prosecution said he would show that a large quantity of bricks used in the construction of the house and stables and outhouses were brought from Armathwaite Station, where they had been sent for the purposes of the Barron Wood Tunnel; also that a large amount of stone was brought from Lazonby quarry and used for the purpose of building a bridge on the road between Westerman's house and Cumwhinton Station. The case of the bridge was extremely singular, because, except the advantage Westerman might have gained from having a handsome bridge and fine road between his house and the station, and position it gave him in the neighbourhood for having got the work done, he did not seem to have got any personal benefit.

As a matter of fact however, many hundreds of tons of the company stone and many hundreds of pounds of the company money had been expended on the bridge. All the bricks and stone for Westerman's house and the bridge were brought to Cumwhinton from Lazonby and Armathwaite on ballast trains, and carted from the station. As Lambert had control over the station, the prosecution contended that he must have connived at these frauds. Errick also joined the frauds, and drew into his own pocket the money which ought to have gone to the company for carting those very goods from the station to Westerman's house. It seemed that Errick has two horses, and made a contract with himself to do this work for the company, using the name of Thomas Bamford, and regularly drew the pay, signing for it 'Thomas Bamford' who, he said, had given him authority to do so. In order to shut Lambert's mouth regarding these transactions he was allowed a share in them. It seemed that he made a contract with Tickle to deliver coal at the brickyard, and, with the cognisance of Westerman and Errick he used the company's ballast trains to carry them free, and so make his profit the greater. The prisoners were committed for trial.

Carlisle Journal, 2 November 1877

FARM IN THE VALE OF EDEN TO LET

To be LET, on LEASE, with Entry at Candlemas next, BARON WOOD FARM, in the Parish of Lazonby and County of Cumberland; 7 Miles from Penrith ,and 11 from Carlisle.

The holding comprises 1,564 acres, of which about 350 Acres are Arable, and the remainder Pasture and sheep-walk. By the aid of steam, however, much of the latter might be advantageously broken up. The farm adjoins the River Eden; is intersected by the Settle and Carlisle Railway; is only 1½ miles from Armathwaite Station on that line; and has the benefit of a private siding convenient to the homestead. A good dwelling house and additional farm buildings, were erected in 1862.

For particulars apply to Mr T Bowstead, Land Agent, Edenhall, near Penrith.

A NEW RAILWAY TO SCOTLAND

The Manchester Guardian, 14 November 1877

THE TRIAL: THE ENGINEER

Mr Higgins (QC) said the transactions which were to be investigated occurred upon that part of the Midland system which lay between Settle and Carlisle and more particularly within a few miles of Carlisle. The permanent way of the Midland system was under the charge of a chief engineer and two assistants and two divisional engineers whose head-quarters were at Derby. The line was divided by an imaginary line at Derby, and the two divisional engineers, one took the section north of that place and the other the section south of Derby. After the sub-engineer, the entire control of the permanent way of the Settle and Carlisle portion on the northern division of the line was in the hand of the superintendant, who was the prisoner Westerman. The next officer under the superintendant was the inspector, and upon the length of the line between Settle and Carlisle there were four or five inspectors. The prisoner Errick was one of them and it was within the length of the line under his charge from Carlisle to Newbiggin that all the transactions which were the subject made against the prisoner took place.

THE STATION MASTER

The other officer of the company, Lambert was the station master at Cumwhinton Station. He was allowed by the company to combine the business of a coal dealer with his work as station master, and the charge against him was that serving coal from his yard at Cumwhinton Station to Tickle's brickyard, he took the opportunity, instead of sending them by the regular money earning goods train of the company to send them by the ballast trains, and so defraud the company of this freight. There was one matter for consideration however in respect to this charge against Lambert. It was believed that the coal came from the North that was some of the Cumberland collieries and that they were sent to Lambert upon the Midland line from Carlisle.

If it turned out that the carriage from Carlisle to Tickle's brickyard near Cumwhinton by the ordinary goods train of the company was the same as the carriage from Carlisle to Cumwhinton, then it would appear that the company had not been defrauded out of this freight of the coal. But if that were so there would still remain this charge that if the other three prisoners or two of them had been guilty of conspiring together to cheat and defraud the company it was almost impossible that Lambert did not know of all that was taking place. The plan of the line that was put in showed near Cumwhinton Station a house which was now almost completed.

The jury would be asked to come to the conclusion that the house was built by Westerman out of materials and with labour belonging to the company and for which the company never received a single penny, it was a house which would let for some £60 or £70 a year and the real charge against Westerman was that he along with others conspired together to obtain goods, materials, and labour for the purpose of building the house without payment to the company. In addition to building this house Westerman, in order to improve the approaches to the house, raised a bridge that crossed a beck constructed considerable earth works and large and heavy retaining walls thus getting rid of a disagreeable dip in the road, and bringing the road up to something like level. All this was done with materials and labour belonging to the company and with out payment to them.

BRICKS SAND AND MORTAR

Further south from Carlisle the plan showed the brickyard rented from the company by Tickle and beyond this place still continuing south two stations Armathwaite and Lazonby. At Lazonby the company discovered a very valuable bed of sand which led them to erect a mortar mill for the purpose of grinding and manufacturing mortar for the railway works. Armathwaite, where they had sidings was a depot for the very large quantities of bricks sent there for the purpose of lining the tunnel which was in the immediate neighbourhood, so that within a short distance of Tickle's brickyard were both mortar and bricks ready to hand belonging to the company.

With reference to the brickyard he should explain that it was used by the company when they were constructing their line, but that on the 1st January last it had been disused for some time previously, there were no kilns or drying sheds upon it and no apparatus whatsoever for carrying out the business of brick making. In that month however the prisoner Tickle entered into an agreement with the Midland Company, whereby he became the tenant of the brickyard and commenced the business of brick and tile making under the style of the Cumwhinton Brick and Tile Company. Considering the state of the yard when the agreement was signed one of the first things to be done was to get the necessary materials for making floors or flats and the jury would find that Tickle applied to the company for certain quantities of sand from their sand hill at Lazonby for the purpose of making those flats. The sand was supplied and charged to him at the rate of 10s per wagon or truck load and the money was paid. That sand, a steam engine, and a mill for grinding up the clay were the only things which entered the yard that Tickle ever paid for, the other materials necessary in brick making were taken from the railway company.

HORSES AND FODDER

The jury would have from the indictment that there was also a charge of stealing hay, it was the duty of Westerman and Errick to send in returns to the company chief officers at Derby of the quantities of grass taken from the slopes of the line, and of the moneys for which it was sold. If any of the grass was not sold but was made into hay, the proper practice for the prisoners to have pursued, was to send it down the line to Carlisle, where it would meet with a ready market. The jury would however find that a quantity of hay was not sent down to Carlisle, but was stacked at Scotby upon land which was rented by Errick, and upon another piece of land occupied of the company by Westerman at Lazonby. Then again as to certain charges illegally made for the service of horses, it would be shown that Westermen and Errick had horses of their own, and by pretending sometimes that the horses belonged to the company and at other times stating the real fact that the horses were their own, they were able to get pay for work which it was alleged was done, but never done at all. In conclusion it might be asked how was all this done?

WESTERMAN'S HOUSE

How could Westermen build a large house with materials and labour of the railway company without the knowledge of his brother officials. The jury would find that the whole of these things had been accomplished through the service of ballast trains of which Westerman and Errick had the control. The ballast trains, conveyed the materials which went to build Westerman's house, to raise the bridge and to furnish Tickle's brickyard. Westerman and Errick and Tickle were all of them in at this, and it was by Westerman's order with the knowledge of Tickle and Errick that from time to time the ballast trains coming from Armathwaite, from Lazonby, and from Carlisle, stopped at the brickyard at Howe's sidings, and at other places, when there was no occasion to stop there for any legitimate purpose of the company that men were carried by the ballast trains without their paying fares, and that the trains were stopped and bricks taken from Armathwaite were thrown into the brickyard and at a spot convenient for their removal to the site of Westerman's house.

BUILDING MATERIALS

In the course of evidence it was stated that the prisoner Errick, as an inspector, would be bound to obey orders of Westerman. He would however be expected to report any improper order that might be given him. The guard of a ballast train stated that in March and April last, he delivered at Tickle's brickyard about seventeen truckloads of bricks and several wagons of mortar, the former coming from Armathwaite and the mortar from Lazonby. He also took to Tickle's brickyard a wagon load of wheelbarrows which had been put on his train at Carlisle. He had orders from Westerman for conveyance of these materials. In January, March and April he likewise took six truck loads of bricks from Barron Wood to Cumwhinton, and in April and May he took fifteen trucks of coal from Cumwhinton to Tickle's brickyard. The coal trucks were unloaded by men travelling with the ballast train, and they were removed from Cumwhinton by orders of the prisoner Lambert. In the first instance, having no right to take orders from

Lambert, the guard of the ballast train refused to remove the coal, but Lambert having stated that he had Westerman's authority to send them, the guard gave way and took them.

THE TICKLE BROTHERS

It was further shown that the gentlemen at the time of these alleged frauds, occupying the position of divisional engineer of the northern section of the line, was a Mr Tickle, brother of the prisoner Tickle, and that Mr Tickle, the engineer, had been seen at his brother's brickyard giving orders for the delivery of machinery from the ballast train, when Errick was present. On the occasion in question, Mr Tickle the engineer directed that the breakdown crane from the locomotive department of the company should be used in unloading the machinery, and this was done. At divers times the ballast train made a special run from Carlisle to Cumwhinton, and visa versa, to convey the prisoner Tickle to and from his brickyard and it was stated that on two occasions his brick makers had been conveyed to and from their work in the same way. The evidence of the guard of a second ballast train went to show that at different times, in the first half of the present year, large quantities of bricks, timber, sleepers, stone and rubble amounting to some scores of truck loads, were removed from different parts of the Settle and Carlisle line by the ballast train service to Cumwhinton Station.

Manchester Guardian, 15 November 1877

FURTHER EVIDENCE

In continuing his evidence, the witness Bryce said that on the 26 July the ballast train of which he was the guard, worked between Newbiggin and Lazonby when the ganger and his men collected twelve truck loads of hay which had been cut upon the slopes of the railway. The hay was taken to Lazonby siding, which was bordered by Westerman's land. On the 27 July fifteen truck loads of hay were taken by ballast train from the railway slopes between Cumwhinton and Little Salkeld. Thirteen of the loads were left at Lazonby siding and two at Scotby, where the prisoner Errick occupied some land. Subsequently witness saw Errick with two horses and carts carrying the hay from the company's premises to his own. Witness had taken large quantities of rubble and dressed stone to Cumwhinton from various depots and quarries belonging to the company. The rubble was utilised for making his road leading to the house which was being erected by Westerman near the Cumwhiton Station, and also for raising a bridge over the adjoining beck. Among the stone was a quantity of kerbstones, which were used for edges of footpaths and for the tops of walls.

EVIDENCE OF CHARLES SIMMS

Charles Simms, ganger of the ballast train of which the last witness was guard, said that large quantities of the stone and timber were conveyed to Cumwhiton by the ballast train were so taken by the orders of the prisoner Westerman. Of the hay which was taken to Cumwhiton, two stacks were built upon Westerman's land.

EVIDENCE OF JAMES WITHERINGTON

James Witherington a brick maker living at Kingstown, said he was formerly foreman to the prisoner Tickle at his brickyard near Cumwhiton, he began to make bricks by hand for Tickle some time in March last. Two or three days after he went to work for Tickle a drying shed was erected of timber, bricks and slates. The bricks came by ballast train on the Midland Railway both from Armathwaite and Carlisle. He did not know how many there were but they would number at least 20,000. An office was built but not with the company's bricks, firebricks being used. The company's joiners were employed to put the roof on the shed, the timber which made the staging over the clayhole came by ballast train from Armathwaite, and to the best of witness knowledge, the mortar which was used came ready made by ballast train from Armathwaite. The men employed in the erection of the shed, etc., came from Cumwhinton by the company's workman's train. About a week after witness entered the employ of Tickle, sixteen new barrows came by the ballast train and they were in use in Tickle's yard when witness left. On one occasion Tickle complained that the brickyard was costing a good deal of money. Witness remarked that it had not cost a great deal yet as, he got a good deal of the worked done for nothing. Tickle thereupon replied that he had heard the company's men saying so. A week after that Tickle found fault with witness's brick making, and discharged him. Tickle had never made a complaint before.

EVIDENCE OF ISAAC DELVRIDGE

Isaac Delvridge a foreman mason in the employ of the Midland Railway residing at Cumwhiton, said about Whitsuntide he was building a brick kiln at Tickle's yard. Witness was living at Carlisle then, and received a message. He subsequently saw Tickle at Westerman's office, and Westerman told him that Tickle wanted him to go as soon as he could get the men together and on the following day he got together a dozen or fifteen men and went to Tickle's yard. The men's time was entered in the company's books and they were paid by the company. Tickle was present while the kiln was in course of erection. About four of the company's men under the control of witness, were also employed for a month or six weeks in the erection of Westerman's house near Cumwhiton Station.

EVIDENCE OF JOHN GIGGLESWICK

John Giggleswick, said he was a carpenter, and worked for the Midland Railway Company. In March eighteen wheelbarrows were made at the company's works at Settle. When they were finished, he saw them placed upon a railway truck and he had since seen them at Tickle's brickyard at Cumwhiton fifteen wheelbarrows having wheels which he himself had constructed at Settle. He had also made in the company's workshop at Settle hutches which were used for keeping the rain off newly made bricks, and he afterwards saw some of them in the brickyard at Cumwhinton. More than twenty hutches were made at the works.

EVIDENCE OF THOMAS OSBORNE

Thomas Osborne a bricklayer, in the employ of the Midland Railway Company, said that about March last he with a number of workmen were engaged in altering a wall and road in front of Westerman's new house at Cumwhinton. They did the work by the orders of Westerman, and were employed about twelve week. About 400 wagon loads of rubble were employed. A stone wall along the side of the road near the bridge 70 yards long and fifteen feet high, six foot broad at the bottom and tapering towards the top was also constructed. A large quantity of stone was used. Witness had seen building materials being carted from the railway to the house which Westerman was erecting.

Mr Materson (defence), The road where we made the bridge was in very bad condition and the works constituted a great improvement. The road which led to the bridge in front of Westerman's new house, had been made steeper by the erection of the railway bridge, before I and the other men received orders to improve it.

EVIDENCE OF JOSEPH MARKLAND

Joseph Markland a clerk in the office of the prisoner Westerman said he received his orders from Westerman. If goods were sold by the company, an order for the delivery of such goods would come to witness through the engineers department at Derby, and it would then be sent to the inspector of the district. Witness kept an invoice book and in that he entered the names of persons to whom the goods were sold. Witness also kept the locomotive book, which ought to show the work done by the ballast engine. There were no entries concerning the work at the brick yard in that book. With respect to that work he received instructions from Westerman not to enter any work done there by ballast engines, and he carried out those instructions. He received similar instructions with regard to the stone and other materials sent to Cumwhition Station.

Manchester Guardian, 16 November 1877

GUARDS AND LOCOMOTIVE RECORDS

Mr Beal solicitor to the Midland Railway company said on the previous evening he compared the locomotive power book and the guards journal. The locomotive power book ought to contain every item contained in the guards journal, but the entries which referred to the taking of materials to the brickyard were not transferred to the locomotive book. There were only a few entries as regarded the things taken to Cumwhinton Station. Markland recalled, said in reply to the judge, that the locomotive power book was entirely in his handwriting. Looking at the guards book for 31 May he found an entry, sixteen wagons of stone from Lazonby Quarry to Cumwhinton. In the locomotive book relating to the same entry, under the head of remarks appeared the words stone for wall. Witness said he did not know why he entered these words. In the guards journal under date 21 June there was an entry. Two wagons of stone from Lazonby Quarry to Cumwhinton and two wagons of sand detached at Cumwhinton. In the book which witness kept, it was entered. Four wagons of stone from Barron Wood to Cumwhinton. With the words 'stone for siding'. He did not know if he turned two wagons of sand, with two of stone, and added the words 'for sidings' he could not remember.

The judge called attention to two other entries for fourteen loads of stone, when the guards book said twelve wagons of stone, and two of mortar. Witness: I did it because it would be easier to copy into the book, it would make less entries. In answer to further questions the witness said, that Mr Westerman came frequently to his office but did not look at the book that had just been referred to. James Eite a clerk in the office kept the time books relating to the work of the gangers by the ballast train. When the gangers did not state upon what work they had been employed, witness took his instructions as to how he should make the entry from Herrick. He had made no charge in the books for work done at the brickyard, because he had received no instruction to do so. He had made no entries as to work done at Westerman's house or at the bridge leading to the house. There were entries relating to the approach roads. On one occasion witness asked Herrick, if anything was to be charged for the bridge, and he answered not this week. Witness made no entry as to hay cut along the line it was not his province.

GOODS INVOICES

Walter Frith, agent for the Midland Company at Carlisle, gave evidence as to the payment to Herrick of certain sums of money due to persons named Bamford and Butler for horse hire. Receipts were given with the money and Herrick returned them receipted in the usual way the following week. Henry Loveday, chief inspector of the traffic department of the Midland Railway said the prisoner Lambert was station master at Cumwhinton. The station masters of the Midland line were under the traffic department. When any goods arrived at the station it would be his duty to take care that he had an invoice with such goods. With regards to goods arriving by ballast train there was no provision for dealing with them by the traffic department, because goods arriving by these trains would only be for the company's use, it would be very irregular that large quantities of stone, timber, sand, mortar etc., should come by ballast train to Cumwhinton Station unless for the company's work, and if any goods came that way not for the company it would be Lambert's duty to report it to the goods manager, and to take any steps he might consider proper. The road leading from the station to Westerman's house could be seen from the station, and if goods were carried to Westerman's house from Cumwhinton Station, the station master must have seen it.

THE QUESTION OF COAL

On the 22 September witness went to Cumwhiton Station and spoke to Lambert about investigating the matter, with regard to the question of the coal. Lambert told him that he had supplied coal to Tickle, being allowed by the company to sell coal as a private trader and a great part of the coal, not all of it, had been taken from Cumwhiton Station to the brickyard by ballast train. He said the coal supplied by him was about 353 tons and that when he arranged to supply coal to Tickle, Tickle told him if he saw Westerman he would arrange to take it from the station to the brickyard and have it unloaded. In consequence of that Lambert saw Westerman and the arrangement was made.

The witness asked Lambert why he had allowed the irregularities to go on, and whether it was for any profit he might make in selling the coal. Lambert denied making any profit, and that it was in consequence of the position of the parties concerned that he had not reported the irregularities. He further told the witness of the houses Westerman was building, one large house, and two small cottages, and said that large quantities of stone had been received by ballast train and had been carried from the station to Westerman's ground by the same horses and carts that were used for the works in connection with the railway. Some bricks had, he said, arrived in Caledonian wagons for Westermam without an invoice, and he had reported the circumstances to Derby.

He explained that it was in consequence of complaint at the wrong sending of wagons, which had been made through the railway clearing house. He also said he had had a conversation with Herrick and Westerman at Cumwhiton Station, when Westerman wished to have the wagon number book recopied out, leaving out the numbers of the wagons which had brought materials to his house. Lambert declined to have anything to do with recopying the book. Westerman later denied asking for the book to be recopied. Westerman wrote to the chief engineer at Derby offering to pay for materials for his house, and blamed Tickle for his being involved in the fraud.

LAMBERT AND HERRICK

Mr Mattinson defending Herrick said I believe he had been 31 years in the service of the company and nothing was known against his character up to the present transaction. Lambert had been 9½ years in the passenger department, and previous to that in the goods department, and had been a good character. Several witnesses gave evidence of having been employed in carting materials from the station to Westerman's house in the course of erection, and were paid at the expense of the company.

Mr Johnson chief engineer of the Midland Railway, living in Derby, said in the spring of last year the tunnel at Barron Wood was being lined with bricks, the bricks for the purpose being sent from Armathwaite, he had never given authority for the sale of mortar from Lazonby mill or of wheelbarrows or other articles, the company never sold things of that kind. It was never known until the investigation that the company's men were employed at the Cumwhinton brickyard, it was the duty of Herrick as the inspector to know what the men were doing along that part of the line, and to have entered the work in his time book. The witness said that he was not aware that Westerman returned 30,000 bricks to the company in lieu of those he had used in the construction of his house. The jury addressing the judge said that they were of the opinion that there was no case against Lambert. The judge said he has been guilty of great irregularities but that was not a crime and Lambert was discharged.

Manchester Guardian, 17 November 1877

THE VERDICT

The day was spent summing up the case. The main points being:- Mr Ambrose QC., defending Tickle, addressed the jury, reminding them that Tickle was not a servant of the company, and was making bricks for the tunnel at cost price and should be found innocent. Then Mr Mattinson, defending Herrick, addressed the jury. Herrick did not order the bricks and mortar to be taken to the brick yard, or any workmen to work at the brickyard. He was under orders from his superior Westerman. He did not report the materials being used in building the house, as there was no rule that he should make a report. The jury retired to consider their verdicts, returning into court with a verdict of guilty against each of the prisoners, but recommended Herrick to mercy. The judge summed up, and gave Westerman, eleven months in prison as he had already served a month. Tickle, to twelve months in prison and Herrick, six months in prison.

This item was found in the *Nottingham Journal* dated 21 August 1882 regarding Edwin Westerman:-

All persons who have any claim against the estate of Edwin Westerman, who sailed on the *Drummond Castle* to South Africa and who was formally permanent way inspector from Peterborough to Lynn, Nottingham, and Mansfield, Erewash Valley, and latterly Superintendent on the Settle and Carlisle Railway are particularly requested to send their name to his wife, Louisa Westerman, Milliner and Draper, 36 Arkwright Street, and if correct, will be paid forthwith, and all parties owing money to the said Edwin Westerman's estate will please pay his wife Louisa Westermen.

It appears from the 1882 shipping news that the *Drummond Castle* was quarantined on its outward voyage in February and May due to an outbreak of small pox?

In the 1884 *Bulmers Directory* the Cumwhinton Brick & Tile Works was owned by Thomas Hamilton, who later changed their name to Messrs Wright in 1918. Their private siding is shown on the Midland Railway map as an extension of the northerly head shunt of the Howe & Co siding they were eventually taken out of service in 1924. Bulmer also gives William Stowell as station master at Cumwhinton.

Penrith Observer, 6 November 1877

FATAL ACCIDENT ON THE MIDLAND RAILWAY

On Friday last an inquest was held at Crow Hill near Appleby, before G. R. Thompson, Esq., coroner on the body of William Sutton, a driller on the Midland Railway. From the evidence adducted it appears that deceased had left work at the ordinary hour on Wednesday evening and proceeded homewards along the railway. The driver of the express train, which leaves Carlisle at 12-10 a.m., stopped at Crosby Garrett and informed a signalman that a man was lying on the side of the line, north of Griseburn. He roused up the station master, who proceeded to the spot indicated, and found the deceased lying with his face downward, and quite dead.

On the arrival of the evening express at Carlisle, a coat, which was identified as belonging to deceased, was found hanging on one of the buffers of the engine; and it was conjectured that deceased, in getting out of the way of an approaching up goods train, had been knocked down by the express train running in the opposite direction, and killed instantaneously. The only mark of injury found on the body was a wound on the side of the head. Deceased was about 36 years of age, and had been employed on the line for 18 months. He was supposed to be a native of Cheshire but the railway officials were unable to discover any relative. The jury returned a verdict of 'Accidentally killed on the railway'.

Griseburn Viaduct has seven spans and is 142 yards long and 74 feet high over Potts Beck.

Chapter Ten
1878

*Lancaster Guardian,*2 January 1878

IMPORTANT ARBITRATION CASE: CRAGG v MIDLAND RAILWAY Co.

In this case Miss Ellen Cragg was the owner of a freehold estate at Deepdale, in Dent through which passes the new Settle and Carlisle railway abstraction the farm house, other buildings, and about five and a half acres of the best land. In addition to these, the owner claimed a large compensation for valuable strata of black marble, which was formerly worked by Mr Nixon. The surveyors for the parties not being able to agree, the case was referred to arbitration of Sir Henry A. Hunt, of London, the surveyor appointed by the board of trade, who lately held sittings at the Institute of Surveyors…

 Many professional experts brought forward in the interest of the claimant, valued the total compensation as high as £12,000…

 Others were of the opinion that from £1,300 to £1,500 would be a fair compensation, the main question being as to the value of the marble, which one witness thought worth £500 a year…

This navvy hut at Appleby was left by the contractors or was subsequently moved to this position after the Settle and Carlisle line was built. It has now been removed and rebuilt at Settle station. During the move an old 1878 newspaper was found pasted on the inside. This provides some conclusive evidence that it was used by navvies as contemporary reports describe hut interiors decorated with pasted up newspaper and magazine prints (photograph by Peter Robinson).

The result of the arbitration is that Sir Henry Hunt has awarded the sum of £1,800 as compensation.

John Blackmore was engineer for the Newcastle and Carlisle Railway, while at Carlisle Blackmore became friendly with contractor and architect Paul Nixon. His partner William Smith Denton was building major viaducts at Wetheral and Corby. Blackmore eventually married Paul's niece Ann Nixon. The ceremony took place on 22 December 1835 at Dent where the family had a marble works and which Paul had adopted as his retirement home.

Sir Arthur Hunt 1810-1889 was a civil engineer. Born in Westminster, Hunt trained as a surveyor before setting up his own civil engineering practice in 1828. Among the clients he worked for were a large number of railway companies, including The London Brighton and South Coast Railway the Eastern Counties and The Metropolitan Railway of London.

Cumberland and Westmorland Advertiser, 22 January 1878

FOG CLOSE SALE SPECIAL TRAIN ARRANGEMENTS

The Midland express leaving Carlisle at 5-35 p.m. will by request, stop at Lazonby, Appleby, and Kirkby Stephen, to-morrow evening, for the convenience of parties returning from Mr Relph's very important sale of farming stock.

The sale reported in the paper for 15 January 1878 was at Fog Close, Kirkoswald:
'Important Displenishing Sale Mr Joseph Relph who is declining farming, to sell by auction on Wednesday and Thursday 23 and 24 of January the entire herd of cattle, horses, sheep, swine, agricultural implements, dairy utensils and a portion of house hold furniture.'

Penrith Herald, 8 June 1878

RAILWAY EXTENTION

The new railway from Askrigg to Hawes was opened on Saturday. Four years ago the North Eastern Railway Company commenced the construction of a line from Leyburn to Hawes to connect the east coast route with the Settle and Carlisle section of the Midland Railway, and with the exception of four miles from Askrigg to Hawes it was opened last year. The line which is being made by the Midland Company from Moorcock, on the Settle and Carlisle section, to Hawes will not be ready for some time yet.

Penrith Herald, 6 July 1878

PROPOSED CONNECTION BETWEEN THE MIDLAND RAILWAY AND PENRITH

Last night a large and influential meeting, at which some of the leading professional men and tradesmen were present, was held in the Market Hall, Penrith, to take into consideration the proposal to form a railway from Penrith to some point of junction on the Midland Railway. John Jameson, Esq., J. P. Moorhouses, presides, and introduced the subject to the meeting, after which Mr Addison moved a resolution that a committee be formed to take steps for a survey for a line of railway between Penrith and Lazonby.

Mr J. Atkinson, of Winderwath, expressed the great interest he felt in the town and trade of Penrith. He had had a scheme under consideration, by which a line could advantageously be brought from a point on the Midland a little out of Langwathby on the Culgaith road, over the Eden, thence past Udford Wood, Woodside, Whinfell Park, Clifton Dykes, to Yanwath, and so into Penrith, either by an independent line or on the London and North Western. He did not, however, make a proposition in favour of any particular route, but recommended that a committee should be formed to take the matter in all its bearings into consideration. If Penrith was to flourish a line must be made.

Mr C. Fairer then proposed the following amendment: 'That it is expedient that a line of railway from Penrith to some point on the Midland Line be constructed, and that a committee be appointed to inquire and report to a future meeting on the best and most advantageous route for the proposed line, and that such committee be authorised to raise the necessary funds to employ a competent railway engineer to make a survey and to advise and assist the committee in carrying out the resolution; that such a committee be composed of the following gentlemen with power to add to their number: Hon. A. Erskine, John Jameson, James Atkinson, John Powley, W. B. Arnison, John Pattinson (Corn Market), W. Little, James Graham, T. G. Cant, Dr. Taylor, C. Fairer, R. B. Smith, Thomas Altham, J. R. Barron, and T. Bowstead.' Mr W. B. Arnison seconded the amendment, and strongly advocated the importance of some junction with the Midland in the interests of the town of Penrith, from which, he said, much traffic and business had been diverted to Carlisle.

Mr Nevison spoke in favour of some project being carried out, and concluded with the sensible suggestion that a subscription should be entered into on the spot to meet costs of all preliminary enquiries. Mr Addison spoke in favour of the Lazonby route in its engineering facilities, and more likely from its quarries to give a good return in traffic.

Mr George Watson questioned the engineering references made by Mr Addison, and stated that his own opinion had been that the most advantageous point of connection with the Midland was between Langwathby and Lazonby, just after the great engineering difficulty of crossing the Eden; from thence he would come by Great Salkeld to Halfway Well, and tunnel from thence to about Forest Hill.

The chairman then put the amendment and the resolution, when the former was carried by a large majority. A subscription was afterwards entered into, when about £600 was subscribed. A vote of thanks to the respected chairman brought the proceedings to a close.

> James Atkinson, Brewer, New Brewery, Middgate, Penrith
> John Powley, Penrith
> W. B. Arnison, Greenfield House, Scot Lane, Penrith
> John Pattinson, Corn Market, Grocer Tea Dealer, 2 Little Dockray, Penrith
> James Graham, Grocer, 6 and 7 Market Square, Penrith
> T. G. Cant, Solicitor, 28 South End Road, Penrith
> Dr. Michael Taylor, Hutton Hall.
> Christopher Fairer, Solicitor, 28 South End Road, Penrith
> Thomas Altham, Ironmonger, 22 Devonshire Street, Penrith
> William Nevison, Tobacconist, 9 Crown Square, Penrith. Snuff manufactures and Snuff mill, Maybrough House, Eamont Bridge.
> George Watson, 18 Wordworth Street, Architect & Surveyor, St Andrews Church Yard, Penrith
> W. Little, Abbots Bank, Friar Street, Penrith

Leeds Mercury, 2 August 1878

THE HAWES BRANCH

This line is now open for public traffic. About five o'clock yesterday afternoon a goods train left Hawes Junction, on the Settle and Carlisle Railway with a number of officials, for Hawes town, at which place it arrived about six o'clock. Shortly afterwards it left for the junction. Upon its arrival and departure the public did not show any demonstration, but seemed to look upon the matter as an everyday occurrence. This line is an extension of the Northallerton and Leyburn branch, to join the Midland Railway at Hawes Junction on the Settle and Carlisle Line. The construction of the line from Leyburn to within a short distance of Hawes Station has been carried out by the North Eastern Railway Company, and from that point to the junction the Midland Company have executed the work.

The line from Leyburn to Askrigg was opened for traffic on the 1st February last year; but on account of the Midland Company not having completed their part of the line approaching to Hawes Station, the portion from Askrigg to that place was only opened on the 1st of last June. The remainder of the line from Hawes town to the Junction, near to Moorcock, a distance of six miles, has been most difficult of construction, on account of the treacherous nature of the ground, the company having in many places to deviate from the original scheme, so as to avoid dangerous bogs. It has taken the company nearly seven years to complete this short distance.

The making of the North Eastern portion of the line, from Leyburn to Hawes, a distance of seventeen miles, has not been so difficult to construct. The formation of the country has been followed, the line winding along the foot of the hills, thus avoiding high embankments and deep cuttings. From Hawes, proceeding westwards, there are some heavy gradients, the steepest being 1 in 70, and the lowest 1 in 350. About a mile from Hawes Station there is a viaduct of four arches crossing Apperset Gill, and after proceeding about half way between Hawes and the junction there is a tunnel 341 yards long, passing through which the line is carried up a slight incline until it reaches Dandmire Gill. At this point the Midland Company have met with difficulties almost insurmountable. In obtaining a foundation for the construction of the line , some thousands of loads of ballast had to be tipped, the contractors in many cases losing some of their wagons, and in one instance nearly losing a locomotive.

From Mossdale Moor, two miles from the Moorcock Inn, the line runs close by the side of the Kirkby Stephen and Hawes high road. Messers J. Gibbs and Sons, of Aberdeen, have had the contract for the North Eastern Railway Company, while the Midland Company have entrusted their work to Messrs Benton and Woodiwiss, of Derby. This line will afford a convenient link between the main line on the east coast in direct communication with those on the west, affording great facilities to travellers from the continent of Europe to America.

Carlisle Express & Examiner, 3 August 1878

TO CONTRACTORS AND BUILDERS

THE DIRECTORS of the MIDLAND RAILWAY COMPANY are prepared to receive TENDERS for the ERECTION of a small ENGINE SHED, at HAWES JUNCTION, Settle and Carlisle Railway Plans and Specifications may be seen, quantities and particulars obtained on application at the Engineers Office, Derby; or to Mr VICKERS, Clerk of Works, Skipton, on and after 30th inst.

Sealed tenders to be forwarded by post to the Secretary of the Way and Works Committee, Midland Railway, Derby, not later than 9 a.m. on TUESDAY, AUGUST 6th.

The directors do not bind themselves to accept the lowest or any Tender, nor pay any expenses attending the same.

JAMES WILLIAMS, Secretary, Derby, 23 July 1878

Penrith Herald, 10 August 1878

THE PROPOSED JUNCTION WITH THE MIDLAND

On Thursday last, a meeting of the committee appointed to consider the best route from Penrith to the Midland railway, met by appointment Mr Wood, C. E., Carlisle, in the Public Offices, Penrith, and gave him instructions to survey the various routes proposed. A small sub-committee consisting of Messrs. Fairer, Pattinson, Seatree, and Bowstead were appointed to confer with Mr Wood as occasion arose.

Leeds Mercury, 14 August 1878

PROPOSED NEW FAIR IN WENSLEYDALE

In view of the opening of the Hawes branch of the Settle and Carlisle Railway (the Midland extension) the inhabitants of Wensleydale are considering the advisableness of establishing a new fair for the sale of sheep and lambs. The movement has assumed a somewhat definite form. It is understood that the first fair will be held in September. Thousands of sheep and lambs have hitherto been taken to distant, markets every year, the entire dale being devoted to sheep grazing.

After 1878 the stations of the Hawes branch in upper Wensleydale were used extensively by Swaledale sheep farmers. Although fleeces were dispatched by rail in the summer, it was the months of September and October when the important sheep fairs took place that were the busiest times for the stations on the line.

Leeds Mercury, 31 August 1878

THE COLLISION AT SETTLE JUNCTION

Col. Yolland has reported to the Board of Trade on the collision which occurred on the 26 June, between a passenger train and a goods train at Settle Junction, on the Midland Railway. Six passengers and four of the company's servants are stated to have been injured on this occasion. 'Taking therefore, into consideration the whole of the statements (says Col. Yolland), I have arrived at the conclusion that the driver of the up goods train was mistaken in supposing that the up home signal at Settle junction had been taken off for him to proceed, and that the collision was entirely due to his carelessness. At the same time it must be remarked that this goods train was permitted to leave Settle Station either four or six minutes before its proper time, and that the collision at Settle Junction occurred at 12-30pm, or four minutes before the train was due there, the passenger train being two minutes late. I cannot think it is right to permit any trains to run before their appointed times. The next point deserving of 'the careful consideration of the directors and officers of the Midland Railway' had reference to the practice, still continued on that line, of permitting trains, that may possibly come into collision with each other, to approach a junction at the same time, especially such a junction as that at Settle. This subject is frequently brought to the notice of the various railway companies by inspection officers of the Board of Trade in their reports on collisions that occur at junctions, and I am happy to say that many of the principal railway companies have altered their practice in this respect, and I trust that the example thus set will be followed on so important a line as the Midland Railway. There is still one other subject to which I must call attention. If the passenger train had been fitted with continuous brakes, placed under control of the engine driver, it is probable that this collision might have been altogether avoided, or greatly mitigated in its effects.

Carlisle Express & Examiner, 7 September 1878

TO CONTRACTORS AND BUILDERS

THE DIRECTORS of the MIDLAND RAILWAY COMPANY are prepared to receive TENDERS for the ERRECTION of TWO COTTAGES, near HAWES JUNCTION, Settle and Carlisle Railway

Plans and Specifications may be seen, quantities and particulars obtained on application at the Engineers Office, Derby; or to Mr HENDERSON, Clerk of Works, Skipton Station, on and after TUESDAY, 10th inst.

Sealed tenders to be forwarded by post to the Secretary of the Way and Works Committee, Midland Railway, Derby, not later than 9am on TUESDAY, 17th inst..

The directors do not bind themselves to accept the lowest or any Tender, nor pay any expenses attending the same.

JAMES WILLIAMS, Secretary, Derby, 5 September 1878

The Standard, 22 November 1878

IN PARLIAMENT SESSION 1879

Midland Railway Company (additional powers) new railways, footpaths, and other works and stopping up footpaths and additional lands in the counties of Cumberland etc.,

To empower the company to purchase, by compulsion or agreement, and to hold lands, houses and buildings for all or any of the purposes aforesaid, and also for extending their station, sidings, warehouses, coal wharf, depot, mineral, goods, and other accommodation, and for providing accommodation for persons belonging to the labouring classes who may be displaced under the powers of the intended act, and for another purposes connected with their undertaking, the lands, houses and buildings following, or some of them (that is to say):

Certain lands, houses, and buildings situate in the parish of Kirkland, in the county of Cumberland and on the north east side of and adjoining the company's Settle and Carlisle railway near the distance post on that railway marked 60¾ miles.

Certain lands, houses and buildings situate in the said parish of Kirkland, on the south west side and adjoining the company's Settle and Carlisle Railway near the level crossing thereof by the public road from Culgaith to Millrig.

In 1873 the Rev G. W. Atkinson and other landowners asked for a station at Culgaith, but were told Culgaith was not considered suitable. Eventually the Midland conceded and a station was opened in 1880. The lands referred to would have been for the construction of a goods siding opposite the signalbox.

The 60¾ mile post is around about the station at Cotehill. Where there was a siding to Knothill Plaster Works and a long station approach road.

Armathwaite Station in circa 1907 with the signal box that was brought into use in July 1899 and operated by William Smith. Photograph courtesy of the Cumbria Railway Association.

Chapter Eleven
1879

Penrith Herald, 29 March 1879

THE PROPOSED RAILWAY FROM LAZONBY TO PENRITH

On Thursday afternoon, a public meeting was held in the Market Hall for the purpose of receiving the report of the committee, and considering what further steps should be taken with regard the construction of the projected railway from Lazonby to Penrith. Mr Thomas Altham was called to the chair. Amongst those present were Messrs. J. Anderson, C. Fairer, G. Watson, W. Seatree, J. R. Barron, T. Hodgson, J. Laggett, W. Grisenthwaite, A. Sutcliffe, J. Scott, R. Thornborrow, M. D. Jackson, E. Addison, G. Pollard, E. Horeley, T. Mackell, etc.

The Chairman called upon Mr Fairer (the Hon Secretary) to read the following report:-

The committee having undertaken the duty entrusted to them, held their first meeting on the 25 July, when they appointed Mr Jameson their chairman, and resolved to employ an engineer to make a survey of the three routes suggested at the public meeting, for the line of railway from Penrith to the Midland line at or near Lazonby, another to the line via Great Salkeld, another to Langwathby, as well as any other route that the engineer might think feasible and proper; also to prepare a plan and estimate of the cost of each route, and to report thereon to the committee.

For the purpose Mr Wood, C.E., Carlisle, was employed, and he was instructed in surveying the Lazonby route, to take into consideration the question of how far working of the stone quarries could afford a profitable traffic for the sale of stone by means of that route. He was also instructed to report on the most advantages position for the terminus at Penrith.

At the next meeting of the committee held on the 8 August Mr Wood received his instructions, and on the 3 October he reported to a meeting of the committee held on that day, that he had surveyed four routes shown on the plan then laid before the committee as follows:-

One from Lazonby, past Maiden Hill direct to Penrith, in length 7 miles 45 chains, estimated cost exclusive of land £56,600; 56 acres of land required.

One from Lazonby, past Salkeld Dykes to the London and North Western Line at Plumpton Station, in length 5 miles 63 chains (5¾), estimated cost £ 36,700; 40 acres of land required.

One from Lazonby, past Salkeld Dykes to the London and North Western at Kitchen Hill, in length 6 miles, estimated cost £40,200; 45 acres of land required. Same route extended to Penrith 8¼ miles, estimated cost £56,000; 62 acres of land required.

One from Langwathby to Penrith 5 miles 61 chains, estimated cost £52,500 (£32,600 to Friar Street); 42 acres of land required.

The Honorary Secretary was instructed at that meeting to ask the Midland Company what support they would give to a line from Lazonby direct to an independent station at Penrith, and, if constructed upon what terms they would work it; also to ask the London and North Western Company what support they would give a line form Lazonby to their line at Kitchen Hill, and what facilities they would offer for the running over their line from that point to Penrith, and in the event of the line being constructed, upon what terms they would work it.

At the next meeting of the committee held on 11 November, a letter was read from the London and North Western Company intimating that, after giving the subject their most careful consideration they did not see their way to afford any assistance towards construction of the proposed line.

A letter was at the same time laid before the committee from the Midland Company, in which they stated that, 'they did not feel competent to express an opinion upon a scheme of this character until the details are before them,' and pointed out that 'the North-Eastern Company's Railway which forms a junction with the Settle and Carlisle Railway at Appleby, already affords a route between the Midland system and Penrith.'

The engineer was instructed at that meeting to supply plans and particulars of two of the proposed routes shown on his plan, namely, the one from Langwathby, and the one from Lazonby, by way of Salkeld Dykes towards Kitchen Hill, but running into an independent station at Penrith.

The engineer having as requested prepared a plan and particulars of the two routes indicated, the same were forwarded to the Midland Company, and at the next meeting of the committee held on the 10 December, the following correspondence was read:-

Penrith, 22 November, 1878.

Proposed Branch Line of Railway from the Midland Line to Penrith.

Dear Sir, Your letter of the 6th instant has been laid before the committee appointed at the public meeting held in Penrith on the 5 July last, to promote the construction of this line, and they have requested their engineer (Mr Wood, C.E., Carlisle) to give the details of two routes surveyed by him at the request of the committee, with a plan showing the course of each. With regard to the general necessity for such a line and the traffic which it might be expected to command, the committee are of the opinion that if constructed by your company, with the assistance of the people of this district, and worked by you in connection with your Settle and Carlisle line, a public want would be met, and a decided advantage gained by connecting your system with this district, by a considerable acquisition of both passenger and goods traffic which now requires an outlet in that direction

The loop line at Appleby referred to in your letter has not been made available in any way as a means of connecting the Midland system with Penrith, and although it would be of some advantage in the mean time if the North Eastern Company's trains were to run over it into your station at Appleby and on to Penrith in connection with yours, it would not supply the want felt for the proposed line from Langwathby or Lazonby to Penrith.

The committee are persuaded that your company will not fail to perceive that advantages likely to accrue from the proposed branch line to see their way to undertake its construction.

Yours Faithfully Chris Fairer, Hon Sec., Midland Railway, Sectary's Office.

Westmorland Gazette, 17 May 1879

APPLEBY PETTY SESSIONS

At this court, on Saturday, before Mr W Hopes, Admiral Eliott, and Mr James Atkinson, Mr Rogers, superintendent of permanent way on the Settle and Carlisle Railway applied, on behalf of the Midland Railway Company, for a licence to store mixed explosives, consisting of dynamite, blasting powder, and fuses, in a storeroom at Griseburn Quarry, on the south side of Helm Tunnel. Superintendent Spencer said that he had inspected the place on the previous day, and found it admirably adapted for the purpose; the store room, which was on a level with the ground, was hewn out of a solid rock, and was in every respect a most suitable place for the storage of explosives. – The Chairman: How far is it from the nearest dwelling? – Superintendent Spencer: Fully 600 yards. – The licence was granted.

Cumberland and Westmorland Herald, 4 December 1878,
CONCLUSION TO THE LAZONBY BRANCH RAILWAY

Dear Sir, I beg to inform you that I read your letter of the 22 November before my board at their meeting to-day, and I am instructed to say to you in reply that my directors are not prepared to incur any liability either towards making the line themselves or towards entering into any arrangement should such a line be made by other persons. I am yours faithfully J. Williams, Sec.

After considering the unfavourable replies of the London and North Eastern and Midland companies, and having regard to the commercial depression then prevailing, the committee adjourned the further

Citadel Station, Carlisle, with two Midland Railway 2-4-0s on a passenger train circa 1900. Photograph courtesy of Cumbria Railway Association.

consideration of the subject until the 11th instant, when, after again considering the whole subject, they arrived at the conclusion that any further negotiations with the two companies after the decided answer received from them, would be hopeless at present, and resolved to report the result of their proceedings to a public meeting.

Mr Watson, in moving the adoption of the report, said he thought all they had to do was to thank the committee for the very great pains they had taken in investigating the scheme, and in getting all the information they could. He regretted the very cold manner in which both companies had met the proposal. That being the case, it now rested with the meeting, he supposed, to propose any further measures, to give up the whole thing as a bad job, or to attempt to carry out the scheme without the assistance of the companies…

The Chairman said that in 1873-4 they had a good deal of correspondence with the Midland Company relative to the line from Langwathby to Penrith, and they held out a promise to do what they could for its promotion. Mr Fairer had a long correspondence with them, and at last they put the committee off from time to time, and they said that their commitments were so great that they must decline to have anything to do with it…

The Chairman hoped they would not lose sight of this, that the present was not the proper time for going further into the matter. Trade was very bad, money was very scarce and bad to get, and he thought they were all poorer than they were this time last year. They however, ought not lose sight of the matter.

Chapter Twelve
1880-1889

Lancaster Gazette, 3 April 1880

MIDLAND RAILWAY EXTENTION

On Thursday, the Midland Railway Company opened for merchandise the mineral traffic to two important new stations on the Settle and Carlisle line, Ormside, in Westmorland, situate on the main line between Crosby Garrett and Appleby, is one; the other is Culgaith (Cumberland), which is also situate on the main line, between Newbiggin and Langwathby. The London and North Western and North Eastern Railway companies have previously dealt with traffic to and from these places.

Cumberland and Westmorland Advertiser, 8 June 1880

ADDITIONAL RAILWAY ACCOMODATION TO PENRITH

We have great pleasure in drawing attention to the Midland Railway Company's advertisement in our last weeks issue, informing the public that from and after 1st June 1880, a new service of trains will be run over the Eden Valley Railway between Appleby and Penrith in connection with the main line of the Midland Railway Company. The trains are now running. The down trains on the Midland from Sheffield, Leeds, and Bradford stop at Appleby daily at 9a.m., 12-49p.m., and 5-21p.m., and run on to Penrith, arriving there at 9-45a.m., 1-22p.m., and 5-55p.m. The up trains leave Penrith daily at 9-20a.m., 1p.m., and 5-35p.m., to Appleby, and on direct to Bradford, Leeds, and Sheffield. A very influential memorial from the inhabitants of Penrith and district, promoted by the Penrith Local Board of Health, was presented to the Midland and North-Eastern Companies upward of two years ago, urging the two companies to carry out the arrangement which we now find has been in force since the 1st inst.

Cumberland and Westmorland Advertiser, 8 June 1880

We hear that the committee of gentlemen appointed to promote a branch line of railway from Penrith to Lazonby or Langwathby, of which Mr Jameson is chairman and Mr Fairer is the hon. secretary, are about to consider a project for constructing a tramway from Penrith along the turnpike road to Langwathby, which it is supposed, would answer the purposes of a line of railway, which cannot be constructed in consequence of the refusal of the Midland Company to be party to it.

Penrith Herald, 28 August 1880.

RAILWAY ACCIDENT

An alarming accident has occurred upon the Midland Railway about 25 miles north of Settle. As the express from Manchester, Leeds, and Bradford was running northwards through the Blea Moor tunnel, the longest on the line, the Westinghouse brake went wrong near the engine, and the train was unexpectedly brought to a stand still. While it was standing in the tunnel it was run into by a Pullman express from London, which, according to the tables, should reach the tunnel about twelve minutes after the Manchester express. Happily no serious damage was done. The men in charge of the first train had relied upon the observance of the rule that no second train should be allowed to enter the tunnel until the first had cleared it; but after they had been in the tunnel about a quarter of an hour, they heard the Pullman train come thundering along. The passengers in the Manchester train heard it too, and on finding the doors of their carriages locked they were naturally in great terror.

The guard then ran back with signals, and he was able to place some detonating signals upon the rails; but it is reported that he fell before he had gone as far as he had intended, and the Pullman express had not sufficient distance in which to pull up after the first alarm of danger had been received. The driver, however, was able to moderate the speed of his train very considerably and so avert a most terrible disaster. The guards van of the first train was smashed to pieces; the engine of the Pullman train was thrown off the line; a dog in the first train was killed; and a great many passengers complained that they had suffered severely from the shaking they had received. The trains were both very full of passengers.

The scene of confusion and alarm in the tunnel was beyond description. The splintered guards van at the tail of the first train and the engine of the second lay in great disorder about half a mile from the north end of the tunnel. The driver of the first train had steamed away out of harm's way when he heard the Pullman approaching, leaving behind him his train, which he was unable to move in consequence of the accident which had happened to the brake. By and by the passengers of both trains were collected and put into carriages of the first portion, and a new train was thus made up outside the tunnel. It reached Carlisle about a quarter past eight o'clock, two hours late. Many of the passengers went forward to Scotland, but some stayed all night at Carlisle. Some of them complained that they had lost all their luggage and had been un-courteously treated after the accident happened. How the signal man at the tunnel permitted the Pullman train to enter the tunnel before the Manchester express had gone through it is at present unexplained.

Penrith Herald, 25 September 1880

A BREAKDOWN

On Thursday, as the Liverpool and Manchester section of the afternoon train by the Midland line to Carlisle was passing Appleby, the engine broke down, and the train had to be taken northwards by the Pullman, which came up shortly after. No damage was done to the train or to the permanent way. The train arrived in Carlisle about an hour late.

Penrith Herald, 23 October 1880

THE RAILWAY ACCIDENT NEAR KIRKBY STEPHEN

The report of Major General Hutchinson on the collision in Bleamoor Tunnel, on the Settle and Carlisle section (Midland Railway) has been published. He attributes the collision between the down express from Leeds, and the down express from St Pancras, to three causes.

First, the stoppage of the Leeds train in the tunnel owing to the flexible tube connecting the air pipes under the tender and front van having been blown off the tender pipe, whereby the automatic character of the Westinghouse air brake, with which the whole of the train, except the engine, was fitted, was brought into play; Secondly, the improper working of the block telegraph system between Bleamoor and Dent Head; and third, the failure of the guard of the Leeds train to go back at once to protect the rear of the train.

When James Allport, the Midland Railway general manager, visited America he was shown the Westinghouse air brake that effectively in an emergency would operate the brakes in every part of the train. The Midland began to adopt this system. With a change of policy in the late 1870s, the Saunders Automatic vacuum brake eventually became fitted as standard.

Lancaster Gazette, 23 October 1880

CLAIM AGAINST THE MIDLAND RAILWAY COMPANY
THE SETTLE AND CARLISLE RAILWAY

There is now being heard at the Institution of Surveyors, Westminster, before Mr W. C. Gully, QC., a claim which has been referred to arbitration, in which the plaintiffs, Messrs Benson and Woodiwiss, contractors, Stretford, near Manchester, and at Derby, seek to recover £40,000 damages from the Midland Railway Company. Mr C. Russell QC, was counsel for the claimants, and Mr R. E. Webster QC, on behalf of the railway company.

Mr Russell in opening the case, stated that the original contract between the plaintiffs and the railway company was for the construction of four miles of railway, commencing about twelve miles north of Settle and running northward, but, as the company decided to seek powers to abandon the line, that contract was rescinded and the plaintiffs were compensated for damages. The company did not succeed in obtaining parliamentary sanction to the abandonment of the line, and in November 1869, an agreement was come to between the plaintiffs and the railway company for the construction of seventeen miles eight chains of the line for £334,800, but the formal contract was not signed until the 26 April 1870.

Between those two dates several letters were written by the plaintiffs to the defendants, complaining of the delay in the acquisition of land and the supply of plans, thus showing that the agreement of November 1869, was being acted upon. The company afterwards obtained powers for the deviation of the line, and the work which the plaintiffs were called upon to do exceeding the former contract by £200,000. There was great delay in the execution of the works, owing partly to the weather but in a greater degree to the peculiarity of the soil, which was boulder clay, that, being utterly useless for embankments, had to be deposited on land acquired for the purpose.

In September 1871, the plaintiffs asked the railway company to make them 30 per cent allowance for this extra work, and for the delay in the acquisition of land. In November 1872, the company agreed to allow 15 per cent on the whole contract as a bonus, they having themselves suffered a loss of 50 per cent by taking another contract for another portion of the line into their own hands. Some of the plans were not delivered to the plaintiffs until 1875, and suggestions were made as late as September 1876, although the original contract limited the time for completion of the works in 1872.

The plaintiffs contended that the defendants were not entitled to put £200,000 additional work upon them, and delay it until 1876 for want of facilities which they were bound to give, and yet that work to be done at the contract price, not with standing that materials and labour were enhanced in price. They had further claim for extras, and that the whole amounted to £130,000, the particulars of which were given to Mr Crossley, the company's engineer, who, after going through them declared the plaintiff to be entitled to £22,270, which was paid to them.

The contention of the plaintiffs was that this sum was only for the extras which he as engineer to the company allowed, and that he never had the matter before him as arbitrator between the parties on the whole question, inasmuch as his connection with the railway company made him an interested party, to whose appointment as sole arbitrator the plaintiffs would naturally have objected. Sundry payments had been made by the company, and the balance now claimed was within a small sum of £40,000. The company's defence was that the whole matter was dealt with by Mr Crossley, and that the contract of 1870 was the only thing to be looked to whereas the plaintiff held that for some purposes there was a pre-existent contract in November 1869 which was partially acted upon. Mr Woodwiss, one of the plaintiffs, was called, and a number of witnesses are being examined as to the nature and extent of the delay in the work, and the consequent loss to the plaintiffs. The case has been proceeding the whole week.

The Nottingham Guardian, 28 October 1881 published the outcome of the claim:

The arbitration in which Messrs Benton and Woodwiss, the contractors, were plaintiffs, and the Midland Railway Company the defendants, has been arranged. The claim was for £40,000, for delay in furnishing land and instructions, and for work done beyond that planned in a contract between the parties. The terms of the settlement were that the plaintiffs withdrew their claim, and each side paid their own costs.

Penrith Observer, 26 October 1880

NEW TELEGRAPH LINE

A new telegraph line is being constructed between London and Edinburgh via the Midland Railway. The poles are erected the entire distance. A staff of men are, at present at work on the wires, and have completed as far as Kirkby Stephen.

Cumberland and Westmorland Advertiser, 21 December 1880

SINGULAR ACCIDENT ON THE MIDLAND RAILWAY

On Wednesday, Dr Elliot, coroner for the city of Carlisle, held an inquest at the Infirmary into the death of John White, a labourer on the Midland Railway. On Tuesday White and other men were engaged in laying out telegraph poles on the Midland Railway. There were several wagons laden with the poles, and the labourers who had to throw them out on the side of the line were riding in the wagons. When the accident occurred the train, which had engine and tender and guard's van attached, was about a mile south of Langwathby, and was proceeding the poles not being discharged at the place, at the rate of seven or eight miles an hour. White and some other men, W. Robinson, Slater, and Samuel Cresswell were all together in the second wagon of the train. Whilst thus proceeding along, one of the loose poles slid out of its place and was shaken over the side of the wagon. Its butt end caught the ground and the upper end was brought sharply over the wagon striking White and Slater. The former was most seriously injured on the side of the head and knocked insensible. As soon as possible the train was stopped and the poor man brought to the infirmary, but died within a short time. The jury returned a verdict of 'Accidental death', commending White's widow and children to the care of the directors of the Midland Railway. They also wished to direct attention to the present method of distributing telegraph poles with a view to such accidents as these being prevented.

1881

The Northern Echo, 13 January 1881

ATTEMPT TO WRECK AN EXPRESS TRAIN

A diabolical attempt to upset the Pullman Express has just been discovered on the Midland Railway, near Appleby, Westmorland. A thick telegraph pole was cut into three pieces by the night express, and must have been placed on the rails purposely. Detectives are on the spot making an investigation. The occurrence has occasioned great alarm.

According to earlier newspaper reports workmen have been building a new telegraph line along the railway. Was the pole one that was badly stacked and rolled on to the line or was it a deliberate act?

The Penrith Herald, 15 January 1881

FATAL ACCIDENT ON THE RAILWAY NEAR KIRKBY STEPHEN

On Tuesday morning a sad accident occurred in the Birkett Tunnel, near Kirkby Stephen, on the Midland Railway. It appears that a platelayer, named Thomas Cornthwaite, was working in the tunnel, when in trying to get out of the way of one train he stepped in front of another, which knocked him down and ran over both arms. Death was instantaneous. An inquest was held on Wednesday last at the Magistrates Room, Kirkby Stephen, touching the death, before T. Wilson Esq. coroner for the district, when a verdict of Accidental death was returned. Deceased leaves a wife and family of small children.

The Leeds Mercury, 7 March 1881

THE SNOW BLOCK ON THE SETTLE AND CARLISLE RAILWAY

The news from the scene of the snow-block on the Settle and Carlisle Railway at Dent Cutting, is much more favourable, and although the heavy rains of Saturday night and yesterday morning do not seem to have cleared away the huge accumulation of snow, the large number of workers in the drift are likely to make a passage today (Monday). From the information courteously given to our Skipton correspondent by the head passenger official at Skipton, and the guard of the goods train that was buried in the block on Thursday, it appears that the drift is not much less than half a mile in length, and the snow is in most of the places from 15 to 20 feet deep. The snow is deepest on the up line.

On Saturday night there were five engines blocked in the drift. The goods train which left Skipton on Thursday arrived in Skipton at 10 o'clock on Saturday night and although the guard, driver and fireman of the train had a supply of provisions with them, they were 15 hours without food. The wagons of the train which were left in the drift on Thursday are most of them entirely buried in the snow. When our parcel left there were nearly 400 men employed digging out the snow on the Skipton side of the drift. They have been supplied from the neighbourhood of Settle, Skipton, etc., and a large quantity of provisions was sent from Skipton on Saturday, as well as an additional supply yesterday afternoon. The high winds of Saturday night broke down the Midland Company's telegraph wires, and thus communication in that way has been cut off. A Post Office telegram, however, states that the storm during Saturday and Sunday morning was dreadful.

On the Carlisle side of the drift a gang of men are employed shifting snow, and, owing to the united endeavours of the men employed, and the efforts of the officials to keep them going, it was thought that a passage would be made late last night. The trains are still worked by the London and North Western line via Ingleton, and in most cases the delay is little more than half an hour. An eyewitness states that the scene in the beautiful valley of Dent is one that has been seldom witnessed. In some places the drifts of snow are like mountains, and the sight of large bodies of men working yards below at the embedded railway wagons is exceedingly striking. The rain of Saturday night seems to have had the effect of hardening the snow which can be walked upon in some places. It is stated that the cars on the Pullman expresses have been taken off because of the narrow bridges on the London and North Western line.

Penrith Observer, 12 July 1881

SUDDEN DEATH IN THE PULLMAN EXPRESS

When the Pullman express arrived at the Citadel Station, Carlisle, on Friday morning, at 4-50, a railway porter named Joseph Little found Joseph McQueen, upholsterer, Kilmarnock, dead in a third class compartment. He was lying on the floor, with his boots off. The incident was reported to the city police, and the body of the man was removed to the mortuary near the Police Office and examined. No marks of violence were found on his person, and his property appeared undisturbed. He wore a gold watch and chain and three rings, and had a purse containing between thirty and forty shillings. The guard of the train said that he saw him enter the train at London. Some time during last month he would seem to have left Greenock to reside with his daughter at Chelsea, and it further appears that he must have been in bad health during that time, as he had an order as outpatient for St Georges Hospital. The circumstances show that he died not long before he reached Carlisle. His boots were off, but the soles were wet, as if he had left the train at the last stopping place, and even at six o'clock, when he was examined at the mortuary, some warmth was still perceptible at the chest.

The Pullman sleeping car express left St Pancras at 9-15pm, reaching Skipton at 2-49am. There the train split with the Edinburgh section leaving at 2-55am, and running non-stop to Carlisle which was reached at 4-55am. The train was made up of two Pullman cars, three 12 wheeled bogie carriages, three 8 wheelers, three 6 wheelers, and several vans. At this time there were no corridors or inter carriage connections in 3rd and some 1st class carriages. Passengers travelled in single compartments making it very difficult in the event of a lone passenger being taken ill or other emergency.

The Penrith Herald, 22 July 1881

THE MIDLAND RAILWAY SIGNALMEN

Seventeen delegates of signalmen along the Midland Railway from London to Carlisle had an interview on Tuesday with the Board of Directors at Derby, in order to support the memorial recently presented for removal of grievances. Various speakers referred to the injustice and hardships of the present system, and pointed out, among other things, the necessity of reducing the working hours from twelve and thirteen to eight, of increasing the pay in different classes by three shillings, and of improving the working uniform. In conclusion, the directors intimated that their representatives would receive careful and favourable consideration, and that the result would be announced in due course.

While the Midland Company are considering the grievances of their servants we might suggest that they should also give ear to the complaints of the public at this end of their system. The Settle and Carlisle was chiefly promoted as a through line, and as such it has undoubtedly conferred a great boon upon the north-west of England by breaking up the monopoly of the London and North Western and securing a reduction of rates and fares; but as a local line it has not conferred the advantages that might have been expected. The service of local trains, in spite of many protests, remain sadly restricted, and is timed so as to afford the public vey insufficient accommodation. More frequent trains between Appleby and Carlisle would be a great advantage, and would certainly develop a paying local traffic in a very short time. At all events the experiment is worth trying.

Penrith Observer, 20 December 1881

FATAL RAILWAY ACCIDENT AT GRISBURN

An inquest was held on Wednesday last by Mr T. Wilson, coroner for Westmorland, at the house of Mr Alexander Lunham, of Griseburn, in the parish of Asby, touching the death of a lad named Harry Neale Walker, who had been killed on the Midland Railway, near Griseburn, on the previous Monday. The following evidence was adduced: Thomas Walker said, I am an engine man in the employment of the Midland Railway Company, and reside at Griseburn, in the parish of Asby. I identified the body of the deceased, Harry Neale Walker, as that of my son; he was eight years of age. I last saw him alive on Monday morning last about 8 o'clock, when he was going to school at Asby. I don't know whether he crossed the line or not then. I have frequently told the deceased not to cross the line, more particularly at night time. Deceased understood the signals very well. The usual road from Griseburn to Asby is by the 'bridle road' from Griseburn on to the public road. A little after 5 o'clock on Monday night last, Mr Gregson's boy came running into our house and said "Harry was killed". I went out immediately, and I met Mr Gregson bringing Mr Lunham's boy in his arms and then went forward to look for my boy, and found him lying in the four foot of the down line. He was quite dead.

John Thomas Lunham, son of Alexander Lunham, residing at Griseburn, said, I was coming across the line on Monday night about 5-5pm from school. Deceased was with me. We looked up the line to see if there was any train coming down. Walker (deceased) was walking in the four foot on the down line. I was walking in the six foot, and whilst watching the up train the down train came and knocked me down.

William Gregson, said, I am foreman of the quarry at Griseburn. About 5-5pm on Monday last I was in my house at Griseburn, and heard the last witness halloing out for help. I went up the railway a bit and met him. He was hobbling along. I took him up in my arms and was bringing him away, and I asked him where Harry (deceased) was. I went back a bit and found deceased lying in the four foot. He was quite dead.

William Love, said, I am an engine driver in the employment of the Midland Railway Company. I was driving the passenger train towards Carlisle on Monday evening last which is due at Griseburn about five minutes past five. It was then quite dark. The train was in good time.

The jury returned a verdict of 'accidentally killed', and attached no blame to anybody.

1882

The Newcastle Courant, 30 June 1882

THE YORE VALLEY RAILWAY

(*Courant,* 23 June) The Midland line to Hawes, from the Settle and Carlisle line, was intended to form a junction with the Melmerby branch of the North Eastern Railway. When the Midland Company resolved on making its Settle and Carlisle Railway, powers were obtained for making the Melmerby branch to unite with it. But when the Midland Company decided to apply to Parliament in 1869, to abandon the Settle and Carlisle, it was thought that the Melmerby and Hawes extension was unnecessary, and powers for its abandonment were also sought and were successful. Meanwhile the Midland Bill abandonment was rejected, and the Settle and Carlisle line had therefore to be made. So for the third time the North Eastern Company in 1870 had to ask that the deceased powers of the Melmerby line might be revived, and their present request was granted. ENGINEER.

Penrith Observer, 21 November 1882

RAILWAY ACCIDENT NEAR KIRKBY STEPHEN

ON Saturday night as a mineral train was proceeding at a rapid pace near Newbiggin, the engine left the rails and pitched head foremost on to an adjoining highway, the whole train following. Fortunately none of the men were injured. The break-down gangs were at work all day on Sunday, and the line was eventually cleared.

Penrith Observe, 5 December 1882

FATAL ACCIDENT NEAR ORMSIDE

On Friday afternoon Mr T Wilson held an inquest at the Midland Railway Station, Ormside, touching the death of John Hunter (42), a labourer on the line, who was killed by a passing goods train, on Thursday morning last. Mr James Sowerby, of Ormside Lodge was foreman of the Jury.

William Smith Webster, labourer, Helm Cottages, Ormside, said yesterday morning, about seven o'clock, he was going up the 'down road' towards the Helm Tunnel, and when he had passed the bridge leading over the line he saw deceased walking in the four foot and at that time a goods train passing on the up line in the direction of Settle. Another goods train came immediately afterwards on the down line, and when he saw it he called to the deceased and said, "Look up Jack, there's a train coming." The deceased could not possibly get out of the way before the train struck him. He then went to the place, and found the deceased lying in the four foot. He was quite dead. The whistle of the engine attached to the train running towards Carlisle was sounded when within twenty yards from the deceased. They who are employed by the Railway Company, are especially cautioned to desist from work upon a train approaching, and not to cross over the other lines, but to move to the side of the road, clear of all the lines, to secure themselves from risk.

Robert Wells, said he was fireman in the employment of the Midland Railway Company, and lived at 39, Charles Street, Carlisle. He was on the engine of the goods train travelling in the direction of Carlisle yesterday morning, when it struck the deceased. He was standing right in the four foot and he first saw him when the train was about twelve yards from him. He applied the whistle once. The wind was blowing strongly at the time, from the north (this would be a direction almost immediately in front of the deceased.) By the Foreman. The deceased did not appear to make any attempt to get out of the way. The train was pulled up at a short distance from the place where the accident occurred. He examined the engine afterwards and found spots of blood on it.

The Coroner having briefly summed up the evidence addressed the jury at once returned a verdict of 'Accidentally killed by a goods train on the Midland Railway.'

The Penrith Herald, 9 December 1882

Snow… The Pullman express leaving London at 10am, and due at Carlisle at 5-54pm, unaware of the plight of its forerunner, came on till it got near Dent, a part of the line which is both elevated and exposed to the full sweep of every storm. Here it was brought to a stand; and it was soon barred behind as well; so that the passengers, who included Mr Ferguson, M.P., for Carlisle and Mr R. A. Allison, Scaleby Hall, had as the other case, to weather the night. Their prospects of sustenance were at first gloomy; but officials, were equal to the emergency; and by foraging about the neighbourhood the belated travellers were able to make out fairly in that respect. The Pullman cars were comfortably warm and lighted, and in them the company congregated throughout the night, passing their enforced imprisonment on the moors in a manner as satisfactory as possible under the circumstances. It was not till Tuesday afternoon that by putting on gangs of workmen to clear the snow, and by applying the power of three engines to each, that the trains were got out. One reached Carlisle about 8 o'clock, and the other about 4 o'clock, Mr Ferguson and Mr Allison arriving in the latter, safe and sound.

Before the fact of the block was known, the 5-56 train for the south went forward from Carlisle on Wednesday evening, but was stopped on this side of the Hawes wreath; and while it was delayed there, it also got fast behind, so that it could not return, and the passengers, as in other cases, had to make up their minds for passing the night out. They, however, found some entertainment in the neighbourhood, and were even better off than some of their companions in misfortune on the other side of the snow barrier, of whom by the way, they could see or hear nothing. The train was got out on Thursday forenoon, and returned to Carlisle about 12 o'clock. Since Wednesday night the Midland trains have come and gone by the London and North Western system to Ingleton, all of them being, however, very late.

1883

Penrith Observer, 9 January 1883

MALLERSTANG AND THE MIDLAND RAILWAY

To the editor of the Penrith Observer

Sir, It is very tantalising, to say the least of it, for the inhabitants of Mallerstang (274 souls) to see the well appointed trains of the Midland running past their very doors, yet not one of them stopping for their convenience. Near the church, or not far from Pendragon Castle, where two roads converge, a station might be conveniently built, and reached by a gradual accent. If two trains each way stopped, when required, it would be a great boon to the inhabitants, who, as it is, have to go either to Kirkby Stephen (4½ miles), or Hawes junction (7½ miles) to secure the privilege of a seat. The valley is rich in stock and dairy produce, and the Company in a short time would be gainers.

I am Sir, Yours faithfully, John Wharton,
  Stainmore Parsonage, 2 January 1883.

A NEW RAILWAY TO SCOTLAND

Penrith Observer, 23 January 1883

A RAILWAY STATION FOR MALLERSTANG

A public meeting of the landowners and occupiers was held in the Board School on Tuesday evening, as to moving the Midland Railway Company to provide a railway station for the district. It was resolved to petition the Company and agitate the matter thoroughly.

The Penrith Herald, 7 July 1883

AN INTENDING VISITOR TO THE RACES STOPPED ON HIS WAY

A youth named Thomas Killroy, 18 years of age, who described himself as an apprentice brushmaker at Manchester, was on Thursday charged at Appleby, with travelling on the Midland Railway from Manchester to Appleby, without having paid his fare. The charge was proved by Mr John Hobday, a detective officer in the employment of the Midland Railway Company, who stated that on examining the carriages composing a special train from Manchester to Carlisle, at Appleby on Tuesday morning, he found the defendant concealed under the seat of a carriage which was filled with racing men. On being apprehended defendant said he was going to the races to sell coconuts. He had eleven pence halfpenny in his possession, but no ticket. In default of paying a penalty of 10shillings, defendant was sent to Carlisle Goal for seven days.

Penrith Observer, 24 July 1883

MALLERSTANG

We understand that last week a memorial was sent off for the presentation to the chairman of directors signed by all the landowners and farmers throughout the dale, requesting the Midland Railway Company to take into their consideration the great want of a station for Mallerstang. The people of Mallerstang wish to tender their best thanks to Lord Hothfield, the Earl and Countess of Bective, the Hon. Wm. Lowther, M.P., and other friends for their ready help and the kindly interest they have taken in the scheme throughout. The memorialists trust that the Midland Company may be able to grant their request, knowing how much such a boon would be welcomed by the inhabitants of Mallerstang.

Penrith Observer, 4 September 1883

RUNAWAY CARRIAGE ON THE EDEN VALLEY LINE

Early yesterday morning a number of horse boxes, carriage trucks, vans, and a first class carriage, belonging to the Midland Railway Company, were taken to Clifton Station on the North Eastern line, for the accommodation of Lord Lonsdale, to form a special for Weldon (Midland Line), via Appleby. In the shunting operations the empty first class carriage was detached from the others before the points were set to admit it into the siding. The line at this point is a falling gradient towards Appleby, there being no means of stopping it. The signalman at Clifton communicated the occurrence to the Cliburn official, who wisely switched the carriage off into a siding, which terminates at an embankment, over which the carriage was thrown. Had not this been done in a few moments the carriage would have met a mineral train from Kirkby Stephen, when the consequences might have been more serious.

Weldon Corby is the station for Brigstock where the North Pytchley hounds were housed. The 5th Earl during hunting in the Brigstock, Lowick, Thrapston area was reported on the 18 September 1883 as having a hunting accident while out with the North Pytchley hounds.

Clifton station was on the Eden Valley Line and not to be confused with Clifton Lowther on the LNWR Lancaster to Carlisle line. In the Act for the Eden Valley Line the 5th Earl of Lonsdale Hugh Cecil Lowther (The Yellow Earl), was given the powers to call on the NER to build the station at Clifton along with the approach roads. He also had his own private waiting room at Clifton. When travelling the Earl's personal entourage numbered over a hundred and whenever he moved from house to house a special train was reserved for his household. If he travelled over night a first class sleeper was reserved for himself and another for his dogs. Along the route station masters paraded on the platforms of their stations, at whatever hour to see the Lonsdale train safely through.

The Leeds Mercury, 25 September 1883

TRAVELLING WITHOUT A TICKET

At the Settle police court on Saturday, before the Rev. H. J. Swale and Mr C. Ingleby, David Pickles (44) who describes himself as a brewer's assistant, living at Leeds Road, Bradford, was charged in custody with having travelled on the Midland Railway from Carlisle to Hellifield that morning with intent to defraud the company, not having obtained a ticket. It seems to have come to the knowledge of the company's detective department that numbers of betting men who had been attending Ayr races had succeeded in evading payment of the fare from Carlisle to Hellifield by booking at the latter place to stations southwards on their arrival there, without being asked for the ticket they ought to have procured at Carlisle. On Saturday morning Detective Holiday was at Hellifield Station awaiting the arrival of the Carlisle express, due at the former place at 3am. Passengers got out of the train, and going to the booking office, asked for a ticket for Bradford. On being asked to produce the ticket by which he had travelled there, prisoner stated that he was a native of Hellifield. He was then apprehended and conveyed to Settle. On the other passengers by the same train being requested to produce their tickets it was found that several of them had none, but as they promptly proffered payment of the fare they were allowed to proceed, Detective Holiday having stated the facts, Pickles was fined £2/8s, including costs, which sum was paid.

Penrith Observer, 30 October 1883

CROSBY GARRETT POSTAL

The Post Office Authorities, who have hitherto required parties to call at the local office in the village for their letters, have now put on a special messenger for the delivery of letters at the railway cottages and station house.

1884

Penrith Observer, 22 January 1884

PRESENTATION AT LANGWATHBY

At Langwathby, on Wednesday, the 9th inst., Mr Shaw, late station master, was presented with a handsome timepiece and a purse of gold, subscribed for by a few friends there and in the neighbourhood, in recognition of his uniform courtesy and obliging manner during a service of nearly eight years that he has held the position of station master. A suitable inscription on the time piece recorded Mr Shaw's kindness and attention to all who came in contact with him. A few friends met in the school room, and the presentation was made by Mr Powley, who expressed the general regret on losing his services. The Rev W Lovejoy, the vicar, bore testimony to the esteem in which Mr Shaw was held. The Rev J Mitchell then addressed a few words to the meeting, remarking that faithful service never went without its reward. A letter was read from Mr Bowstead, Edenhall, who was not able to be present, speaking in highest praise of Mr Shaw's attention. In replying Mr Shaw acknowledged, in feeling terms, his pleasure in accepting such a mark of regard from his friends. The Midland Railway Company have lately promoted him to a more important post on their line at Bentham, near Lancaster, where he carries the good wishes of all his friends in the north, The time piece was supplied by Mr Wilson, silversmith, Penrith.

Penrith Observer, 8 April 1884

A RAILWAY STATION FOR MALLERSTANG

We understand that negotiations are in progress in this matter, and there is some hope of success, but the cost of the land for the station and road thereto is serious, and is at present hindering any rapid settlement of the situation.

Penrith Observer, 18 November 1884

SERIOUS ACCIDENT AT ARMATHWAITE

Early on Thursday afternoon a serious accident occurred to a man named Richard Dean, in the service of the Midland Railway Company, at Armathwaite. It seems that Dean, who belongs to Bentham, near Lancaster, was employed in loading wood into a wagon, which was standing on a siding off the railway, when the bark of a tree upon which he was standing gave way, and he slipped, falling violently on his head upon one of the lines of rails some ten feet beneath. One side of his head was laid open. He was immediately conveyed to the Infirmary at Carlisle where he now lies in a very precarious condition.

1885

Witney Express & Midland Counties & Oxford Herald, 4 February 1885

As a luggage train on the Settle and Carlisle Railway was passing Dent Head the other afternoon one of the wagons left the metals, owing to the large accumulation of snow upon the track. Both lines were immediately blocked, and the Pullman express trains to and from St Pancras were each delayed for three hours in consequence.

Yorkshire Post & Intelligencer, 6 April 1885

At an early hour on Saturday morning a goods train travelling from Carlisle to Leeds on the Settle and Carlisle Railway met with an accident of a rather serious character whilst passing the Horton-in-Ribblesdale Station. From some cause which has not yet transpired a number of wagons containing fat cattle and merchandise left the rails. One animal was killed outright, and four others were so seriously injured that they had to be slaughtered forthwith. Messers C. Harrison , of Giggleswick, and Robert Preston, of Longpreston, to whom the cattle belonged, were at the time in the guards van, and they and the guard received a very severe shaking, Mr Harrison's face also being injured. The sides of the cattle trucks had been entirely carried away, whilst several others were almost demolished, and a quantity of lace curtains and wearing apparel was scattered upon the permanent way, which, as might have been expected, was considerably damaged. Traffic was delayed for some time.

Penrith Observer, 28 July 1885

OFFICIAL RAILWAY GUIDES

Messers. Cassell and Company have just published profusely illustrated Guides to the Midland and Great Western Railways. Most of the places of interest on the two systems are described with care, and full and sectional maps are given of the route of both railways. Many beautiful views are given of the English Lake District; and places of interest in and around Penrith, Keswick, Windermere, etc., are described in an interesting manner.

The Manchester Times, 15 August 1885

WATERSPOUT IN WESTMORLAND

A remarkable descent of water took place at Armathwaite a few days ago, and did considerable damage. A dark cloud seemed suddenly to collapse overhead, and after a few drops of rain a waterspout fell on the Station Hill on the west side of the railway arch of the Settle and Carlisle Railway. The road was soon ploughed up to a considerable depth, and the torrent rolled down the brow, carrying stones and earth with it, until it was brought to a stop at the walls and gates leading to Armathwaite Castle, the castle being flooded to the extent of many feet. Fears were for some time apprehended for the village, but the large gates were opened with promptness, which allowed the water to spread. Great damage was occasioned.

Penrith Observer, 10 September 1885

Editorial:- The proposal to form a railway from Langwathby or some point contiguous thereto to Penrith and Pooley Bridge has reached another stage. Necessarily the line would be of great benefit to Penrith, but I find some critics saying that the advantages would not be so great as sanguine people suppose. The only appreciable difference, they assert, so far as Penrith is concerned would be the probable bringing in of east fellsiders to do their marketing instead of availing themselves of the cheap fares to Carlisle. But that event would depend greatly upon the state of the Penrith market, for it is notorious fact that many of the country folks now come in on Tuesdays only to get rid of their produce, preferring to take advantage of the easy rates to Carlisle on Saturdays to do their buying, because they say it is a cheaper and better market. The folks on the western side are to a considerable extent bound to patronise Penrith, because excepting Keswick, there is no other market easy of access for them. Taking a broader view of the case, however, the line, might make a considerable difference to both Penrith and Pooley Bridge, and what was advantageous to one place would benefit the other, from a tourist point of view. A direct line from the Midland would undoubtedly tend to open up the district, and make it what it ought to be, one of the chief health and pleasure resorts in the kingdom.

1886

The Liverpool Mercury, 15 January 1886

…During the construction of a tunnel on the Settle and Carlisle Railway, the roof gave way in one place, and left a hole 60 feet high. Now, to fill up a hole in the ground is an easy matter, but when it is within a mountain overhead the task is not so simple. In this instance it was done by putting timbers across from rock to rock at the highest part of the hole, and then working downwards until the arch of the tunnel was reached, and no spaces was left except a hole large enough for the last work man to crawl through and then that was filled up…

North Eastern Daily Gazette, 26 January 1886

BLOCK ON THE RAILWAY

Yesterday afternoon as an up luggage train was passing Dent Head, on the Settle and Carlisle Railway one of the wagons left the rails in consequences of the heavy accumulation of snow at that place. Both the up and down lines were immediately blocked. The afternoon Pullman express from Glasgow to St Pancras was delayed at Dent Head for three hours, and the down Pullman from St Pancras to Edinburgh was detained a similar time. The traffic had to be worked upon a single line, the down line being utilized. Although a break-down gang of considerable number was engaged, the up line was not completely cleared at night fall. The men engaged upon the work stated that the snow lay to a depth which has not been equalled for many years past. In places where it has drifted the wreaths are over two yards in depth.

The wind which prevailed yesterday made it difficult to maintain an upright position. Snow, sleet, and rain alternated, a perfect hurricane prevailing during the greater part of the day. Great anxiety was caused by the delay to the Pullman trains.

Penrith Observer, 2 Feburary 1886

FATAL ACCIDENT NEAR ASBY

On Friday last an inquest was held at Griseburne, in the parish of Asby, before T. Wilson, Esq., coroner, touching the death of Alfred Edwin Ladds, who was killed on the Midland Railway on the previous day… The first witness called was James Ladds, foreman platelayer in the employment of the Midland Railway Company, living at Griseburne, who identified the body of deceased as that of his son, who was five years and nine months old. At about ten o clock on the previous morning he left the deceased outside the gate of the sidings, and cautioned him to be careful of the train. He knew it was his intention to go to George Jackson's farm for butter about that time, but he was not aware that his son intended to cross the line. By the foreman, he had gone that way before, but not within the last four months. James Bolt, signalman on the Midland Railway at Griseburne, noticed the deceased walking along the footpath on the line side in the direction of the bridge over the line, at 9-44 on the previous morning. Thomas Sowerby, flagman attached to the small ballast train on the Midland Railway at Griseburne, said they had two brakes and fifteen wagons standing in the siding about 9-45 yesterday morning. About this time the engine, with another 11 wagons, was run into the siding and he attached them to the others. When he came out the road was quite clear, and the signal was given to the guard to start the train. When witness got into the six foot he looked to the rear of the train and observed an object under the brakes, about 70 yards distant. He at once gave the signal and the train was pulled up directly. Witness hastened to see what the obstruction was, and found the body of deceased lying on its right side across the line… He informed the guard of the accident, and afterwards told the father. The coroner having briefly summed up, the jury returned a verdict of "Accidently crushed by the wheel of a brake van attached to a ballast train on the Midland Railway."

The Leeds Mercury, 2 March 1886

A TRAIN EMBEDDED IN THE SNOW ON THE SETTLE AND CARLISLE LINE.

Our correspondent telegraphs yesterday that North Ribblesdale was visited by one of the most violent snowstorms ever experienced in this region. Snow commenced to fall between six and seven o'clock in the morning, and continued with ever increasing fury until night fall. As the day advanced the wind became stronger, and culminated in a hurricane. About seven o'clock the snow drifted to such an extent that locomotion became impracticable, the drifts ranging from a foot to several yards in depth. Many of the country roads now impassable. On the Settle and Carlisle Railway which is especially liable to be blocked, the 4-10 'pickup' train from Carlisle was delayed at Hawes Junction about two hours and the 5-38 express from Carlisle had not reached Settle at ten o'clock. It was stated to have become embedded in the snow at Dent Head. Snowploughs were employed constantly during the evening, but the line could not, it appears, be kept open. Sheep have been overblown in vast numbers, the farmers not being able to herd them, as their male servants leave home on the 1st of March for the purpose of attending the statute hiring's.

The Leeds Mercury, 20 March 1886.

THE BLOCK ON THE SETTLE AND CARLISLE RAILWAY.

The Settle and Carlisle Railway which was blocked on Thursday through an immense snow slip, was got clear yesterday morning. The Scots express trains between Carlisle and Manchester were very little delayed. The snow slip was caused by a stiff gale of wind, which dislodged the vast accumulations of snow on the railway embankments at Dent, and both lines were buried. One passenger train dashed into the fallen snow, and was completely buried.

Penrith Observer, 20 April 1886

FATAL ACCIDENT AT APPLEBY, A MAN AND A HORSE KILLED

A very sad and deplorable accident occurred at Appleby, soon after two o'clock yesterday afternoon whereby Mr Thomas Ellwood, farmer, of Sideaway Bank, near Kings Meaburn, and a valuable cart horse, which he was driving at the time, met with almost instantaneous death. It appeared that Mr Ellwood had been to the Midland Railway Yard for a load of coals, and on returning he was riding on the front of the cart. On passing the passenger station, the horse, which was a young one, was startled by an express train, which was leaving the station and he at once dashed off down Clifford Street, at full gallop. This street is a very steep one, and although the poor animal had evidently endeavoured to check himself at the foot of it, the momentum behind was too much for him and he was driven headlong through the stone wall, which borders the garden now or lately occupied by Mr J. P. Shepherd. The horse was killed on the spot and Mr Ellwood, having been ejected right over the animal's head, fell with a crash among the debris, and sustained a fracture of the skull, from the effects of which he died in a few minutes... In the course of the afternoon the scene of the deplorable accident was viewed by many hundreds of people.

1887

Railway News, Summer 1887

THE MIDLAND TOURS TO SCOTLAND AND THE NORTH

The summer service of express trains to and from Scotland, via the Settle and Carlisle route of the Midland Railway is now in operation. Two trains per day, one at 8-25am, and the other at 9-15pm, leave St Pancras Station and reach Greenock in time for the passengers to join the *Columbia* or *Iona* steamers for the Highlands. There is no charge of carriage by these trains. Saloon and family carriages, and family sleeping saloons can be attached on application at the London station to run through to any railway station in Scotland. Arrangements can be made for the dispatch of heavy luggage in advance of passengers, who will be spared all trouble and annoyance in respect to the usual impediments of travel. A very liberal and complete service is provided for Matlock, Buxton and other places of seaside or pleasure resort in Yorkshire, Lancashire, and the Lake District. Tourist tickets are issued at temptingly low rates available for two months. Care has been taken to provide adequately for the important service of refreshments. A dinner of five courses, with desert, and no fees to waiter, is prepared at Normanton, and half-an-hour is allowed for the discussion and disposal of the good things so liberally provided. A telegram handed to the guard, no charge for transmission, will secure a special dinner, which will be served for family parties in the saloon, or compartment which they occupy. Carriages are supplied, on application, for invalids, which may be attached at any station on the company's line. Compartments of carriages may be retained by four first-class passengers. It is difficult to discover a want in the shape of creature comfort, or luxury of travelling, which is not at the command of passengers by the Midland Railway. In no other country in the world does such service of trains exist as that which is provided by the Midland, Eastern, and Western routes to Scotland and the north. There are eight up Midland trains to Carlisle in the day, and seven to Glasgow and Edinburgh, and the same number of down trains. There is a service of five trains daily each way for Dundee and Perth, and two to Aberdeen, via the new Tay Bridge, and Inverness has its contingent of three trains daily each way. It remains to be added that all trains on the Midland are first and third class. The programme of the season does credit to the organizing powers of Mr Noble, the general manager of the company.

A NEW RAILWAY TO SCOTLAND

Penrith Observer, 9 August 1887

THE SETTLE AND CARLISLE BRANCH

The strike of drivers and firemen took full effect on this branch at midnight on Thursday. All goods trains stopped at stations, or, if not at the nearest siding; fires were drawn out, and the engines and trains left. At Aisgill Moor seven trains were so shunted and left, at Kirkby Stephen three, and at Appleby several. The men then left the station premises, and walked about until the morning trains were available for them , when they left for their homes, paying their fares as ordinary passengers. The passenger trains were not much behind so far, but goods traffic is practically suspended. A curious circumstance occurred at Kirkby Stephen. A goods train pulled up about midnight in charge of a driver who was not, but a fireman who was, a society man. The fireman promptly left the engine, and the driver was obliged to stop, owing to the regulation forbidding and train to proceed without both fireman and driver, but, shunting his train, he proceeded up the line till he picked up a man, and resumed his journey to Carlisle which he completed in safety.

Penrith Observer, 9 August 1887

THE MIDLAND STRIKE: THE SITUATION AT CARLISLE

The intervention of Sunday enabled the local officials of the Carlisle section of the Midland line to clear all their sidings and bring up the arrears of goods traffic ready for a clear start on Monday morning. With the exception of two meat trains, which had to be handed to the London and North Western Company on Thursday morning, the Midland Company have been able to carry all their traffic themselves. As the drivers and firemen of passenger trains remained at their work little delay has been experienced in that department of the traffic. A large number of drivers and firemen from the Scots lines have passed through Carlisle to fill up the vacancies. At Carlisle the places were all filled up on Friday, and there were several sets to spare. Thirteen drivers and nineteen firemen who had joined the strike are to be discharged from the Company's services, their places having been supplied by others.

More details from the *Spectator* newspaper:-

Till last week, the men on the Midland Railway practically worked at fixed weekly wages. They were paid so much a week, and for this pay the Company could call for a week's work; but whether they were called on to work out their full time or not, they received a week's pay. Instead of this arrangement, the Board of Directors determined to substitute what was in effect piece-work. They gave notice that in future the men were to be called on as before when there was work to be done, but that they were only to be paid for the number of hours during which they were actually on duty. In favour of the change of system, it was alleged, among other things, that the old plan imperilled the discipline and efficiency of the Company's servants; that the wages actually earned by the men would be as large, only more fairly distributed; and that the shirking practised by the lazy, and the consequent overwork of the willing, would be got rid of. It was found, the Directors declare, that many men, knowing that their wages would not suffer, did not come forward when called on, and that it was often difficult to get on without throwing too great a burden upon those who were conscientious enough to come when wanted. To all this the men replied that the existing plan had worked well for twenty years, and had made the Midland line stand high in the opinion of the public for the efficiency of its train-service.

At 12 at night on Thursday week, the old contracts under which the men were working came to an end, and at that hour the strike began. The men actually engaged in running goods trains drew up at the first danger-signal reached after midnight, raked out the engine fires, and left their trains. It does not appear that this was done in the case of passenger trains, nor did any loss, of, or, indeed, danger to life arise from the action thus taken. We notice that the men are blamed even by those who support them otherwise, for thus abandoning the trains.

The way in which the men's loyalty to the strike was maintained seems, again, to have been quite unobjectionable. There was no intimidation, and almost none of that jeering at, or mobbing of, the men who remained at work or who filled the places of the strikers, which is almost as bad as intimidation

The public has, on the whole, expressed a great deal of sympathy for the men. That they have done so can hardly be wondered at when we consider what a splendid body of men the engine-drivers are.

The Leeds Mercury, 2 November 1887

FATAL ACCIDENT AT DENT

Yesterday morning, after a sudden fall had been recorded in the barometer to 27, a terrific storm of wind was experienced at Dent, which is one of the most exposed situations on the Settle and Carlisle Railway. About ten o'clock the force of the tempest broke away the roof of a cattle truck as the train was passing over a viaduct near Dent and the detached part, after being carried some distance, fell in the midst of a gang of platelayers who were working on the viaduct. One of them, named John Ward (46), the foreman, was struck on the head by the falling framework. The sides of the skull was smashed in, and the man was rendered immediately unconscious. He was conveyed by a special train to the Leeds Infirmary, Dr Buck accompanying him. After lingering for some hours, the unfortunate man succumbed to his injuries shortly after nine o'clock last evening. Two platelayers were struck by the roof, but their injuries were not of a serious character.

The Leeds Mercury, 4 November 1887

THE FATAL ACCIDENT ON THE RAILWAY AT DENT

Mr J. C. Malcolm, the Borough Coroner, held an inquest at the Leeds Town Hall yesterday, relative to the death of John Ward (46), the foreman of a gang of platelayers, who received fatal injuries on the Settle and Carlisle Railway on Tuesday… He was conveyed to Dent, and thence by special train to Leeds, where he was taken to the Infirmary, in which institution he died the same evening. From the evidence adduced yesterday it appears the viaduct is 100 feet high, and was exposed to the full force of the wind. Mr Joseph Elliot, an examiner of trains, said the truck was of an old fashioned type, and the top was nailed on. There were frequent reports of these tops lifting, and orders had been issued that trucks of that kind should receive special attention. The jury retired to consider their verdict, but on returning the foreman stated that they thought they had not sufficient evidence before them, and expressed a desire to see the truck and roof. The inquiry was consequently adjourned.

Penrith Observer, 8 November 1887

THE RAILWAY RATING APPEAL AT CARLISLE

The adjourned Cumberland Quarter Sessions gave judgment on Wednesday in the important appeals by the Midland Railway Company against the assessment of a portion of their line between Settle and Carlisle. It will be remembered that the Assessment Committee of the Carlisle Union assessed the seven odd miles of railway in the parish of Wetheral at £3,643, or, roughly speaking, £300 per mile, and that the Company appealed against that valuation, and contended that the railway should be assessed at £1,479, or again roughly speaking, about £200 per mile. The unanimous judgment of the court was that the company had not made out their case, and that the assessment must stand. The appeal was, therefore, dismissed, with costs; as were also, by agreement, three other appeals which had been entered by the Company against assessments made in Cotehill, Cumwhitton, and St Cuthbert's Without.

1888

Penrith Observer, 13 March 1888

TWO RAILWAY FATALITIES

A goods guard named James Ward met with a shocking death at Hawes Junction, on the Settle and Carlisle Railway, on Saturday. He was coupling a wagon, when by some means he fell beneath the wheels and was frightfully mangled, and died immediately. On Saturday afternoon about three o'clock, a platelayer named Richard Ellison, (52), while crossing the goods yard at Hawes, was caught between the buffers of two trucks attached to a Midland engine, and crushed so severely that he expired almost immediately.

Penrith Observer, 11 September 1888

RAILWAY ACCIDENT ON THE MIDLAND LINE

A serious block occurred at Kirkby Stephen early on Tuesday morning. A heavily laden goods train was proceeding in the direction of Carlisle, when by some means not ascertained two of the wagons were thrown off the rails. They were smashed to pieces, the contents being scattered about the metals, and the main line blocked. All the fast expresses from Scotland to various centres were delayed some hours. The guard of the goods train was slightly injured. A breakdown gang was telegraphed for from Carlisle. In the meanwhile the traffic was worked through a loop line and thence on to the main line. The 9-15 Scots express from Glasgow, due in Manchester at five minutes to four, did not arrive in Victoria Station until 25 minutes to seven.

1889

Penrith Observer, 10 September 1889

BREAKDOWN ON THE MIDLAND RAILWAY

On Tuesday evening last the engine attached to the Glasgow fast express train from London broke down, owing to the bursting of a tube, immediately after passing Appleby Station. The disabled engine was shunted into a siding, and after an hour's delay the Glasgow train was attached to the Edinburgh express, which then proceeded en route for Carlisle.

---

* "Ann Stansfield, who lived in an old thatched cottage in Culgaith was a widow (her husband having been killed on the railway) made herself a little money by mangling her neighbours' washing. Her charge was three pence a basketful of clothes. She had a very primitive kind of mangle consisting of one roller with a handle attached. Underneath the roller was a big flat stone on which the clothes were laid out, and when the handle was turned the roller went over them flattening them out."

from *The Story of Culgaith and its People,* Ada Huddart 1959.

Chapter Thirteen
1890-1899

The Penrith Herald, 1 February 1890

A PLATE LAYER KILLED ON THE MIDLAND RAILWAY

Yesterday morning, the dead body of James Stansfield, a platelayer on the Midland railway, was found near the entrance of the Culgaith tunnel, in a horribly mutilated condition. The deceased, who was a married man with a large family, resided at the level crossing cottage near Culgaith station. He left home in the morning at seven o'clock to proceed to his work, and was not seen again till 8-40, when his body was found as stated, a passing train having run over it and cut it to pieces. An inquest will be held at Culgaith.

The Penrith Herald, 8 February 1890

THE ACCIDENT AT CULGAITH

Last week we published particulars of the death of a platelayer named James Stansfield on the railway near Culgaith. He had been walking along the line to his work, which at that time lay between two tunnels, close to Culgaith village, and it is supposed that when entering the tunnel he stepped out of the up track, to evade an approaching train, into that of the down line with out perceiving that a goods train was also coming in that direction. This train overtook him, and striking him on the head killed him instantly. The sad event happened about 7-10 am and the body was discovered by the ganger, Mr Symes about 8-30, when coming through the tunnel. He called for assistance of the other platelayers, who conveyed the remains to the waiting room at Culgaith station. From the marks on the line, the deceased seemed to have been struck when about ten yards inside the tunnel but the body was found 37 yards from the entrance, and was lying in the four foot of the down line. A passenger train leaving Culgaith at 7-47 would pass over the body as it had not then been found. An inquest was held on Saturday morning at Culgaith station before Mr Lee deputy coroner…

Mr Symes identified the body and testified to finding it as stated above. The driver said that he was in charge of an express goods train from Liverpool. In accordance with instructions he sounded the whistle before reaching the tunnel, but he saw no person, and was not aware of the accident till he received information at Carlisle. He had been a driver for 17 years, and this was his first accident. The jury returned a verdict of accidental death, with no blame attached to anyone. The deceased lived in the cottage adjoining the station, and it was part of his duties to mind the gates at the level crossing at Culgaith station, after the last of the stopping trains had gone. He was 41 years old, and leaves a widow and seven children, three of whom are at service. He was a very quiet, steady man, with a hobby for gardening, and was well known as a successful exhibitor at many of the local flower shows.*

It is coincidence that the deceased father was killed by a passing train on the Midland Railway near Newbiggin, just over thirteen years ago.

The Leeds Times, 12 April 1890

On Tuesday, whilst some shunting operations were going on at the Craven Lime Works, Midland Railway, near Settle, a signal failed to act. The result was that a goods train ran into the rear of some detached wagons, and smashed a number of them. A breakdown gang were occupied all day in clearing the way, traffic meanwhile being conducted on a single line.

A NEW RAILWAY TO SCOTLAND

The Penrith Observer, 22 February 1890

THE NEW ROUTE TO THE LAKES

On Tuesday Messrs. Cook had another of their popular trips, via the new route, to the Westmorland Lakes, from Leeds and Bradford to Patterdale. The tourists, numbering 123 (including a number of ladies), arrived at Appleby, by Midland train, 9-30am. Provision was made by Mr Rigg, of the King's Head Hotel, for the conveyance of the party by vehicles from Appleby by Brougham Park, and thence to Pooley Bridge, where the steamer was in waiting to convey the visitors through the picturesque scenery surrounding the lake to Patterdale. The day throughout was exceptionally fine. Messrs Cook are to be complimented on this as on the previous occasion. Great credit is also due to Mr Rigg for conveyances, which were carried out with general satisfaction. The only mar to the day's result was the loss of a horse valued at £35, belonging to Mr Rigg which took ill on the return journey, and succumbed to inflammation on Wednesday morning.

And now for something a little different! A story form the other side of the world.

Hawke's Bay Herald, New Zealand, 27 September 1890

…we relate an episode in the humble career of a signalman, Andrew Agge, who may be found on duty in his box at Culgaith, a little station on the Midland twenty three miles south of Carlisle.

Mr Agge is on duty nearly every day, and must break his fast without leaving his post. The confinement and mental strain tell on his system. The strongest man cannot stand it long without feeling its effects. It makes one think of the passionate exclamation in Tom Hood's *Song of the Sprit* " Oh, God! That bread should be so dear. And flesh and blood so cheap."

Our friend has been at the same work for many years, although he was only 35 when these lines were written. In 1884 he began to think that he was about to break down. "I don't know what ails me." He would say, " but I can't eat." What he forced down produced no sense of satisfaction or strength. Sometimes he was alarmed at finding he could scarcely walk on account of giddiness. He said to himself "What if I should be seized with this at some moment when there is trouble on the line, and I need all my wits about me?"

Other features of this ailment were pains in the chest and sides, costiveness, yellow skin and eyes, bad taste in the mouth, risings of foul gases in the throat, etc. The doctor said Agge must give up his confined work or risk utter disability. He could not. Wife and children were in the way. So he remained at his post and grew worse. But his work was always right, telegrams were properly received and sent, and no train got into trouble through any neglect or fault of his. His disease, indigestion dyspepsia, took a step further, and brought on kidney and bladder trouble. The doctor, at Appleby, said, "Mr Agge, you are poisoned with the foul stuff in your stomach and blood." His doom seemed to be sealed. It was like a death warrant. Six months more rolled by. On duty one morning he was attacked with so great and so sharp a distress he could neither sit nor stand. He says, "I tumbled down on that locker and lay there till all the forenoon. Signals might be given, the telegraph needle might click, but I heeded them no more than a man in the grave heeds the beating of the rain against his own tombstone."

He was alone at first, but help arrived, and the poor signalman was carried home. Physicians laboured on his case without avail. Around his bed were his five little children, the mother being absent in an institution, to be treated for a serious ailment.

Here he lay for weeks, part of the time unconscious. Nothing was to be done but to wait for the end. Then the torpid faculties awakened for a moment.

Memory flashed up, he recalled the fact that a medicine which he had used with benefit years before,

---

* Post Office Directory, Cumberland, for 1901, Andrew Agg listed as Signalman.

and then thrown aside and forgotten, was concealed in a secret place at the signal box.

He sent for it, and took a dose. Soon his bowels moved, the kidneys acted, the pain was eased, he felt better. With brightened hope he sent to Carlisle for more. It arrived, he used it, and in a few days the doctors were astonished to find their patient out of doors, and on the road to recovery. He regained his health completely, and in speaking of his experience, said to the writer. "What a wonderful thing it was that, on what promised to be my death bed, I suddenly remembered where I had put that half used bottle of Mothers Seigel's Curative Syrup. That flash of memory probably saved me from death."*

1892

Penrith Observer, 23 February 1892

PRESENTATION TO THE LATE STATION MASTER AT APPLEBY

Mr Moss, who was for some time station master at Appleby Midland Station, and who is now in charge of the station at Kirkby Stephen, was a few days ago presented with a splendid dinning room clock, subscribed for by his late staff at the Appleby Station... The clock, which was supplied by Messrs. Gibson & Son, Appleby, was of black marble, richly ornamented with gilt, and the dial was of ivory with a dead gold background. Mr Moss, whilst at Appleby, was very highly respected not only by his own staff but by the tradesmen and inhabitants of Appleby in general. He was always prompt and obliging, and the news of his removal was received with general regret.

The Sheffield and Rotherham Independent, 28 September 1892

MIDLAND RAILWAY STATION CHANGES

...Mr Dickinson, from Clowne, Derbyshire, has gone to Langwathby, Cumberland, and for the time being Mr Masters is in charge at Clowne.

1893

Penrith Observer, 14 November 1893

ROBBERY AT KIRKBY STEPHEN

Early on Saturday morning it was discovered that the booking office at the Midland Railway Station, Kirkby Stephen, had been broken into by the window facing the railway, after having broken a pane and undone the latch. When searching for cash he was disappointed, as the office had been cleared of all money on the previous evening. Halfpenny stamps to the value of 6s/6½d are missing, and these appear to be the only booty the depredator thought it worth his while to secure. Information was given to the police, but there is no clue. Several similar offences were committed in the district two years ago.

Penrith Observer, 5 December 1893

SHOCKING ACCIDENT NEAR LITTLE SALKELD
AN EDENHALL RIVER WATCHER CUT TO PIECES ON THE RAILWAY

Yesterday morning Mr J. B. Lee, Coroner, held an inquest at Little Salkeld Station, on the Midland Railway, into the circumstances attending the death of Elijah Braithwaite. whose remains were found at 7-45 on Saturday morning on the railway between Little Salkeld and Lazonby stations...

Elijah Braithwaite, who resided at Dolphenby Cottage, Edenhall, was 41 years of age. He was water bailiff in the employ of the Eden Conservancy Board... Joseph Thompson, platelayer, Little Salkeld, said he was examining his length of line at about 7-40 on Saturday morning when he found a piece of a coat and a shoe lying at the Long Meg siding, and about 100 yards further on he found the body of a man lying close to the bridge in the four foot way on the up line. Police constable Railton came up at the time, and they picked up a piece of paper, which was found to be the deceased's appointment form.

Witness had been a platelayer for seven years. He had occasionally seen deceased cross the bridge to get from one side of the river to the other, but not within the last six months. He thought deceased had permission to cross the bridge.

There was a cottage on the brow, and a signal box close to where the body was found. The signal box, however, was closed at five o'clock in the evening, as it was only used for the Long Meg Alabaster Works... He knew the deceased was in the habit of going along the railway, and on one occasion witness left him as he was going over the bridge at twelve o'clock at night. Deceased used to say he could get a good view of the river from the bridge. If the deceased had wanted to have gone to his home the road would have been the better way... He must have left Lazonby at about 10-30 on Friday night, and that would give him time to get to the siding just as the 11-11 goods train would be passing...

Inspector Nicholson, said deceased had no authority, but his appointment for being on the line. The appointment, however, was considered sufficient authority as it gave him power to go into any place except a house or its immediate surroundings. He knew it had been the habit of deceased to cross the bridge frequently. It was a common thing for watchmen at Lazonby and Kirkoswald to walk along the bridge, because they could get a full view of the water for a good distance. Deceased had never said that he had been threatened by anyone, nor was he afraid of being injured. Deceased was a big, powerful man, and had been in the employ of the Conservancy Board for six years... The jury returned a verdict to the effect that deceased was accidently killed on the railway at Long Meg sidings.

1894

Penrith Observer 13 February 1894

SAD RAIL FATALITY AT LAZONBY

On Friday evening Mr J. C. Wannop, deputy coroner for the city, held an inquest at the Carlisle Infirmary on the body of James Ferguson, 66 years of age, who lived at Surtees Lane, Botchergate, and died at the infirmary at half past seven on Tuesday night. A fortnight ago deceased, who had rather peculiar ways, left his home, and had been found lying on the roadside near Penrith. He had been taken by order of the magistrates to the workhouse at Penrith, and was allowed out a day or two later, after his friends had been communicated with in Carlisle. He had not come home, however, and on Wednesday morning the driver of a goods train, Robert Winter, who was doing some shunting in a siding near Lazonby heard a groaning beneath his engine. It was about five o'clock, and dark, but by the aid of his lamp he discovered the deceased below the engine. He assisted him to rise, and afterwards Dr Macdonald, Kirkoswald, bandaged deceased's arm and attended to his injuries... A verdict of 'Accidentally killed' was returned.

The Leeds Mercury 8 June 1894

TEMPERANCE DEMONSTRATION AT LANGWATHBY

The Vale of Eden Band of Hope Union which this year attains its majority, held a most successful demonstration at Edenhall, the seat of Sir R. G. Musgrave, Bart., yesterday. The weather was gloriously fine, and the beautiful grounds and walks looked at their best. A procession of 3,000 children, accompanied by the Carlisle Artillery Prize Band and several local bands, was formed at Langwathby Station at noon, and marched to the fete grounds. During the afternoon selections of vocal music were given by the Penrith Glee Society, and prizes were offered to Band of Hope children for competition in recitation. Various other amusements were provided, and addresses on the temperance question were delivered by Mr Guy Hayler, Newcastle-on Tyne, and others.

The Band of Hope was started in 1847, a temperance movement founded to curb excessive drinking by children and young adults. The movement spread country wide and by 1887 there were 1½ million members of all Christian denominations. In 1897 with 3 million members Queen Victoria became patron. The demonstrations or gatherings took place at Easter or Whitsontide when members would march to a suitable venue where after an address by the local clergy they spent time in recreation followed by a tea. Children from the whole Eden Valley area would have come by special trains to Langwathby to take part.

The Yorkshire Herald, 1 December 1894

COLLISION NEAR CARLISLE NARROW ESCAPE OF A MIDLAND EXPRESS

On Monday night a railway collision occurred on the Midland Railway at Lazonby. The last local Midland train to Appleby is made up of Glasgow and South Western carriages, and returns to Carlisle empty. On the way back the train ran into a wagon used for loading timber at Lazonby. The wreckage is described as very great. The Midland dining express was close behind, and had a narrow escape. It reached Carlisle an hour and a half late.

Penrith Observer, 4 December 1894

THE RECENT RAILWAY ACCIDENT AT LAZONBY

Yesterday morning an inquiry was held at Lazonby Railway Station, by three of the Midland Railway permanent officials, into the circumstances of the accident which occurred on the line a week ago. All the men in any way connected with the disaster were under examination, and the inquiry lasted three and a half hours. The men most interested in the affair will not know the result of the inquiry until eight or ten days hence. The enquiry was strictly private.

1895

The Sheffield and Rotherham Independent, 15 October 1895

ONE OF THE PRETTIST SPOTS IN ENGLAND

Joseph Foster, the landlord of the Bridge End Inn, Helwith Bridge, Horton-in-Ribblesdale, appealed against the decision of the West Riding Justices at Ingleton, who had refused to renew his licence. Mr Walter Beveley and Mr Shepherd appeared for the appellant and Mr Thomas and Mr Stephen H. West for the respondents. At the recent Brewers Sessions the justices declined to renew the licences on two grounds, non adaptability of the premises and no necessity. In support of the appellant it was said the house is extremely extensively used by members of the Manchester Angling Club, who lease a long length of the River Ribble, which flows by the house, and that shooting parties also used the house for sleeping when grouse shooting in the dales. It was also asserted that the district is one of the prettiest spots in England, is much frequented by tourists and tradesmen from Settle and other places; that the postmen leaves letters there for persons; that the Medical Officer for the district uses the house as his vaccination station and that there are some slate and lime quarries in the locality. On the other hand, it was said that the premises consist of two cottages made into one house, to which a licence was granted some years age when the Settle and Carlisle Railway was being constructed in the locality. After three hours had been spent in hearing the appeal it was dismissed with costs.

1896

Penrith Observer, 15 December 1896

THE PROPOSED BRIDGE AT THE APPLEBY MIDLAND STATION

In view of the action of the Appleby Town Council in regard to this matter a prominent official of the railway company yesterday pointed out to our Appleby correspondent a return of the Board of Trade for the six months ending in June, from which it appeared that during that period nine persons had been killed and 14 injured in crossing the lines at railway stations and of these seven were killed and eleven injured at stations where there was either a subway or over bridge, thus apparently bearing out the chairman of director's remark to the late mayor (Lord Hothfield) that passengers will not use these means of communication when they are provided.

1897
Penrith Observer, 1 June 1897

SERIOUS ACCIDENT AT LANGWATHBY

This morning Mr Dickinson, stationmaster at Langwathby, met with a nasty accident. While some timber was being unloaded he was struck on the side of the head by the truck, and knocked down. It was feared that his jaw was broken, while the unfortunate man was also badly cut about the ear and head. Efficent first aid was rendered, by the foreman, and Mr Dickinson was put to bed, where he was afterwards attended by Dr Winship. The extent of his injuries is not yet accurately known.

Penrith Observer, 29 June 1897

MIDLAND RAILWAY TRAIN ALTERATIONS

The inhabitants of the villages situated between Appleby and Carlisle have been grumbling for a long time past at the local train service on the Midland Railway. They will, therefore, be glad to hear that there will commence with July a complete re-arrangement of the running of the trains. The present 8-45am train from Carlisle is changed to 8-30, and will be followed at 9-15 by an express to Appleby. The 2-15pm train, which, at present, only runs on Saturdays, will leave Carlisle at that time every day for Langwathby, but on Saturdays to Appleby. The present 3-30 train from Carlisle will leave at 4-10 in future. A new train will leave Appleby for Carlisle at 12-40pm, stopping at each station. At 5-22pm a train is timed to leave Langwathby daily for Carlisle, but on Saturdays will start from Appleby.

1898
The Penrith Observer, 10 May 1898

EXTRAORDINARY ACCIDENT AT APPLEBY

A remarkable occurrence was witnessed on the Eden Bridge at Appleby on Wednesday forenoon. The Midland Railway Company's lorry was taking a load of goods from the station into the town; the contents included sacks of feeding stuffs, cases, etc., the whole weighing probably not much under a couple of tons. When the horse got to the crown of the bridge it suddenly swerved, and before the driver, Tom Hayton, had any idea of what was about to happen the animal leapt over the wall and was hanging head downwards towards the river. The front part of the vehicle was lifted on the parapet, a fact, considering the weight, which amazed the onlookers, both at the time and afterwards.

The horse was suspended for a few seconds, and then the shafts broke off and the harness also gave way, so that the animal dropped into the deep water almost under the arch on the Appleby side of the bridge. It could not get out owing to the sharp ascent, but Hayton by running round and wading into the middle of the river was able to reach the reins by the aid of a walking stick; he led the horse across the stream and on to the Bongate road at the end of Mr R. Yare's house. To the surprise of everyone who had witnesses its escapade, the horse appeared to be no worse for the occurrence, and was taken away to its stable. The attempt to get the wagon from the bridge was attended with considerable difficulty. The goods were taken off, and then the wagon was lifted down. This caused one of the large coping stones of the embrasure of the bridge to topple into the river, and several others were broken.

The Penrith Observer, 27 September 1898

NARROW ESCAPE OF A MIDLAND EXPRESS

On Saturday evening the Midland express train, which left Carlisle for the south at 5-45pm, had a narrow escape from wreckage when it reached Ribblehead. One of the tyres of a driving wheel on the engine came off as the train was running along at a good speed, and the fragments hit one of the steam pipes, with the result that all the steam ran out of the engine with a loud noise. Fortunately no further harm occurred to the train, which was brought to a stand. The engine having completely broken down, a message had to be conveyed on foot to the nearest signal cabin. As the signal cabins are far apart on the fells at this section of the line, much delay was caused before a new engine could be got from Hellifield to take on the disabled train, the passengers in which had been alarmed by the sudden stoppage, and had got out of the train on to the bank. Owing to the train having passed one signal cabin but not arrived at the next, the signalman there, according to the rules, had to stop the dining express due in Carlisle at 8-55pm, until the nature of the mishap was ascertained. This train consequently did not reach Carlisle till 10-45pm.

1899

Penrith Herald, 7 January 1899

RAILWAYMEN'S ENTERTAINMENT AT CROSBY GARRETT

A public entertainment and supper, under the auspices of the Midland Railway staff at Crosby Garrett was given in the Board School on Thursday evening week. Mr Reynolds, stationmaster, who initiated the proceedings, secured the services of the Kirkby Stephen Orchestral Society's Band, whose music, rare indeed in this locality, gave great pleasure to the large audience… After the last performance by the band, a move was made to the class-room, where a sumptuous supper was provided… The rooms were tastefully decorated for the occasion by the railway staff, assisted by Mr and Mrs Gledhill, the schoolmaster and mistress. About 180 sat down to supper. Any surplus funds will serve to defray the expenses of fixing a lamp at the Railway Cottages.

The Penrith Observer, 24 January 1899

LANDSLIP ON THE RAILWAY AT KIRKBY STEPHEN

About eleven o'clock on Wednesday night, when the storm was at its height, a landslip occurred on the Midland Railway, in the first cutting north of Kirkby Stephen Station. Owing to the recent heavy rain the embankment at this particular place had suffered considerable damage the previous few days, and its unsafe condition was known to the local railway officials. A special watch was therefore kept upon it, and a man was stationed on duty in this capacity when the landslip occurred and the metals of the south line became embedded beneath 50 tons of earth. A gang of labourers was speedily set to work removing the obstruction, and in the meantime the traffic from the south was carried over the north line between Crosby Garrett and Kirkby Stephen, and in this way only a slight delay was occasioned. By five o clock on Thursday morning the obstructed line was cleared sufficiently for trains to pass.

Liverpool Mercury, 14 July 1899

THE GREAT THUNDER STORM

A Kirkby Stephen (Westmorland) correspondent says, further reports of the storm show the damage to have been much more serious than supposed. A waterspout burst on Hartley Fell, and tore a huge rent in the mountainside visible for miles. The signal cabin at Kirkby Stephen Midland Station was struck by lighting, and the signalman injured by the flying glass. The River Swale, swollen by the rain, carried away every bridge for ten miles.

A NEW RAILWAY TO SCOTLAND

The Leeds Times, 29 July 1899

HOLIDAY NOTES: AFTERNOON IN A TUNNEL

…My first acquaintance with the Settle and Carlisle line was at the period of its formation. The engineers had completed the lofty viaducts, pierced the tunnels through the hard rock, and were having a hard fight with the 'slurry' slipping stuff that would roll down the cuttings after heavy rain, and swamp the efforts of the navvies. The other day, when travelling on the line, it was noticeable that the 'slurry' was still at its old game of 'slip', but the engineers have overcome this propensity, in some degree by drainage. In the winter time, at the higher levels, the snow was a great trouble. This has been guarded against at Dent Head by the erection of snow guards, on the side of the line, to keep the heavy masses gathering in that region from blocking the deep cuttings. My experience in Blea Moor tunnel on the highest level, was something to be remembered for a lifetime.

Accompanied by a guide who had a candle stuck in his hat, and carried one in each hand, I also having a couple of candles, we advanced into the darksome hole in the hillside, first 'paying toll' to a stalwart navvy. The scene was grim and weird in its significance. Dimly illuminated by candles stuck in the hats of the miners and by others placed in various positions the swarthy faces of the men had a singular aspect as they plied hammer, chisel and pick, or pressed holes for 'shot' to blow up the hard rock, which the reverberating sound of the heavily struck tools was deafening. It was a kind of pandemonium. Occasionally a shout was heard 'Look out'. The miners rushed to places of safety. We followed suit as a loud explosion burst upon the ear and masses of stones and rock were hurled in various directions. The miners immediately after resumed their work.

We slowly progressed, other 'tolls' having to be paid and several 'shots' were fired, but at length a narrow opening, just sufficient to crawl through admitted us to the other portion of the tunnel. 'Heavy toll' was then necessary to enable us to pass through. It was no easy task walking, amongst stones, large and small, varied by shouts of 'Look out' when down fell heavy stones of large size within a few yards of where we had stood. This was fine fun for the miners, but not for us. Finally a glimmer of light was seen ahead. Immediately 'Look out' was again the cry. My guide exclaimed, 'Run, sir, run!' I complied but had only gone a few yards when I fell over a stone, flopped into a pool of water, my candles and those of the guide were extinguished, and a heavy stone, tons weight, landed from the roof on the very spot we had just quitted. This was my first and last tunnel exploration. I didn't want another experience of the kind. However, we completed our two mile journey underground, and came into the glorious evening sunlight at Dent Head. Heaven upon earth as it appeared to us, in a prettiness. The grand prospect that greeted the eye at that fine outlook amongst the hills atoned for all the difficulties we had undergone. Tunnel driving has been improved since that period.

That adventure is always remembered when passing through the tunnels of that region whether in the splendid corridor day cars or in the cosy sleeping coaches... the journey through the hills has no terrors, even in the most inclement weather. Thanks to the enterprise of the company and their engineers, we are, in these modern days, blessed with comforts in these travelling hotels of which our ancestors never dreamed. Surely we ought to feel grateful for these good things.

Chapter Thirteen
1900-1908

The Penrith Observer, 16 January 1900

CURIOUS ACCIDENT AT APPLEBY

On Sunday morning an accident occurred at the Midland Railway Station, Appleby, to a train examiner. Daniel Gerrard, who resides in Carlisle, but has been for the past few weeks been relieving one of the men from Appleby owing to illness, went on duty at six o'clock in the morning. He had examined the train and was according to his statement, returning to the cabin at 6-25, when he slipped, and the train passed over his right arm. He went into the cabin, where Mr John Beeby rendered first aid until Dr de Montmorency arrive. The doctor amputated the limb above the elbow, Gerrard was immediately afterwards despatched to Carlisle Infirmary.

The Penrith Observer, 20 March 1900

A MIDLAND EXPRESS ON FIRE: NARROW ESCAPE OF PASSENGERS

An accident of a peculiar nature occurred on the Midland Railway between Bleamoor Tunnel and Settle on Sunday morning to the express from the Waverley Station, Edinburgh, to St Pancras, which left Carlisle at 12-50am. In the centre of the train was a sleeping car for first class passengers, and in the car were three passengers from Edinburgh to the south along with the car conductor. At the rear end of the car was a heating stove with an oil lamp in the ceiling above. As the express was travelling full speed through Bleamoor Tunnel the car conductor noticed that the rear end of the car was in flames. He at once pulled the communication cord, but it snapped. Still the train rushed on until the driver saw the signals against him at the bottom of the hill near Settle, and it transpired that the stoppage had been brought about by the signalmen in the cabins which the train had passed seeing that the car was in flames and sending the 'stop and examine' electric signal on with all speed from cabin to cabin. The three passengers in the car left it at Settle Station, and the car was detached from the train, which subsequently resumed the journey to London, the sleeping car passengers, who had been greatly alarmed , having to be accommodated in ordinary first class compartments. The escape from an awful death had been marvellous, for had the front end of the car been the scene of the fire instead of the rear end, the consequences would have been serious owing to the communication cord snapping. The rear end of the car was so much burned that the cause of the fire cannot be positively ascertained, but it is believed to have been due either to the heating stove or the oil lamp. The sleeping cars on these night expresses are still heated with stoves, but the dining cars run on the day expresses on the Midland have steam pipe heating apparatus supplied from the engine.

The Penrith Observer, 7 August 1900

THE ROYAL VISIT TO EDENHALL.
DEPARTURE OF THE PRINCESS VICTORIA: INTERESTING INCIDENT

The Princess Victoria of Wales, after having been about the fortnight the guest of Sir Richard and Lady Musgrave at Edenhall, left Penrith on Monday at midnight for London, a sleeping berth being reserved for her use… During her stay in Cumberland the Princess was, generally speaking favoured with good weather, which enabled her and Lady Musgrave to spend a great deal of their time in cycling, an exercise of which the Princess is passionately fond. Many interesting places in the district have been visited during her stay. A rather notable incident attaches to her last cycle run in Cumberland. The Princess and Lady Musgrave went out on Monday afternoon for a 'spin' and for some reason, probably because the weather was rather oppressive, the two ladies resolved to take the train from a local station to Langwathby. They accordingly booked first class, and had their cycles put into the van. But instead of taking their seats in a first class compartment requested the driver and a fireman to allow them, as a favour, to travel to their destination on the engine, so as to experience the sensation of travelling on a locomotive while in rapid motion, and also to observe its work. The rules of the railway company prohibit drivers taking any person on their engines without authority, so the driver, while most anxious to accede to their wishes, had no alternative but to reluctantly decline to grant their request, as it would have constituted a breach of the laws of the service. No doubt had application been made to the railway authorities permission would only too readily have been granted for the ladies to have their desire gratified, but there was no time for anything of the kind to be done, and the workmen were extremely sorry that they could not oblige. The Princess and Lady Musgrave readily understood the situation in which the men were placed and they did not press their request further. Needless to say both the engine driver and fireman were profuse in their expressions of regret. Princess Victoria cordially thanked the locomotive attendants for their courtesy, and expressed her admiration for their sense of duty. The two ladies then tripped away to their first class compartment.

The Leeds Times, 8 September 1900

THROUGH THE DALES

The railway companies, in their desire to please their customers, are rivalling one another in the costliness of their trains, in the size of their coaches, and in the comfort of the fittings. The Midland are evidently determined to bear away the palm in this respect. Their new trains are models of pleasure and comfort. The through trains to the north are conspicuous in this respect. Travelling by the Settle route to the north, the other day, it was a treat to spend an hour in the Carlisle railway station, where one could see the best trains of the great companies that compete for the north and south traffic. The Midland line, as many readers know, is noted for its picturesqueness, especially from Settle to Carlisle, and in its route through the valleys of the Aire, the Ribble, and the Eden, with extensive outlooks over the wild or beautiful country traversed. The companies find, however, that these trains, besides being costly to build, are expensive to work, their great weight necessitating the employment of very powerful locomotives. Some of the latter weigh 80 tons, and with coaches varying from 30 to more than 40 tons weight, it may readily be imagined that the entire weight of a new first class train is something enormous. Some idea of the extent of the traffic may be gained by a knowledge of the fact that, on Saturday, one train from the north was so crowded that it had to be run in four sections, each with two engines. That train was an hour and forty minutes last at Carlisle.

1901

The Penrith Observer, 12 February 1901

BRIDGE FIRE ON THE RAILWAY

On Tuesday evening the driver of a train proceeding in the direction of Kirkby Stephen, on the Midland Railway, observed that a wooden bridge which crosses the line near to Birkett Tunnel was on fire, and on arriving at Kirkby Stephen station he reported the occurrence to the officials there. With all practicable speed a light engine was run to the scene and the fire was extinguished, the damage done being inconsiderable.

The Penrith Herald, 16 March 1901

SAD DEATH OF FARMER NEAR LAZONBY

…Mr John Wales, a retired farmer, who lived with his son-in-law, Mr John Nelson, Force Mill Farm, had been found dead on the road adjoining the Midland Railway near Force Mill, early in the morning… The facts relating to his death were inquired into by Mr J. B. Lee, coroner, who held an inquest yesterday at Force Mill… John Nelson, farmer, Force Mill, said that deceased was his father-in-law, and was 63 years of age. He last saw him between twelve and one on Tuesday at Penrith Auction Mart, and he was then in his ordinary health. Deceased came to Langwathby with the carrier Mrs Graham, to see a friend… From Langwathby deceased came towards home along the railway, a thing which he frequently did when he was at Langwathby. It was very dark on Tuesday night. Witness passed the place where the body was found at 9-30pm. The 'cut' across the railway was often used by people. He had known people to be cautioned for crossing the railway. A water watcher was once killed at the viaduct while crossing the line…

  John Thompson, platelayer, Kirkoswald, said he had been employed by the Midland Railway for 21 years. He remembered the other accident which the previous witness had spoken of. Witness produced a copy of the printed bye-laws forbidding people to trespass on the line. There was a notice board at each end of the viaduct to a similar effect. He had never seen deceased trespassing on the line. He found the body under the bridge about 6-45 on Wednesday morning. Deceased was lying on his left side, and was quite dead. His walking stick was still in his hand… William Bonson, farm labourer, Edenhall, said he saw deceased at ten o'clock on Tuesday night at the Fish Hotel, Langwathby. He was with him for about two hours. They parted at closing time, and he said that he was going home down the line. Deceased was quite sober… In answer to a juryman, the witness said that he expected deceased would use the public road as far as the viaduct and then cross.

  PC Wilkinson, Lazonby, said that he examined the body and found a compound fracture of the skull… On examining the bridge, witness found from two distinct marks that it was evident that deceased had fallen off the embankment wall from a height of about ten feet… The coroner, in summing up, said that as deceased was a trespasser, the railway company could not be responsible. As to the immediate cause of death it was quite clear that the deceased died from the result of the fall. There was one matter he might mention. There were special obligations upon the railway and similar companies which a coroner's inquest could take cognisance of in the interest and safety of the public. If they wished the jury could add a presentment to their verdict with a view of lessening the danger. He mentioned this because during the last week he had had three inquests, and in two the cause of death was through trespassing on railway lines. Since 1893 he had had eight similar inquests. Some discussion took place amongst the jury, who eventually decided to return a verdict of accidental death, and to add no rider of any kind.

The Penrith Herald, 27 April 1901

TRESPASS ON THE RAILWAY NEAR LANGWATHBY

The recent fatality at the viaduct by which the Midland Railway crosses the Eden between Langwathby and Lazonby has had the effect of stirring up the railway authorities and causing them to enforce their bye-laws more strictly. The viaduct in question is the only bridge over the Eden between Langwathby and Lazonby, and persons wishing to reach the other side of the river have, in order to avoid a long detour, made use of the bridge, thus of course, besides running the risk of a passing train, breaking the company's bye-laws. The railway authorities evidently decided to make an example of someone and the unlucky individual was William Little Musgrave, labourer, Lazonby. He appeared at the Penrith Police Court on Tuesday and pleaded guilty to a charge of trespassing on the line. Detective Inspector Hobday representing the company said that the recent fatality at the viaduct brought forth special comments in the newspapers and the authorities decided that some special steps should be taken to prevent this sort of thing. The case was not brought forward in a vindictive spirit but after the accident they felt that some thing must be done to protect the lives of the people Mr F. E. Abbot (Scott and Alan, Penrith) appeared on defendant's behalf and in defence said that it was the custom in the neighbourhood to use this bridge to cross the river and he simply did what others had done. Defendant was extremely sorry, and being a poor man he hoped the Bench would deal as leniently as possible with him

Mr Hobday said that it was not a public highway. Mr Abbot had made it appear to the Bench that people used it as such. Mr Abbot, No, but they use it frequently.

A fine of 5s and costs (25s 6d in all) was imposed.

Note: Using railway viaducts by local people to cross rivers appears to have been an accepted occurrence despite the dangers involved. Ada Huddart recalls in her 1959 book *The Story of Culgaith and its People*: "Towards the end of the last century, a small private school for girls was held at Williamsgill (south west of Culgaith) Dobson had the farm then, and his daughter Minnie took in a few day scholars from Culgaith and other neighbouring villages. The girls from Culgaith walked across the fields and over Newbiggin Viaduct (Crodundle Viaduct) some of the more daring ones walking on the edge of the parapet."

The Penrith Observer 15 October 1901

REMARKABLE ACCIDENT AT ORMSIDE: MARVELLOUS ESCAPE ON THE VIADUCT

At about ten o'clock on Saturday night the people in Ormside were startled by a loud crash on the Midland Railway, and by the moving lights and escaping steam there seemed to be an accident on the viaduct. This fine bridge is 100 feet high over the River Eden. By the prompt precautions of the station officials at Ormside and Appleby any further injury was prevented, and after slight delay at Appleby, an express was allowed to proceed southward. The block was caused by damage to a goods train, which had become divided and was running in two sections on a slight incline. Somehow the rear portion was allowed to collide with the front wagons, still governed by the engine. One of these was lifted off the rails. However, regardless of the terrible shock the driver bravely continued his haulage, so preventing the derailed truck from toppling over and, what was of more serious importance, dragged the wreck clear over the dangerous bridge. There was some waste of good ale in the more heavily laden rear wagons.

1902
The Penrith Observer, 17 June 1902

REMARKABLE ACCIDENT AT APPLEBY: A RAILWAY BRIDGE DRAGGED DOWN

At ten minutes past five on Friday a serious mishap occurred at the Midland Station, Appleby. A goods train was being shunted through the station, and amongst the wagons was one conveying a crane, the jib of which had not been lowered. The train was going fairly fast, and the jib of the crane catching the iron bridge connecting the two platforms, brought it down across the line, leaving only the side supports standing. There were also two wagons thrown off the metals. The staff were soon at work, and quickly had the derailed vehicles put to rights again. The line, however, was blocked, and it was some time before the portion of the bridge which rested on the platforms and one of the wagons of the train was drawn across the up line clear of traffic. The trains, however, were considerably delayed. The 5-20 down express did not pass until 6-50, and the up train, due shortly after five o'clock passed at 6-45. The 5-27 to Carlisle left at 7 o'clock, and the 5-35 slow and 5-55 express for the south left at 7-25 and 7-30 respectively. A breakdown gang from Carlisle arrived during the evening, and both lines were clear when the 6-55 slow from the south left for Carlisle about eight o'clock. The bridge was only erected last November. There was no one injured, the bridge being clear of traffic when the accident happened.

The Penrith Herald, 12 July 1902

PRESENTATION AT LAZONBY

Mr M. A. Hall, who has for five years been stationmaster at Lazonby, has recently been transferred to Redlett, a larger and more important station near St Albans. When the fact became known that Mr Hall was about to leave the district, it was the unanimous wish of the many friends he had made that he should not be allowed to leave without receiving a token of the good will and esteem in which he was held. With the view of promoting a suitable testimonial a committee was formed representing Lazonby and Kirkoswald, and the district… The result of their efforts was seen on Monday night, when Mr Hall was the recipient of several handsome gifts. Owing to the fact that the farmers were busy in the fields there was not a large attendance at the ceremony, which took place in the reading room… They knew he was the paid official of a large company, but there were thousands of little acts that were not paid for, and which, in the case of Mr Hall, they valued very highly indeed. They would like to refer to Mrs Hall, who had been exceedingly kind to many of the girls in the parish. They bitterly regretted they were loosing them but wished them success in their new sphere. Cannon Wilson then asked Mr Hall to accept a very handsome silver tea and coffee service and tray, the latter bearing the inscription 'Presented to Mark Albert Hall by his friends in recognition of his kindness and courtesy as station master at Lazonby and Kirkoswald Station. July 7, 1902.'

Cannon Wilson then presented to Mr Hall on behalf of the railway employees at Lazonby, a silver mounted walking stick and a cigar case… The stick bore the inscription 'Presented to Mr Hall by the traffic and permanent way men at Lazonby station, July 1902.'

The Penrith Observer, 9 September 1902

A LOCAL EXPRESS RECORD: PRODIGIOUS SPEED FROM HAWES TO APPLEBY

Ever since the Midland Railway awoke from its lethargy last year, up to which period the management had been content with the old jog-trot average speed of 40 miles an hour, a substantial acceleration has taken place in the express service between London and Scotland by way of Carlisle. Large engines weighing 102 tons each have been used with success for over twelve months past on the northern section of the line to save stoppages between Leeds and Carlisle for picking up water. The largest locomotive in Great Britain, recently turned out at Derby, which weighs 115 tons and is the first compound engine used on the line, last week, however, eclipsed all previous performances on the Midland. The culmination took place on Friday night, when the journey of 76¾ miles from Hellifield to Carlisle was covered in 79 minutes. The train was the dining express which left St Pancras at 1-30 on Friday afternoon for St Enoch, Glasgow, and Waverley, Edinburgh. It was equal to 13½ vehicles, and the northern portion of the journey to Carlisle was performed with the one engine referred to in a period of time and an average speed which had not hitherto been equalled under similar conditions either on the Midland or the London and North Western. On the latter system, in fact, all the principle express trains have to be run with two engines, usually a compound with a pilot, in order to keep up time.

The new Midland engine, while compound in construction, works on a different principal for the competing compounds built at Crewe, and its three cylinders can be worked simultaneously at high pressure. It is of such weight that, for the safety of bridges it has been found wise to use it only between Leeds and Carlisle, where all bridges and tunnel work was made up-to-date and of enduring strength in 1876, when the Settle to Carlisle section was opened.

The details of Friday nights run are full of interest. The express left St Pancras at 1-30pm., travelling northward to Hellifield, the last stop prior to Carlisle. At Hellifield the start, owing to delays in the south, was 17 minutes late, the journey to Carlisle being begun at 6-41pm instead of 6-24. Hawes Junction is 1,175 feet above sea level, and the upward gradient between Settle and Hawes is 1 in 100. The 25½ miles from Hellifield to Hawes Junction were covered in 36 minutes, giving an average speed per hour up the ascent of 42½ miles. Then came the sensational part of the journey. The decent of 20½ miles from Hawes Junction to Appleby was negotiated in 16 minutes, or at an average speed of 76⅞ miles per hour, a rate which is about four miles an hour faster than the West Coast 'racing' speed of 1895 from Shap to Penrith. On the final night of that struggle it will be remembered that the West Coast train ran from Shap to Penrith at slightly over 72 miles an hour, but the train was composed only of three vehicles, equal in weight to 4½. The last section of the journey from Appleby to Carlisle took 27 minutes. Appleby is not 30 miles from Citadel Station, as many people suppose. The exact distance between the points is 30¾ miles and the average speed per hour on Friday over the section, including the time lost for the slow down and stop, was 68⅕ miles.

When the train stopped in the Citadel Station the clock hands pointed precisely to 8. The express was therefore five minutes late, but twelve minutes arrears had been knocked off during the journey from Hellifield. On one occasion last year 14 minutes arrears were accounted for in a similar way, but the train then was drawn by two engines. It is also interesting to note that the London and North Western time as a general rule for running the 31½ miles from Shap Summit to Carlisle, with two engines, is 25 minutes, giving an average speed of 75⅗ miles per hour. As both the competing lines commence with a flying start, the Midland performance on Friday, with one engine, at an average of 76⅞ miles, works out the best. The details of the run ranks probably as the record 'one engine, platform-to-platform' performance of the world, considering the weight of the train, the height of the summit, and the average speed.

The Penrith Observer, 16 September 1902

SAD ACCIDENT NEAR ORMSIDE: KILLED ON THE RAILWAY

On Friday morning a sad accident occurred near Ormside Station. John Turner Wappett, was proceeding to his work at Southfields Farm and while going over the viaduct was knocked down by a passing stock train and was killed. The inquest was held at the railway station Ormside, on Friday evening before Mr W. Hewetson, coroner. Stephen Bowman, Little Ormside identified the body as that of his father-in-law, a farm labourer, who resided with witness. Deceased was 65 years of age. That morning deceased and himself set off together about six o'clock to go to work. Deceased got on to the Midland Railway at the station end of the viaduct, so that he might cross the River Eden, over the viaduct. Witness stopped behind and the deceased stepped forward across the viaduct and witness followed probably a quarter of an hour afterwards. When he got across the viaduct witness found the deceased lying on the railway embankment on the left side of the railway going from the station. He was much injured, and was quite dead. Witness went to Southfield and gave information.

In the interval between the deceased crossing the viaduct and in following him, a train passed, going north, travelling at a high speed. The deceased had no leave on the railway. Ralph Musgrave, engine driver, Manningham, said he was the driver of an empty stock train from Bradford to Carlisle. On approaching Ormside Viaduct he noticed a man in the four foot of the down line. As soon as he saw him he put his hand on the whistle, but his mate got it before him and sounded the whistle. He saw the man appear to try to get out of the road. The train was travelling from 30 to 35 mile an hour, and had no chance of pulling up. He stopped at the next signal box and gave information. He found the hat produced on the engine lamp. The engine was not marked. He was probably 50 to 100 yards from the man when he first saw him. Henry Smith, fireman corroborated. Supt. Cheesman, Appleby, said the morning he saw the deceased lying half way down the embankment at the Appleby end of the viaduct, He had him conveyed to the station at Ormside where he examined the body. The jury returned a verdict of accidental death.

THE LACK OF A BRIDGE
(to the editor of the *Penrith Observer.*)

Sir, the particulars of an inquest held here to day you will doubtless report. A neighbour named Wappett while trying to cross the River Eden to his work was killed this morning while trespassing over the Midland Railway viaduct. More than one working man has ceased to live at Ormside because he could not get eastward to any work. The agriculturist on that side of the Eden cannot deliver his produce at Ormside Station, neither can we have safe access to the Brough Hill district. There is no bridge between Appleby and Warcop, a distance of about six miles. To remedy this inconvenience the local government of Ormside lately solicited the co-operation of the Rural District Council towards building some bridge. In answer, Ormside was told to provide an estimate.

After survey, this was promptly done, and reply sent to the Rural District Council, that one of the two estimates was as low as £329. That body which had the legal goverance of such affairs, again refused to help, even by saying whether the estimate met its approval, or what in aid might be expected. However, collectors were proceeding to obtain promise of local subscriptions when the chief landowner refused to contribute. A bridge as proposed at Danby Wath would have been nearly opposite the dwelling of poor Wappett, and would have prevented the risking death by an express train. It happens as an additional local privation that the railway has silted up the ancient stepping stones and put them under water.   Yours, J. Brunskill, Ormside Rectory, Appleby, 12 September 1902.

1903

The Penrith Observer, 31 March 1903

LANDSLIPS AT APPLEBY

A land slip has occurred at the Midland Railway Appleby, owing to the recent heavy rains. On Friday the bank on the down side, about a hundred yards above the north signal box, was observed to be slowly slipping, but as the earth subsided the rails were packed to keep their level, and so allow the traffic to continue to run over the metals. On Sunday morning, however, the trains had to be run at caution, and continued to do so until yesterday noon. About one o'clock the slip got so bad that the down line had to be abandoned altogether, and all the traffic was worked on the up line. A distance of about seventy yards has slipped to as much as five feet. Yesterday afternoon a ballast train arrived from Carlisle, and the work of repairing the bank was commenced last night. A portion of the bank above Garth Heads Road, at Bongate end, collapsed on Friday afternoon and came down on to the roadway, bringing with it the retaining wall. A length of about 30 feet is down.

Manchester Courier & Lancashire General Advertiser, 31 March 1903

MOTOR TRAFFIC OPENING UP THE LAKE DISTRICT

Yesterday it was announced that a number of local gentlemen had formed a limited liability concern, to be called the Penrith and District Road Carrying Company, with the object of conveying merchandise by motor cars. The first regular service will be between Penrith and Patterdale, a distance of fifteen miles, by which communication with the whole of the Ullswater district will be facilitated. This will put an end to the long talked of railway from the Midland railway at Langwathby to Pooley Bridge, at the foot of Ulswater. If the present scheme answers the expectations of the promoters, the system will be extended, both as to the mercantile and passenger cars, to the eastern fellside district.

The Penrith Observer, 8 December 1903

FATAL ACCIDENT AT APPLEBY: A MAN KILLED ON THE RAILWAY

A shocking occurrence took place at the Midland Station, Appleby, about half-past six on Thursday evening, when William Yare was knocked down and killed by a light engine. Yare, who resided at Bongate Cross, was a platelayer, but owing to the stormy weather he had been employed that day in securing the sheets of goods wagons. He had inspected a train which was standing on the up road and passed Mr J. Beeby twice to whom he spoke. He had evidently got to the first crossing on the south side of the station and it is thought that he had attempted to cross the metals of the down road, or was standing on the crossing when he was caught by a light engine which had gone some distance past the footbridge, and then set back to shunt for the down slow passenger at 6-35 p.m. Nobody saw the accident, but when Mr Beeby came back, he was going to the cattle dock, and observed some thing in the line. He thought it was a sheet, but on throwing a light on the object he found it was the deceased. The body was found in the points some distance from the crossing, and must have been carried there by the engine, jamming the points so that the signalman could not get his lever over… The jury found a verdict of 'Accidental death'. The Foreman on behalf of the jury expressed his sympathy with the relatives of the deceased, and said they would give their fees to some deserving poor in Bongate.

1904

Sheffield Daily Telegraph, 9 February 1904

CURRENT TOPICS

The fact that the Directors of the Midland Railway have decided to replace by stronger structures the iron girder bridges between Settle and Carlisle, the company's main line route to Scotland, a distance of seventy one and a half miles, should be welcome news to the firms engaged in this branch of foundry work. This important decision has been arrived at, after a through engineering examination, on account of the heavy four cylinder compound express locomotives, which have a length over the buffers of sixty feet ten inches, and weigh no less than one hundred and twelve tons. They are nearly twice the weight of the engines that worked this line when it was opened for passenger traffic on Wednesday 1st May 1876. The weight of the other rolling stock has been correspondingly increased. The iron girder bridges are numerous, as the line is carried over the beds of the Ribble, the Dent, and the Eden. The viaducts with which the Settle and Carlisle line abounds, Ribblehead, Batty Moss, Dent Head, Arten Gill, Dandry Mire, Lunds, Smardale, Crosby Garrett, Grisburn, Great Ormside, Long Marton, Crowdundle, Armathwaite, Drybeck, and High Stand Gill are built, fortunately for the Midland Railway Company and the contractors, from the excellent stone that was quarried in the neighbourhood.

In February 1898 Ernest Paget the Midland Railway chairman alluded to the Settle and Carlisle line. It appears that half of the track had at one time or another been re-laid since 1875 with rails mostly of 85lb weight, but about 80 miles, or nearly half of the total track mileage, had not been touched. This the company now intended to relay at an estimated cost of £1,000 a mile. Ahrons suggested that engines were making faster times than previously and this was probably caused by harder steel rails, 100lbs weight to the yard replacing the old 85lb rails. This, combined with an increase in the tensile strength of tyres, he thought caused less bending of the rails and flattening of wheel rims which in turn led to a decrease in friction. In any event it would appear that at least half of the rails on the line had lasted twenty years which, according to Paget, was not bad. Especially so since he pointed out that he had authorised their purchase from the Barrow Haematite Company in 1869 for the very low price of £9-5s per ton. (North from Leeds)

1906

The Penrith Observer, 8 May 1906

FIRE AT CROSBY GARRETT STATION

On Friday evening a fire occurred at one of the Midland Railway Company's cottages at Crosby Garrett, in the occupation of a signalman named Whitaker. The outbreak originated in a remarkable manner. It is supposed that a live spark form a passing engine found lodgement in a birds nest, under the eves of the cottage, and immediately set the combustible material of which it was composed ablaze. Some projecting spars of timber, newly painted, quickly caught fire, and very soon the flames began to spread along the roof. Fortunately the outbreak was detected by Mr Whitaker's son, whose attention was attracted by a crackling sound on the roof, and a number of railway workmen and villagers were soon upon the spot. By the operation of a jet of water, thrown up by a small manual engine, and by cutting away the burning spars, the fire was extinguished before any serious damage was sustained by the property. But for the timely discovery the result would have been disastrous, as two at least of the cottages would certainly have been involved in the fire.

The Penrith Observer, 31 December 1906

On the Midland Railway traffic was continued all day, though many of the trains were running considerably behind time. About seven o'clock on Wednesday evening two Kirkby Stephen platelayers had a narrow escape from death while following their employment on the Midland Railway. The night was exceedingly stormy, snow falling almost incessantly, while a gale swept across the country. The men were clearing the rods which work the points close to the station buildings; and in the storm failed to hear the approach of an express until the locomotive was close upon them. On realising their position, the men sprang in opposite directions clear of the track of the train. How near they came to a violent end may be judged from the fact that one of them, Uzziah Robinson, had the sole of his clog taken clean off by the engine, but he sustained no injury beyond a sprained ankle. His companion escaped harm.

1907

The Penrith Observer, 19 March 1907

COTTON WAGON ON FIRE AT KIRKBY STEPHEN

Early on Tuesday morning as a goods train was proceeding along the main Midland Railway line, between Kirkby Stephen and Hawes junction stations, one of the wagons, freighted with cotton, was discovered to be on fire. It is surmised that a spark from the engine had ignited the combustible material. The train was brought to a standstill in the Mallerstang district, and steps were promptly taken to subdue the outbreak. Before this could be done, however, the bulk of the load of cotton had been consumed and the sides of the vehicle were also burned away.

1908

The Penrith Observer, 7 July 1908

A RECORD RUN ON THE MIDLAND

On Wednesday the Midland and Glasgow and South Western Railway Companies began the running of a new express from London to Glasgow, with a conditional stop at Shipley engine sheds junction for change of engines only, and only one other stop in Carlisle, throughout the entire journey of 423 miles. The opening proved successful, and a new record was created on both railways, the distance between St Pancras and Carlisle (308 miles) being covered in 5 hours 51 minutes, while the journey of 115 miles from Carlisle to St Enoch was accomplished for the first time without a stop en route. The express left St Pancras at 11-30 a.m. and was equal to 9½ vehicles. The route was the shortest of the four available, and was via Trent, Erewash Valley, and Eckington, avoiding the run into Leeds and reducing the mileage thereby from 309 to 308. By this method also the changing of the front end of the train to the rear at Leeds was obviated. Engines were changed at Shipley, but there was no other stop between London and Carlisle, and the train, which was six minutes early at Hellifield and twelve at Appleby, reached the Citadel Station at 5-21 p.m., eight minutes ahead of its time. The engine used from London to Shipley was No 1038, driven by Devonport, of Leeds. From Shipley to Carlisle the engine was No 1028, driven by Coad, with Pyman as fireman, both of Leeds. The train left Carlisle for the first non-stop run to St Enoch with the Glasgow and South Western engine No 18, driven by Duff, with Broom as fireman, both of Glasgow. The arrival time in Glasgow was 7-51p.m., nine minutes before time. The various stages of the run were 205¾ miles from London to Shipley, 102¼ miles from Shipley to Carlisle, and 115 miles from Carlisle to Glasgow, via Barrheath. The express created a fresh record on Thursday, the arrival in Carlisle being 5-19 p.m., ten minutes before time and two minutes earlier than on Wednesday. The train passed Hellifield seven minutes early and Appleby ten minutes early. From London to Shipley engine No 1032, driven by George Ward, London was used. From Shipley to Carlisle the engine was No 1035, driven by Devonport, of Leeds. For the journey to Glasgow No 18 engine was again used, and the train reached St Enoch at 7-54, or six minutes ahead of time.

The Manchester Guardian, 28 September 1908

MIDLAND STAFF WITHDRAWN AT CARLISLE

As a result of the agreement entered into between the Midland and London and North Western Railway companies it has been decided to withdraw the Midland Railway Company's passenger staff at Carlisle. Mr J. R. Johnson, who for the past five years has acted as the Midland Railway's passenger agent and district cashier for the Settle and Carlisle section, has been offered and has accepted the post of station master at Bradford, where he will enter upon his duties on October 5th. Before going to Carlisle, Mr Johnson was for twenty years inspector of the staff in the coaching department over the entire Midland system. The rest of the staff will be removed either to other stations on the line or to the goods yard, and the duties which they have discharged since the line was opened to Carlisle in 1876 will be undertaken by the Citadel Station Committee. Of the seven railways which run into Carlisle the Glasgow and South Western will now be the only company left with a passenger staff of its own.

EPILOGUE

Even after 1908 stories about the Settle and Carlisle railway continued finding their way into the newspapers. There were fatal accidents at Hawes Junction in 1910, Ais Gill in 1913, and Little Salkeld in 1918 these have been well documented in other books and journals.

The threatened closure in 1985 and the fight to save the line with its eventual salvation in 1989 provided newspapers and publishers with more column inches of material.

The line is still attracting media attention, with the temporary closure of the northern section in 2016 when 500,000 tons of earth slipped at Eden Brow and its reopening in 2017.

These and many other accounts about the people who engineered, built, worked, and then saved the great Settle and Carlisle Railway have made the line what it is today, one of our most cherished railway journeys in Great Britain.

Snowplough at Ribblehead Station circa 1912, photograph courtesy of Lens of Sutton.

Appendices

APPENDIX A

CONTRACTORS' LOCOMOTIVES

There appears to be few records detailing contractors' locomotives used to build the Settle and Carlisle Railway, this list is certainly not definitive but provides us with some indication of the type of small engines contractors were using at this period in railway construction.

Engines from the Manning Wardle Works

Sheffield and Rotherham Independent, 6 March 1871

At the Boyne Engine Works, Messers Manning Wardle… Hastening forwards a good deal of important home work, for instance, two strong contractors' locomotives for the new line between Manchester and Liverpool. On the royal wedding day they will be christened respectively the 'Louise' and the 'Lorne' (see also 28th March 1873).

The new Manchester and Liverpool line was being constructed by Morton Peto, and included the quadrupling of the Edge Hill to Huyton section. Morton Peto went bankrupt in January 1868 and the contract and equipment was taken over by Benton and Woodiwiss this included the Manning Wardle standard gauge 0-4-0 ST built in 1870 called 'Lorne', (see also 25th March 1873).

Henry Lovatt was using a Manning Wardle 0-6-0 ST called 'H Lovatt No2' on the Great Central Railway. The engine was built in 1872 and started life on the Settle and Carlisle Railway (see *The Making of a Railway* by L. T. C. Rolt).

In 1872 an 0-6-0ST called 'Derby' was delivered from Manning Wardle to Settle for John Ashwell for No 1 contract.

There is evidence that a contractor's Manning Wardle engine No 328 'Sedbergh' an 0-4-0 ST built in 1870 to 5ft 6ins gauge was listed on J. Ashwell's contract No1 for ballasting work in November 1873.

A Manning Wardle 0-6-0 No 327 'Finchley' built in 1870 was used by J. Firbank on contract No3 according to records it was sold to Benton & Woodiwiss in 1872 further records show that Woodiwiss was using a Manning Wardle 0-6-0 ST 327 called 'Batty Wife' and brought from J. M. Finchley in 1872 on his contract, Dent Head to Smardale. Did J. Firbank hire this engine from J. M. Finchley before Finchley sold it to Woodiwiss?

Manning Wardle 0-6-0 ST Class M 'Scotby' No 341 standard gauge built for Eckersley and Bayliss in 1871. Its sister engine 'Newcastle' (as in Newcastle-under-Lyme) is now at the Beamish Museum.

In July 1876 Samuel Johnson the Midland Locomotive Superintendent reported that in the previous January an 0-6-0 tank engine 'Queen' that was used on contract No1 was transferred to the Midland Railway and numbered 1326. From records this may have been a Manning Wardle WYT 0-6-0 No 227 built in 1868 once owned by J. Bradley & Co.

During the 1872/3 period the Midland Railway Locomotive Committee also purchased two Manning Wardle 0-4-0ST No 445 Midland Railway 2066 and No 446 Midland Railway 2067 both H class standard gauge locomotives. A Manning Wardle 0-6-0 Midland Railway 2068 and three other contractors' engines of unspecified class, all of which came from J. Firbank the Settle and Carlisle contractor (*Journal of the Stephenson Locomotive Society* February 1957).

Engines from the Hunslet Engine Company

Hunslet Engine Company, standard gauge 0-6-0 ST, 'Henry Appleby' was purchased by Joseph Firbank for the Smardale to Crowdundle contract in 1870. It was also used on the Basingstoke and Alton Light Railway that was built by Firbank's son Joseph T. Firbank in 1891. In 1897 it was used by the contractor for the Canfield Place to Marylebone section of the Great Central Railway, with a cut down chimney and the cab spectacle plate removed, for use in the restricted tunnel headings.

In 1872 a Hunslet 0-6-0 ST No 72 called 'Wellington' was delivered to J. Firbank at Appleby (*A Hunslet Hundred,* L. T. C. Rolt, 1964)

Russel Wear provides additional information for the article of 26 September 1871 in the *Cumbrian Railway Journal,* October 2017. Hunslet works No 7, called 'Hunslet' a standard gauge 0-6-0 ST with 12 x 18in inside cylinders, was sent new on 10 April 1866 to Waring Bros, at Barnet near London for use on one of their Midland Railway extension contracts. Contract No4 Brent Viaduct was relinquished to J. Firbank on 12 November 1866 and it is likely that the locomotive was passed on to that company.

I have found a reference in the *Hertford Mercury* for 1st August 1868 of an auction sale to take place at Boreham Wood near Elstree of surplus stock owned by J. Firbank on the 12 August for three days – there were no railway locomotives in the auction only stationary and portable engines. This leaves me to believe that the railway locomotives were retained for other contracts.

Kitson Locomotive Works
Finally Williams mentions in his book a contractor's locomotive No 568 working between Settle and Bleamoor during the latter stages of construction. This may have been a Kitson 0-6-0 standard tank built in 1866 and eventually transferred to the Midland Railway No 1321. (references used, newspaper reports, www.leedsengines.info and North of Leeds.)

These are the edited details of four further reports about contractors' plant and engines that were printed in *The Lancaster Guardian.*

1870 A tramway is being laid from Batty Wife Hole to the south end of Bleamoor Tunnel, a distance of two and a half miles. An engine of 12 horse power is in daily use on this tramway.

1871 In the cuttings on the south of Bleamoor Tunnel, two locomotives are employed conveying excavated earth to the bank.

1873 On contract No3 four locomotives, 17 portable engines and steam cranes, 500 earth wagons and 2,000 tons of contractors' temporary rails.

1873 On contract No4 four locomotives and 12 stationary engines.

APPENDIX B

Some of the engineers living and lodging locally are listed in the 1871 census:

Contract No 1 (resident engineer for Arten Gill to Kirkby Stephen) Edgar O. Ferguson lodging at Giggleswick, civil engineer aged 24.

Contract No 2 Frank Lynde (Francis Gascoigne Lynde), living at Kirkby Stephen, civil engineer aged 23 with his wife Elizabeth Ellen 19, Ellen 0, mother-in-law Rebecca Eyre 52.

Contract No 2 James Hay, living at Kirkby Stephen, contractor's agent, aged 48 with his wife Helen 44, George 19, cashier; James 17, civil engineer's assistant; John 14, clerk; David 11; Ellen 8 and Sarah 6.

Contract No 3 Jesse Drage, living at Bongate, Appleby, a civil engineer aged 32 and a widow.

Contract No 3 John Throstle, living at Long Marton, Westmorland, manager aged 52 with his wife Hannah 51, George 22, civil engineer and John 18, accountant.

Contract No 4 Samuel H. Paine, living at Rickergate, Carlisle, a civil engineer aged 44 with his wife Mary aged 39, and John 10, Frank 9, William7, Henry 4 and Charles 0,

Contract No 4 John Allen, living in lodgings at Great Salkeld, civil engineer aged 30 with his wife Caroline Louise 20.

Bibliography

The Midland Railway its rise and progress, Frederick S. Williams, 1877
  (Williams has devoted a whole chapter in his book to the construction of the Settle and Carlisle railway. He writes as if he were an eye witness to some of the works that took place. My research has placed some doubt that this was the case, as whole passages appear to have been lifted from newspaper reports published up to four years prior to his book appearing in print. Interestingly Peter Baughan in his book *North of Leeds* casts some doubt on the story of the engineer Sharland and his involvement with the survey of the Settle to Carlisle line he states that the only documented evidence to these events appear in Williams book? Even so Williams book is certainly worth reading.)

The Making of a Railway, L.T.C. Rolt, 1971
  (a valuable archive of photographs taken during the construction of the Great Central Railway that illustrate the last vestiges of manual railway construction. Now out of print but highly recommended reading)

North of Leeds, Peter Baughan, 1966
  (Extremely detailed account of the line from Leeds to Settle, the building of the Settle and Carlisle and its operation after it opened. Now out of print, was reprinted in the 1980s, but it is worth purchasing the 1966 copy.)

Settle-Carlisle Railway Centenary, David Joy and W. R. Mitchell, 1975

The Settle and Carlisle Railway, O. S. Nock, 1992

The Lost Shanties of Ribblehead, W. R. Mitchell, 1996

How they built the Settle and Carlisle Railway, W. R. Mitchell, 1989
  (more newspaper account of the building of the Settle and Carlisle mainly around the Ribble Head area.)

Stations and Structures of the Settle and Carlisle railway, Anderson and Fox, 2014

Carlisle 150 years of railways Cumbria Railway Association, 1986

The Settle and Carlisle Past and Present, Williams, 2010

Settle and Carlisle: A railway over the Pennines, Mitchell and Joy, 1982

Limestone Industries of the Yorkshire Dales, David Johnson, 2010

The Railway Navvies, Terry Colman, 1965

Ribblehead: The Story of The Great Viaduct on the Settle and Carlisle Line, W. R. Mitchell, 2015

Handbooks of Railway Contractors Locomotives, Vol 1-6, David Cole

Leeds in Steam, Rayner, Ward, Johnston, *Auto Review,* 109, 2015

Friends of the Settle and Carlisle Papers from the national Archive, Peter G. Davis

Cumbrian Railways Journal of the Cumbrian Railway Association, Volume II No 4, October 2013

Article on the Ais Gill Accident, September 1913

Article on Charles Stanley Sharland Engineer who first surveyed the Settle and Carlisle line, Volume 12, No 8, October 2017

Article on contractors locomotives, R. Wear

The Wensleydale Railway, Christine Hallas, 1984 and 1991

Index